SOUTHERN HISTORICAL PRESS, Inc.

- 2023 SUMMER / FALL Catalog -

Reprints *and* New Editions *of*
Genealogical *and* Historical Source material *for*:
Alabama, Arkansas, Delaware, Florida, Georgia, Illinois, Indiana, Kentucky, Louisiana, Maryland, Mississippi, Missouri, New Jersey, North *and* South Carolina, Ohio, Pennsylvania, Tennessee, Texas, Virginia *and* West Virginia

www.southernhistoricalpress.com
1071 Park West Blvd. ◆ [redacted]
Greenville, SC 29602-1267
southernhistoricalpress@gmail.com

Southern Historical Press Inc
Book Publishers

A MESSAGE from the Publisher....

HELP US EXPAND OUR LISTING OF TITLES

We are always trying to expand our listing of Tieles. We welcomb your sugestions of possible reprints and / or newly abstracted but unpublished source material, such as Wills, Deeds, Marriages, Chancery Court Minutes, etc... that you might bring to our attention or submit for possible publication.

SHIPMENT

We normally ship via US Postal Service: 4th Class Book Rate. In most instances we try to ship books within 5 days of receiving the order. However, we do ask that you allow 2 to 3 weeks for delivery of your order.

PRICING / RETURN POLICY

All prices are subject to change without notice. **ALL SALES ARE FINAL.** Books are Not sold on a pre-approval. We accept returns for books sent in error or for damaged or defective books only. Then and only then, we will replace the book with a non damaged or non defective copy of the same title. **NO CASH REFUNDS......**

ALABAMA

1840 Census Index *of* Alabama. By: Betty Sue Drake Posey, Pub. 1973, Reprinted 1991, 128 pages, ISBN #0-89308-331-3.

AL 16 $20.00

Recently a small case of these books was discovered in the warehouse from the 1991 printing. So supplies are limited, order yours today. Counties formed from the creek and Cherokee Cessions of the 1830¿s: Barbour, Benton, Chamber, Cherokee, Coosa, Dekalb, Macon, Marshall, Randolph, Russell, Talladega, and Tallapoosa.

Index *to* Alabama Wills, 1808-1870. By: Alabama Society Daughter of the American Revolution, Pub. 1955, Reprinted 1999, 192 pages, Hard cover, ISBN #0-89308-399-2.

AL 27 $32.50

This book is an index of Wills for the state of Alabama. The Wills used to complete this book were found in a variety of places, such as: Will Books, Deed Books, Probate Records, Court Minutes & Records, Administration Records, Order Books and Records of Estates. This book is arranged alphabetically by surname. Such information found within in this book: person leaving will, a county where the will was found, date and page number.

Marriage, Death & Legal Notices *from* Alabama Newspapers, 1818-1880. By: Pauline J. Gandrud, Pub. 1981, Reprinted 2008, 728 pages, Hard Cover, Index, ISBN #0-89308-209-0.

AL 11 $60.00

These newspaper notices listing approximately 30,000 names of persons have been taken from the various volumes of the late Mrs. Gandrud¿s 245-volume series on Alabama. The editing and compiling of this book took over two years and should make a very significant contribution to historical and genealogical research in Alabama, and also in neighboring states of GA, SC, NC, LA, TN, VA, MD, IN, OH, NY and MS. Not only are the more familiar Marriage and Death notices included in these volumes together with dates, places, and names of family members, but also Legal Notices will include such things as the appointment of guardians, coroners¿ inquests, wills, and many, many other items too numerous to mention. The papers from which these notices are taken from are as follows: Cahaba Press & Alabama State Intelligencer; The Alabama Sentinel published in Greensboro and Tuscaloosa; Voice of Sumter, Sumter Democrat; Livingston Journal all published in Sumter County, AL.; Montgomery Weekly Mail; Wetumpka Argus and Commercial Advertiser; Wetumpka Argus; Gainesville News; Selma Times; Cahaba Gazette; Shelby Guide; The Tuscumbian; Tuscumbia Telegraph; papers from the Tuscaloosa area: Tuscaloosa Telegraph and Patriot, The Democrat Gazette& Flag of the Union, The Republican Banner, Tuscaloosa Times, Tuscaloosa Observer, Northport Spectator; The Jackson Republican. Huntsville and Madison County papers are: Huntsville Advocate, North Alabama Reporter, Huntsville Democrat, The Democrat, Mercury, New South, Argus, Huntsville Republican, Huntsville Confederate, Huntsville Independent, Southern Advocate. Other miscellaneous Alabama papers are: the Choctaw County News, Wilcox County News, Monroe Journal, and Clark County Democrat. Tennessee papers with Alabama data are: Knoxville Register, Knoxville Enquirer, The Post (Knoxville), Memphis Eagle, Nashville Whig, Nashville Whig and the Tennessee Advister, Nashville Republican, The Nashville Union. Other papers with Alabama material are: The Raleigh, N.C. Register, The Richmond, VA. Enquirer and National Intelligancer (DC). The major papers for which notices can be found are the Huntsville papers, Limestone County newspapers, Northport, Tuscaloosa, Cahaba, Demoplis, Selma, Sumter, Montgomery, Wetumpka, and other "Black Belt" county papers.

Alabama Newspapers *and* Family Records, 1819-1890, Marriage & Death Notices *from*. By: Helen S. Foley, Pub. 1981, reprinted 2004, 240 pages, Index, Hard cover, ISBN # 0-89308-208-2.

AL 12 $30.00

These newspapers abstracts cover the central and Eastern portion of the State of Alabama, with papers from the Mobile, Eufaula, Clayton, Bluff City, Montgomery and Henry County areas. Much valuable genealogical information is to be gleaned from this book of source material. Some of the papers from which this material is taken are: Montgomery Republican, Mobile Commercial Register, The Eufaula Democrat, The Spirit of the South, Independent American, Eufaula Express, The Bluff City Times, The Henry County Register, The Clayton Banner, Eufaula Weekly Times & News, Eufaula Times & News, The Eufaula Times, The Eufaula Weekly Bulletin, and Eufaula Daily Times.

Early Settlers *of* Alabama. By: James E. Saunders, Pub. 1899, reprinted 2015, 556 pages, soft cover, Index, ISBN #0-89308-061-6.

AL 1 $45.00

This excellent book on the history of northern Alabama and most especially of Lawrence County is a MUST. The volume is in two parts, part one being ¿Recollections of the Early Settlers of North Alabama ¿, written by Col. Saunders. This part contains a brief history of Lawrence County, AL. and the Tennessee River Valley, sketches of many early families and personalities of the area and their origins as well as Col. Saunders writings on the Civil War. Part two, ¿Notes and Genealogies¿, was compilied by Mrs. Elizabeth Saunders Blair Stubbs, a granddaughter of Col. Saunders. The genealogies cover not only families in Northern Alabama but in other areas of the state, and also other states as well, giving much detail and family origins in this country and abroud. Among the families covered are: Banks, Bankhead, Bibbs, Billups, Blair, Cantzon, Clark, Clay, Coleman, Cox, DuBose, Dudley, Dunn, Eliott, Flint, Foster, Fry, Gholson, Goode, Gray, Harris, Hill, Hopkins, Kennedy, Lanier, Ligon, Lowe, Maclin, Manning, Maury, McCarthy, McGehee, Moore, Oliver, O¿Neal, Phelan, Poellnitz, Ray, Richardson, Saunders, Shelton, Sherrod, Shorter, Speed, Swoope, Tait, Taliaferro, Thompson, Tillman, Urquhart, Walthall, Waykins, Webb, Weeden, Wells, White, Withers, Yates, and

Young

1833 State Census *for* Barbour County, Alabama. By: Helen S. Foley, Pub. 1976, reprinted 2020, 72 pages, Index, soft cover, ISBN #0-89308-177-9.

AL 7 $15.00

No. 53 of Acts of Alabama that in 1833, a census was to be taken of each county in Alabama using the following for: White males under 21; white males over 21; white females under 21; white females over 21; Total amount of whites; Total number of slaves; Total amount of free people of Color; Total amount of inhabitants. This Census is printed in the order of enumeration with a complete alphabetical index at the end. In 1833 Barbour county had 6,280 white persons and total inhabitants of 9,283 person.

Bible Records *of* Barbour County, Alabama. Volume #1. By: Helen S. Foley, Pub. 1976, Reprinted 2020, 84 pages, Index, soft cover, ISBN #0-89308-180-9.

AL 8 $15.00

These Bible records were copied from originals by the author. A listing of the original Bible owners' surnames is shown later, but this no way includes all the families whose entries may be listed in these records: Adams, Wood, Richards-Carter, McLeod, Baxter, Efurd, Johnson, Alston, Harwell, Spratling, Walker-Thompson, Grimmett, Ham-Freeman, Danner, Wilkerson, Screws, Watson, Jackson-Locke-Sylvester, Pickett, Bray, Floyd, Bledsoe, Goree, Stroud-Speir, Stow, Motley, Gilmore, Roberts, Trammell, Cliatt, Taylor, Christian, Matin, Green-Oliver, Bush, Andrew, McKenzie, Bowers, Thomas, Spurlin, Caraway, Tew, Andress, Goodson, McKenzie-Harrison, Wilson, Snipes, Lane, McDonale, Dunnning, Lewis, Faulk, Hardwick, Avent-McLendon, May, Rambo, Sims, Lowman, Corbitt, Turnipseed, McKay, Cade and Sapp.

Bible Records *of* Barbour County, Alabama. Volume #2. By: Helen S. Foley, Pub. 1976, Reprinted 2020, 88 pages, Index, soft cover, ISBN #0-89308-181-7.

AL 9 $15.00

These Bible records were copied from originals by the author. A listing of the original Bible owners' surnames is shown later, but this no way includes all the families whose entries may be listed in these records:Glover, Ventress, McEachern, Lee, Cawthon, Williams, Lamar, Pomeroy, Hyatt, Walton, Srewart, Petry, Spurlock, Vann, Locke, Bush, Horn, Warr, King, Cadenhead, Cox, White, Seay (See), Thomas, Leverett, Burney, Dixon, Motley, Owens, Lee, Jones, McRae, Walker, Wilson, Searcy-Nordan, Floyd, Smith, palmour, Sime & Boyle, Sonday-Sprangler-Wertenberger, Lovelace, Peak, Sanders, Carson, Sanders-Riddle, Riddle-Hamd, Riddle, Ivey-Garland, Downing, Hutchisen, Pierson, Mulkey-Hopkins, DuBose, Foy and Dassinger.

Rural Land Owners *of* Barbour County, Alabama. By: Marie H. Godfrey, Pub. 1990, reprinted 2019, 158 pages, Index, soft cover, ISBN #0-89308-670-3.

AL 23 $20.00

Barbour County was formed in 1832 from parts of Pike and Henry Counties and from Creek Indian lands. All records are for Barbour County unless specified. About 1866, parts of Barbour County were cut off to form Russell and Bulloch counties. This land is shown by an (R) for Russell county and a (B) for Bulloch county following the description.

Barbour County, Alabama, History *of*. By: Mattie T. Thompson, Pub. 1939, Reprinted 2018, 570 pages, ISBN #0-89308-423-9.

AL 2 $48.50

Barbour County was formed in 1832 from parts of Pike and Henry Counties and from Creek Indian lands. Biographies: Alston, Alexander, Adams, Andrews, Baker, Ballowe, Barnett (2), Brown (2), Bennett (2), Bray, Brassell, Bush (2), Britt, Beringer, Bernstein, Bullock, Brannon, Conner, Comer (7), Clayton, (7), Crawford, Cargill, Cato, Crews, Colby, Cochran, Daniel, Davie, Dean, Dent (5), Douglas, Doughtie, Edmundson, Espy (2), Evans, Floyd (2), Flournoy, Foy (7), Foster (2), Florence, Glenn (2), Guice, Hart, Hawkins, Hobdy, Holleman, Hortman, Houston, Hunter, Hyatt, Jelks, Joiner (2), Jones (3), Kendall, Kolb, Lampley, Laseter, Lee (4), Lewy, Margart, Massey, McDowell (2), McEachern (2), McCormick, McDowell (3), McInnis, McKay (4), McKenzie, McLeod, McNab, McRae, Merrill (3), Milton, Moore, Moulthrop, Oppenheimer, Ott, Pappas, Parish, Patterson, Peach, Petty, Pitts (3), Pugh, Quillian, Ramser, Reeves (2), Rhodes, Richards, Roberts, Robertson, Roquemore, Ross, Ryan, Salter, Schloss, Screws, Searcey, Shorter (5), Simpson, Sparks, Speight, Spurlock, Standifer, Stow, Sutlive, Swanson, Thomas (7), Upshaw, Walker (2), Ward, Warren, Weedon, Wellborn, West, Wharton, Whitlock, Williams (2), Winn, and Young.

Barbour County, Alabama, Early Settlers *of*. (Vols 1 & 2). By Helen S. Foley, Pub. 1976, reprinted 2015, 376 pages, soft cover, Index, ISBN 0-89308-160-4.

AL 10 $38.50

Originally published as to separate volumes, these have now been consolidated into one with a complete full name index. The families discussed in this book were selected by the author because they were living in this area when Barbour County was formed in 1832 from parts of Pike and Henry Counties and from Creek Indian lands. Bullock County was cut off from Barbour, as well as part of Russell County. The families listed in this book had patented their land by 1829. This 2 volume work bound in one volume is filled with Georgians by the hundreds who moved into Barbour County. Families being covered: Adams, Ball, Beasley, Beauchamp, bennett, Bizzell, Boswell, Bradley, Breland, Brown, Burch, bush, Byrd, cadenhead, Campbell, Childs, Cole, Cox, Creech, crews, Dansby, Deshazo, Eades, Efurd, faulk, Fenn, floyd, Gillis, Briggs, Grubbs, Harrod, Hartzog, Harwell, Head, Henderson, Hill, Hix, Hobdy, Hood, Jackson, Jernigan, Johnson, Johnston, Jones, Lee, Lewis, McEachern, McGilvray, McInnis, McKenzie, McLeod, McLean, McRae, McSwean, Mann, Minshew, Nix, Norton, parmer, payne, Peterson, pitts, pruett, Pugh, Purifoy, Pynes, Richards, Shipman, Siler, Sutton, Swilley, Thomas, Utsey, Ventress, Walker, Ward, Warren, Watson, Williamson, Williams, Willis, Windham, Winslett, Wise, Wood, and Zorn.

Barbour County, Alabama, 1838-1859, Marriage Records *of*. By Helen S. Foley, Pub. 1990, reprinted 2022, 100 pages, Index, ISBN 0-89308-657-6.

AL 20 $17.50

Barbour County was formed in 1832 from parts of Pike and Henry Counties and from Creek Indian lands. Bullock County was cut off from Barbour, as well as part of Russell County. Contains approximately 2,200 marriages and approximately 6,000 names, including bride and groom, officiating minister and often times the name of the persons home where the marriage took place.

Barbour *and* Henry Counties, Alabama, Newspapers, 1846-1890, Marriage *and* Deaths *from*. By Helen S. Foley, Pub. 1999, 320 pages, Index, Soft Cover, ISBN 0-89308-658-4.

AL 21 $30.00

These newspaper abstracts used to complete this book were compiled from papers on file at the Barbour and Henry Courthouses, the Eufaula Carnegie Library and the Alabama History and Archives. These marriage and deaths not only mention over 11,000 persons from these two counties, but also throughout Georgia and Alabama with many other references to other states as well, including VA., Tex., SC., NC., Fla., and Tenn.

Abstracts *of* Barbour County, Alabama Wills & Estates 1852-1856. By: Helen S. Foley, Pub. 1976, Reprinted 2017, 124 pages, Index, ISBN #0-89308-183-3.

AL 5 $17.50

This book was published back in the early 1970¿s. Due to their limited production run and the fact that they were printed in paperback, makes this reprint an extremely exciting offer for persons researching in this area of Alabama, as many of the original printed copies no longer exists. Barbour County was formed in 1832 from parts of Pike and Henry Counties and from Creek Indian lands.

Clarke County, Alabama, History *of*. By: John S. Graham, Pub. 1923, Reprinted 2018, 354 pages, New Index, ISBN #0-89308-693-2.

AL 24 $35.00

Clarke County is located between the Alabama and Tombigbee Rivers and was initially carved from Washington County in 1812. When Alabama became a Territory in 1817, Clark County was substantially enlarged. This history is similar to most county histories done in this time period in that it covers all the usual topics such as education, newspapers, population, Indian skirmishes, mineral wealth, schools and community leaders. It is especially rich in biographical sketches and has various lists of soldiers including the war records on many men living in the community who had served in the Confederate Army during the Civil War. It is filled with biographical sketches of individuals with detailed genealogies on many of the early pioneer families of the county such as: Adams, Anderson, Ball, Barnes, Bedsole, Bolen, Boroughs, Boyles, Caller, Carlton, Chapman, Davis, Frazier, Garrett, Gillis, Graham, Grant, Gross, Hicks, Jones, Johnson, Kimbell, Kimbrough, Langford, Mathews, McDuffie, McGowan, McLeod, Murphy, Newman, Nichols, Pugh, Rivers, Savage, Stewart, Taylor, Tucker, Turner, Wilson, Wing, and the mention of vast numbers of other pioneer settlers.

History *of* Fayette County, Alabama. By: Herbert & Jeanie Newell, Pub. 1960, 467 pages, Hard Cover, Index, ISBN #0-89308-811-0.

AL 33 $50.00

This book should be in the library of anyone who has or is researching in the State of Alabama due to not only its scarcity but also for its content. When this book was first printed in 1960, it was limited to a print run of only 200 copies. So that when a person tries to locate a copy, it is nearly impossible. Fayette county was created in 1824 from Tuscaloosa county. This book discusses the history of the county through such topics as: economics, transportation, education, religion and government. This book is a genealogical treasure chest, as it is filled with lists of persons from the county such as: heads of household for 1830 & 1840, numerous lists of public servants, ministers for various churches throughout the county, lists of Pensioners for the War of 1812, volunteers from the

Seminole War, Civil War census of 1907, Cemetery records, and many, many other lists concerning persons from the county. But what the family historian / researcher will savior are the Biographical Skecthes of approximately 1,200 early settlers/citizens of the county. This alone makes-up over half of the entire book.

Fayette County, Alabama Cemetery Records. By: Herbet & Jeanie Newell, Pub. 1959, reprinted 2022, 232 pages, soft cover, Index, ISBN #978-1-63914-050-3.

AL 41 $28.50

Fayette county was created in 1824 from Tuscaloosa County. This book is listed by graveyards. It lists the deceased names and date of birth and death. A map is provided with location of the graveyard, along with an index to help locate an individual. It will make a great addition to anyone's collection who is researching in the area of Western Alabama.

Fayette County, Alabama Index *to* Marriage Records, 1850-1970. By: Herbert & Jeanie Newell, Pub. 1970, reprinted 2022, 260 pages, soft cover, Index, ISBN #978-1-63914-059-6.

AL 43 $30.00

Fayette county was created in 1824 from Tuscaloosa County. This book is in alphabetical order by groom. It lists the brides and grooms names along with the book number it was recorded in. It will make a great addition to anyone's collection who is researching in the area of Western Alabama.

Fayette County, Alabama Index *to* Wills *and* Estates, 1851-1974. By: Herbet & Jeanie Newell, Pub. 1977, reprinted 2022, 206 pages, soft cover, Index, ISBN #978-1-63914-058-9.

AL 42 $25.00

Fayette county was created in 1824 from Tuscaloosa county. This book is in alphabetical order by testator. It list the testators name along with the where the information can be found from court minutes, court records or will records and page numbers that it was recorded on. It will make a great addition to anyone's collection who is researching in the area of Western Alabama.

Northern Alabama, Historical *and* Biographical. By: Smith & DeLand, Orig. Pub. 1888, Reprinted 2006, 776 pages plus NEW INDEX, Hard Cover, ISBN #0-89308-839-0.

AL 36 $75.00

First of all, don¿t let the title mislead anyone. This book covers Northern & Central Alabama covering some 32 different counties. It is similar to other vanity sketch books of its kind, such as Goodspeed Publishing Company. The book is broken down into two main issues. The first being a history of the counties and the second being biographical sketches on approx. 832 these early settlers. The counties covered are: Bullock, Butler, Calhoun, Cherokee, Clarke, Clay, Cleburne, Colbert, Cullman, Dallas, Etowah, Greene, Hale, Jackson, Jasper, Jefferson, Lawrence, Lauderdale, Lee, Limestone, Madison, Marengo, Marshall, Montgomery, Morgan, Perry, Pike, Shelby, St. Clair, Sumter, Talladega, and Tuscaloosa.

Old Cahaba Land Office Records & Military Records, 1817-1853. By Marilyn D. Barefield, Pub. 1981, Revised and Reprinted 1999, 300 pages, Hard Cover, Index. ISBN #0-89308-384-4.

AL 29 $35.00

This book contains records of more than 1,800 early purchasers from the land offices in Milledgeville, GA. and Cahaba, Ala. including 1,600 entries not listed in the 1981 version. The section, township, and range, for each entry residents of Autauga, Barbour, Bibb, Butler, Coffee, Conecuh, Covington, Crenshaw, Dale, Dallas, Escambia, Geneva, Greene, Houston, Lowndes, Marengo, Monroe, Montgomery, Perry, Pike, Shelby, and Wilcox counties.

Pickens County, Alabama *from its* First Settlement *in* 1817-1856, History *of.* By Nelson F. Smith, Pub. 1856, Reprinted 1994. 272 pages, Index, Hard cover, ISBN #0-89308-691-6.

AL 25 $30.00

Pickens county was created by the Alabama Legislature in 1820, the year after Alabama was admitted into the Union. The early settlers, most of whom were from the upper districts of South Carolina, are discussed under the topics of living conditions, crops, mills, election precincts, the villages of the county and county officers. A ¿General View of Pickens County¿ includes water courses, towns, geography, agriculture, roads, religion, manufacturers, charter of the inhabitants, minerals, and education facilities. Newspapers, climate, early settlers, eminent men and schools are also discussed in this section. Of particular interest are biographical sketches of judges, county court clerks, sheriffs, commissioners, circuit court clerks, and representatives of the Legislature.

Newspaper Abstracts *from* Pike County, Alabama 1855-1861. (Vol. #1). By: Susie K. Senn, Pub. 1999, 314 pages, Hard Cover, Index, ISBN #0-89308-424-7.

AL 31 $35.00

Pike County was created in the 1821 from Henry County, Alabama. It is surrounded by the present day counties of: Barbour, Bullock, Coffee, Crenshaw, Dale, and Montgomery counties. Due to the many counties carved out of Pike County, (Bullock, Barbour, & Crenshaw Counties), this book will be extremely helpful for researchers looking for individuals in this southeastern portion of the state. These newspaper abstracts were taken from the Independent American, a newspaper published in the town of Troy. Within this book, information will be found on deaths, marriages, administrative notices, murders, trials, hangings, and many, many other items of genealogical interest.

Newspaper Abstracts *from* Pike County, Alabama 1860-1865. (Vol. #2). By: Susie K. Senn. Pub. 2002, 372 pages, Index, ISBN #0-89308-729-7.

AL 32 $38.50

This is the SECOND VOLUME of a series of newspaper abstracts by Susie Senn. These newspaper abstracts were taken from the Southern Advertiser, Troy, AL. during the years of The War of Northern Aggression. There are articles of Secession Meetings and Resistance Club Meetings including some names. There is information on formation of various Militia Units and their training. There are letters from soldiers to their families and to the newspaper editor. There are dead & wounded lists, unit lists, obituaries of soldiers and much, much more concerning Pike county¿s people which at that time covered the now Pike County and parts of what are now Bullock and Crenshaw Counties.

Newspaper Abstracts *from* Pike County, Alabama 1860-1864. (Vol. #3). By: Sussie Senn, Pub. 2009, 300 pages, soft cover, Index, ISBN #0-89308-784-X.

AL 37 $35.00

Here is the Third Volume of newspaper abstracts for the Pike County, AL. The following information comes from The Southern Advertiser, a newspaper published in Troy, AL. during the years of The War of Northern Aggression. The information within this volume differs from the material in volume #2, even though both volumes cover the same time frame. This volume¿s main focus is on hometown news: Obituaries, Marriages, Administration Notices and etc. for Pike county and also other surrounding counties. The information within this volume is new and is completely different from material found in her earlier two books.

Pike County, Alabama Index *to* Will Books 1830-1995, Estate Boxes 1830-1955 *and* General Estate Books 1-25. By: Susie K. Senn, Pub. 2022, 196 pages, Index, soft cover, ISBN #978-1-63914-063-3.

AL 44 $25.00

Pike County was created in 1821 from Henry County, Alabama. It is surrounded by the counties of: Barbour, Bullock, Coffee, Crenshaw, Dale and Montgomery. Due to the many counties carved out of Pike County, (Bullock, Barbour and Crenshaw), this book will be extremely helpful for researchers looking for individuals in this southeastern portion of the state.

Sumter County, Alabama, Pioneer Families *of.* By: Nelle Morris Jenkins, Pub. 1961, Reprinted 2018, 276 pages, Index, ISBN #0-89308-944-3.

AL 19 $30.00

Sumter County was created in 1832 from lands ceded from the Choctaw Nation. Its early settlers were French explorers who came up from Mobile. This book begins with a historical background of the county and then moves into the genealogical records found in old Church records. One chapter is devoted to death notices in early newspapers, another chapter is devoted to Tract Book records, showing who entered the land and information about the family. But the main part is devoted to tombstone inscriptions. Almost every inscription is followed with details about the person¿s family. In most cases the author was able to trace the families back to the Carolinas or Virginia.

Walker County, Alabama, Records *of.* By: Inez Biggerstaff, Pub. 1959, Reprinted 2005, 202 pages, Hard Cover,Index, ISBN #0-89308-812-9.

AL 17 $28.50

Walker county was created in 1821 from Tuskaloosa and Marion counties. It is located in the Northern portion of the state and is surrounded by the counties of: Blount, Fayette, Jefferson, Marion, Tuskaloosa, and Winston. This area of Northern Alabama was a major route for persons migrating westward out of or through Tennessee and Georgia. Due to the fact that the records for this county are ¿DESTROYED¿ prior to 1871 makes this book as well as any other book on Walker County of extreme importance. Material contained in this book: 1840 Census, Lists of 1840 Tax Payers, Marriages 1879-1888, Pensioners from the War of 1812, Bible & Family records containing births, deaths, & marriages, and Cemetery Inscriptions from Not only Walker County but also neighboring counties of: Cullman, Fayette, Marion, Talladega, Tuscaloosa and Winston.

Walker County, Alabama, History *of.* By: John M. Dombhart, Pub. 1937, Reprinted 2015, 382 pages plus NEW INDEX, ISBN #0-89308-725-4.

AL 22 $38.50

Walker County is located in the North Central portion of the state. It was created in the 1830's and was surrounded at the time by the counties of: Blount, Fayette, Franklin, Jefferson, Lawrence, Marion,

Morgan, and Tuscaloosa. Large numbers of early pioneers passed through this portion of the state of Alabama on their way westward with numerous individuals staying on as settlers. The main bulk of this book is devoted to over 500 Biographical Sketches of these early pioneer settlers. Due to these vast numbers, we are unable to list these surnames at this time. This New Index that was specially compiled for this volume contains the names of over 7,300 individuals.

Revolutionary Soldiers *in* Alabama.
By: Thomas M. Owen, Pub. 1911, Reprinted, 2018, 129 pages, soft cover, ISBN #0-89308-986-9.

AL 40 $15.00

This book is arranged alphabetically covering approximately some 537 soldiers who served in the Revolution War. The reader will discover such information such as: age, place of residence, rank, line, and, in some cases, names of wives, dates of marriage, and names of children.

ARKANSAS

1830 Census *of* Arkansas.
By: L.E. Presley, Pub. 1971, reprinted 2004, 88 pages plus New Index, soft cover, ISBN #0-89308-750-5.

AR 24 $20.00

Thius census takes place back when there were only 23 counties: Arkansas, Chicot, Clark, Conway, Crawford, Crittenden, Hempstead, Hot Springs, Independence, Izard, Jackson, Jefferson, Lafayette, Lawrence, Miller, Monroe, Phillips, Pope, Pulaski, St. Francis, Sevier, and Union.

1840 Census *of* Arkansas.
By: L.E. Presley, Pub. 1971, reprinted 2004, 268 pages plus New Index, soft cover, ISBN #0-89308-751-3.

AR 25 $30.00

This census takes place back when there were only 39 counties: Arkansas, Benton, Carroll, Chicot, Clark, Conway, Crawford, Crittenden, Desha, Franklin, Greene, Hempstead, Hot Springs, Independence, Izard, Jackson, Jefferson, Johnson, Lafayette, Lawrence, Madison, Marion, Mississippi, Miller, Monroe, Phillips, Pike, Poinsett, Pope, Pulaski, Randolph, St. Francis, Saline, Scott, Searcy, Sevier, Union, Van Buren, Washington and White.

Arkansas County, Arkansas, History of.
By: W.H. Halliburton, Pub. 1903, Reprinted 2022, 98 pages, Index, ISBN #0-89308-076-4.

AR 2 $25.00

This is the earliest of Arkansas county histories, and to a degree, the history of the entire state. It covers the period in Arkansas history from 1541 to 1873. The material, much of which is from French and Spanish sources, is arranged chronologically. The material that relates to Arkansas County has been abstracted from the county land, probate and court records.

Arkansas Pensioners, 1818-1900:
Records of some Arkansas residents who applied to the Federal Government for benefits arising from service in Federal Military organizations (Revolutionary War, War of 1812, Indiand and Mexican Wars). By: Dorothy Payne, Pub. 1985, Reprinted 2017, 228 pages, Index, Soft Cover, ISBN #0-89308-537-5.

AR 22 $27.50

This book contains abstracts of Federal Pension Applications from the American Revolution, War of 1812, Indian Wars and Mexican War (including several hundred other applications that are identified and indexed, but not abstracted); county records from various counties in Arkansas including marriages, wills, and deeds; 1850 Federal Census Records, many from states other than Arkansas; The complete Regimental Muster Rolls of the Arkansas Volunteers during the Indian Wars of 1836; Muster Rolls of the Mounted Volunteers and The Arkansas Volunteers during the Mexican War, plus the Regimental commanded by Colonel Archibald Yell and John Seldon Roane, the Battalion commanded by Lt. Colonel William Gray, and the Independent Companies of Gaston Mears and Stephen Enyart.

Arkansas Gazette Obituaries Index, 1819-1879.
By: Stephen J. Chism, Pub. 1990, Reprinted 2017, 116 pages, Index, ISBN #0-89308-398-4.

AR 23 $20.00

This index includes 14,329 entries of unequivocal reports of death in which a person (s) is named between the years 1819 and 1879. The Arkansas Gazette for the same period lists 4,201 names under the heading ¿Deaths¿. This can be attributed to the inclusive policy of listing every mention of death, whether it appears in an obituary column or in the text of an article on another subject. If a person identified in an obituary used an alias, the index bears an entry under both the alias and the name given at birth. If the name appears spelled differently in two references of a death, it is listed as it is spelled. This index, arranged alphabetically, contains the last name of the deceased, followed by the first name, middle initial, title as given (Mrs., Mr., Miss., Corp., Capt., Col., etc.), where death appears with month and day of the issue of the newspaper, page and column it appeared on.

Craighead County, Arkansas, History *of.*
By: Harry Lee Williams, Pub. 1930, reprinted 1995, 752 pages, Hard Cover, Index, ISBN #0-89308-400-X.

AR 14 $55.00

Craighead County was part of the territory claimed for France in 1682. This area was transfered to Spain in 1762 as part of the Louisiana Territory. Later it became part of the Missouri Territory. It was carved out of Poinsett and Mississippi Counties, Arkansas in 1859. It is located in the Northeastern corner of the state at the corner of the Missouri Boot. Schools, churches, railroads, Press, 1860 census, first settlers, and Biographical Sketches of first families.

Centennial History *of* Arkansas - Volume #2.
By: Dallas T. Herndon, Pub. 1922, Reprinted 2019, 1058 pages, Index, ISBN #0-89308-069-1.

AR 10 $75.00

When Dallas T. Herndon became Secretary of Arkansas History Commission in 1911, he began to "realize that the state had no history that could be reliable upon as authentic," although several state histories had been published, but whose authors did not have access to reliable sources of information. "With more and more people seeking information on the state, which often required hours and even days of research," Mr. Herndon in the Fall of 1920 entered into arrangements to begin work toward the publication of this three volume series. The Centennial History is divided into three volumes. Volume #1 is concerned with the history of Arkansas from its earliest beginnings and is divided into seven major parts, beginning with the Indians, explorers, French and Spanish domination, etc. and continuing with Arkansas as a Territory, pioneer life, customs and final admission into the Union. In these seven major headings will also be found sections dealing with the Political History, Industrial History, Education, Military (the War with Mexico, Civil War, Reconstruction, etc.) and Local History, which is concerned with the formation of the counties, county officers, population, cities and towns, etc. Volumes #2 of this series contains approximately 1,200 Biographical Sketches of Prominent leaders and individuals through out the state of Arkansas up through the year 1922. As with Goodspeed Histories, it should be noted that these sketches contain a vast storehouse of family history and primary genealogical source material for the person with Arkansas "Roots." Many of these sketches also carry these family histories back into the early 1880's and some instances to the late 1790's. See our website for a full listing of the surnames of the Biographees.

Centennial History *of* Arkansas - Volume #3.
By: Dallas T. Herndon, Pub. 1922, Reprinted 2019, 1076 pages, Index, ISBN #0-89308-070-5.

AR 11 $75.00

When Dallas T. Herndon became Secretary of Arkansas History Commission in 1911, he began to "realize that the state had no history that could be relied upon as authentic," although several state histories had been published, but whose authors did not have access to reliable sources of information. "With more and more people seeking information on the state, which often required hours and even days of research," Mr. Herndon in the Fall of 1920 entered into arrangements to begin work toward the publication of this three volume series. The Centennial History is divided into three volumes. Volume #1 is concerned with the history of Arkansas from its earliest beginnings and is divided into seven major parts, beginning with the Indians, explorers, French and Spanish domination, etc. and concinting with Arkansas as a Territory, pioneer life, customs and final admission into the Union. In these seven major headings will also be found sections dealing with the Political History, Industrial History, Education, Military (the War with Mexico, Civil War, Reconstruction, etc.) and Local History, which is concerned with the formation of the counties, county officers, population, cities and towns, etc. Volumes #2 and #3 of this series contains Biographical Sketches of Prominent leaders and individuals in Arkansas up through the year 1922. As with Goodspeed Histories, it should be noted that these sketches contain a vast storehouse of family history and primary genealogical source material for the person with Arkansas "Roots." Many of these sketches also carry these family histories back into the early 1880's and some instances to the late 1790's.

History *of* Arkansas: the GENERAL History *of the* State.
By: Goodspeed Publishing Company, Pub. 1891, Reprinted 2017, 124 pages, Index, soft cover, ISBN #0-89308-078-0.

AR 15 $17.50

This is the first 124 pages that appears in all of Goodspeeds Histories of Arkansas. It is a detailed history of the state and its creation.

The History *of* Central Arkansas.
Reprinted 2015, 760 pages, Index, ISBN #0-89308-079-9.

AR 16 $60.00

This is probably one of the MOST VALUABLE set of books ever published on Arkansas Families. There are 7 volumes to the set, of which all have been reprinted by SHP, inc. with a NEW FULL NAME INDEX at one point in time. This book is broken into two main sections. The first is devoted to the history of the counties, while the second section contains biographical sketches of some 930 individuals and genealogical data of some 4,750 other families/ individuals for the following counties: Jefferson, Saline, Hot Spring, Pulaski, Garland, Lonoke, Perry, Faulkner and Grant. The New Index that was perepared for this reprint edition contains the names of over 14,500 individuals. Many of these biographical sketches of these early pioneers date well back into the early to mid 1700s.

The History *of* Eastern Arkansas. By: Goodspeed Publishing Company, Pub. 1891, Reprinted 2017, 786 pages, NEW INDEX, ISBN #0-89308-080-2.

AR 17 $62.50

This is probably one of the MOST VALUABLE set of books ever published on Arkansas Families. There are 7 volumes to the set, of which all have been reprinted by SHP, inc. with a NEW FULL NAME INDEX at one point in time. This book is broken into two main sections. The first is devoted to the history of the counties, while the second section contains biographical sketches of some 1,250 individuals and genealogical data of some 4,750 other families/ individuals for the following counties: Arkansas, Crittenden, Cross, Lee, Monroe, Phillip, Prairie, and St. Francis. The New Index that was prepared for this reprint edition contains the names of over 17,500 individuals. Many of these biographical sketches of these early pioneers date well back into the early to mid 1700s.

The History *of* Western Arkansas. By: Goodspeed Publishing Company, Pub. 1891, Reprinted 2017, 576 pages, Index,Hard Cover, ISBN #0-89308-084-5.

AR 21 $58.50

This is probably one of the MOST VALUABLE set of books ever published on Arkansas Families. There are 7 volumes to the set, of which all have been reprinted by SHP, inc. with a NEW FULL NAME INDEX at one point in time. This book is broken into two main sections. The first is devoted to the history of the counties, while the second section contains biographical sketches of some 8,000 individuals and genealogical data of some 3,200 other families/ individuals for the following counties: Conway, Johnson, Logan, Montgomery, Polk, Pope, Scott, and Yell. The New Index that was prepared for this reprint edition contains the names of over 15,000 individuals. Many of these biographical sketches of these early pioneers date well back into the early to mid 1700s. In this volume, the History of Conway County, AR plus the Biographical Sketches of the county were included too. In the original 1891 edition Conway was left out but SHP, inc. with the help of some very knowledgeable librarians have located and included Goodspeeds left out county. A new index was completed for this section also. So please be aware that there are two indexes in this book to cover the original section plus the new section that covers Conway County, AR

History *of* Northeast Arkansas. Reprinted 2002, 1040 pages, Index, ISBN #0-89308-081-0.

AR18 $75.00

This volume contains Biographical Sketches of 1,500 individuals and 6,500 other families listed in these sketches. Counties covered in this volume are: Clay, Craighead, Fulton, Greene, Independence, Izard, Jackson, Lawrence, Mississippi, Poinsett and Sharp.

History *of* Southern Arkansas. By: Goodspeed Publishing Company, Pub. 1891, Reprinted 1984, 1112 pages, Index,Hard Cover, ISBN #0-89308-083-7

AR 20 $75.00

This volume contains Biographical Sketches if 1,750 individuals and 7,000 other families listed in these sketches. Counties covered are: Conway, Johnson, Logan, Montgomery, Polk, Pope, Scott, and Yell. The New Index that was created for this reprint mentions over 15,000 names. In this volume, the History of Conway County, AR. plus the biographical Sketches of the county were included too. In the original 1891 edition, Conway was left out but SHP, inc. with the help of some very knowledgeable librarians have located and included Goodspeeds left out county. A new Index was completed for this section also. So please be aware that thereb are two indexes in this book to cover the original section plus the new section that covers Conway County, AR.

DELAWARE

Calendar *of* Kent County, Delaware Probate Records 1680-1800. By: Leon de Valinger, Jr., Pub. 1944, Reprinted 2018, 688 pages, soft cover, ISBN #0-89308-309-7.

DE 1 $52.50

Kent ounty was created in 1683 and is located in the central portion of the state. Immigrants from England stated settling this region of the St. Johns River about 1670. Probate records are a wonderful source of genealogical information and ar a standard research tool of the family historian. Information to be found within this book: Name of the deceased, the type of document whether it is a will or administration, date of probate, names of heirs, executors, administrators & witnesses, and folio number which will lead the reader to the location of the actual document within the Archives.

New Castle County, Delaware, 1676-1681. (Volume #1), Records *of the* Court *of.* By: The Colonial Society of Pennsylvania, Pub. 1904, Reprinted 2019, soft cover, Vol. 1, (1676-1681): 562 pages, Index, ISBN #0-89308-021-7.

DE 2 $48.50

\New Castle County was one the first three counties in Delaware and was created in 1676. It sits in the northern most portion of the state boarding Maryland, New Jersey and Pennsylvania. This book is a compilation of multiple types of courts such as: Court of Common Pleas and Court of Quarter Sessions and Orphans Court. In these minutes of pleas & quarters sessions you will find appointments of county officials, appointed administrators, marked public roads, granting of licenses to ordinaries, taxes being levied, civil actions of a wide variety,persons being tried for offenses against the peace & dignity of the State, list of jurys, guardian accounts of orphans, Wills, and countless numbers of Deed Acknowledgements.

New Castle County, Delaware, 1681-1699. (Volume #2), Records *of the* Court *of.* By: The Colonial Society of Pennsylvania, Pub. 1904 & 1934, Reprinted 2019, soft cover, Vol. 2, (1681-1699): 252 pages, Index, ISBN #0-89308-022-5.

DE 3 $25.00

New Castle County was one the first three counties in Delaware and was created in 1676. It sits in the northern most portion of the state boarding Maryland, New Jersey and Pennsylvania. This book is a compilation of multiple types of courts such as: Court of Common Pleas and Court of Quarter Sessions and Orphans Court. In these minutes of pleas & quarters sessions you will find appointments of county officials, appointed administrators, marked public roads, granting of licenses to ordinaries, taxes being levied, civil actions of a wide variety,persons being tried for offenses against the peace & dignity of the State, list of jurys, guardian accounts of orphans, Wills, and countless numbers of Deed Acknowledgements.

Sussex County, Delaware, Some Records *of.* By: C.H.B. Turner, Pub. 1909, Reprinted 2021, soft cover, 418 pages, Index, ISBN #978-1-63914-013-8.

DE 4 $35.00

Sussex County was created in 1680 and is the southern most county in the state. It shares boarders with Maryland and the Atlantic Ocean. This book has a wide variety of records within, ranging from: civil, court, church and Bible records. The civil records range from Letters to Petitions to Residents Lists. While the court records cover such things as: Land Grants, Civil Suits, Wills, Administrations and Marriage records. The Church records cover such things as: Letters, Petitions, Subscriber Lists and Vestry records for St. Peter's church. This leaves us to the last type of records: The Bible records. Here one will discover a wealth of genealogical information including things like: births, deaths, and marriages. Also the reader will discover that there are some Kent County records that have been included.

Walter Wharton's Land Survey Register, 1675-1679. By: Albert Cook Myers, Pub. 1955, reprinted 2023, 124 pgs, soft cover, Index, ISBN #978-1-63914-082-4.

DE 5 $18.50

The region that these land surveys cover was called the West Side Delaware River. It ran from New Castle County, Delaware up to Bucks County, Pennsylvania. This book should make a nice addition to anyone's collection researching in this are along the Delaware River.

FLORIDA

Biographical Souvenior *of the* States *of* Georgia *&* Florida. By: F.A. Battle & Company, Pub. 1880, Reprinted 2017, 880 pages, Index, Hard Cover, ISBN #0-89308-040-3.

GA 1 $75.00

This volume is perhaps the RAREST of all books of biographical sketches of persons located within Georgia and Florida. It is so rare that are only 6 original copies known to exist in the Public Libraries of Georgia. This book contains 1,000 biographical histories of individuals living in 1889. That means that these genealogies will carry the reader back several generations going as far back as the mid 1700's. This book should be considered a Statewide reference book for both states. This book should be a welcome addition to the library of anyone who is researching in Georgia & Florida. ***See our website for a list of names of biographies.***

Loyalists *in* EAST FLORIDA, 1774-1785. By: Wilbur H. Siebert, Pub. 1929, Reprinted 2018, 264 pages, Index, soft cover, ISBN #0-89308-979-6.

FL 6 $27.50

This book is the consolidation of two volumes. Part one is a narrative in which the events of the American Revolution involving the participation of British Loyalists of East Florida or those loyalists who went to East Florida from other neighboring provinces / states, either during or at the close of the Revolution, are detailed. Part two consists of the claims of the loyalists who were mentioned in part one.

Effingham County, Georgia 1786-1860, Records *of.* By: Caroline P. Wilson, Judge Huxford & Rev. S.E. Lucas, Jr., Pub. 1976, Reprinted 2017, 416 pages, New Index, ISBN #0-89308-019-5.

GA 21 $35.00

This book is the joining together of two separate works: "Annals of Georgia Vol. #2" and various legal records that appeared within the Georgia Genealogical Magazine between 1961-1975 that covered Effingham County. Records within this book are: Effingham County Deeds 1767-1806; Marriages 1757-1857; Wills 1826-1854; Court minutes 1827-1850; Miscellaneous Records from Ordinary's Office 1791-1834 & 1850-1865, these records contain such things as: administrations, wills, guardianships, deeds of gifts, gifts of personal property and other proceedings; and lists of residents who drew land in the 1805, 1807, 1820 & 1821 Land Lotteries. Other records covering surrounding areas: Alachua County, FL wills 1836-1858; Duval County, FL. marriages 1825-1859; Bulloch Count, GA. marriages 1795-1842; Camden County, GA. marriages 1819-1842; Columbia County, GA. marriages 1806-1812; Screven County, GA. Wills 1808-1850 and Screven County, GA. marriages 1835-1860.

Spanish Land Grants *in* Florida, 1797-1799. (5 Volumes). By: WPA, Pub. 1940, reprinted 2021, soft cover, Index.

Vol. #1, 1752-1786, Unconfirmed Claims: 442 pages, Index, ISBN #978-1-63914-000-8.
FL 1 $40.00

Vol. #2, 1752-1786: 442 pages, Index, ISBN #978-1-63914-001-5.
FL 2 $40.00

Vol. #4, 1787-1793: 412 pages, Index, ISBN #978-1-63914-002-2
FL 3 $40.00

Vol. #4, 1793-1797: 350 pages, Index, ISBN #978-1-63914-003-9.
FL 4 $35.00

Vol. #5, 1797-1799: 410 pages, Index, ISBN #978-1-63914-004-6
FL 5 $40.00

The Spanish Land Grants were land claims filed by settlers in Florida after the transfer of the territory from Spain to the United States in 1821 in order to prove land ownership. Starting in 1790, Spain offered land grants to encourage settlement to the sparsely populated and vulnerable Florida colony. When the United States assumed control of Florida, it agreed to honor any valid land grants. This volume is comprised of confirmed Claims for the years 1797-1799. The value of the translation of the Spanish Land Grants and their supporting documents is also enhanced by the inclusion of geographical data, such as the names and locations of creeks, roads and Indian trails, as well as basic information on the size, location and basis of each claim will be found to be important social and economic data on the English occupation of Florida (1763-1783) and the second Spanish occupation (1783-1821).

GEORGIA

Early Settlers *of* Georgia, A List *of the.* By: E. Merton Coulter and Albert B. Saye, Pub. 1949, Reprinted 2018, 124 pages, soft cover, ISBN #0-89308-943-5.
GA 104 $18.50

This book is a list of the early settlers of Georgia but more importantly a list of the FIRST SETTLERS of Georgia. It is considered a complete list of all those who were sent by the Trustees for establishing the Colony know as Georgia. This book is broken into three parts. Part one is a list in alphabetical order of persons who went from Europe to Georgia at the Trustees' Charge. Part two is a list in alphabetical order of persons who went from Europe to Georgia on their own Account. Giving such information as: Name, Name of Spouse, Age, Marital status, date left Europe, date arriving in Georgia, final destination heading to, Name of Trustees, occupation and etc... And part three, is a list in alphabetical order of the first Shipload of Georgia Settlers.

(Baldwin County) Deaths *from the* Federal Union, 1830-1850. By: Rev. Silas Emmett Lucas, Jr., Pub. 2017, 129 pages, New Index, ISBN #0-89308-603-7.
GA 34 $25.00

Baldwin County was created in 1803 from Wilkinson County. These records of deaths come from The Federal Union, a newspaper that was being published out of Milledgeville, GA. These records were originally to be included in "Marriage & Obituaries from Early Georgia Newspapers". Unfortunately, they were left out but were just recently rediscovered. This book should be considered a companion volume to the abovementioned book. The Index mentions approximately ??,000 names.

Baldwin County, Georgia, History of. By: Anna Maria Green Cook, Pub. 1925, reprinted 2023, 522 pages, Index, soft cover, ISBN #0-89308-777-7.
GA 54 $48.50

Baldwin County, one of the original Georgia counties, was formed in 1805 from lands obtained from the Creek Indians in cessions of 1802 and 1805. It is the parent county to: Bibb, Jasper, Jones, Morgan, Putnam, Newton and Rockdale. This book is similar to other history of books of its era with such topics as: organization of the county, Indians tribes, treaties, old stage roads and Indian trails, religion, trade/commerce, schools, and towns being discussed. The reader will also find sections devoted to lists of soldiers of various wars, marriage records from 1807 to 1820. The genealogists will discover over 200 pages devoted to biographies of approximately 150 families. The new Full names index that was created for this reprint references approximately 6,000 persons. Surnames of biography's: Allen, Barron, Bass, Beckam, Beeson, Bell (2), Bigham, Bonner, Boykin, Brown, Butts, Calloway, Campbell (2), Case (2), Cline, Cobb, Compton, Cone, Conn, Cook, Cooper, Crawford (2), Crowder, DuBignon, Duncan, Edmondson, Ellison, Ennis, Fair, Farell, Fort, Furman, Garrard, Grantland, Green (2), Grieve (2), Gumm, Hall, Hammond, Harper, Harris, Hawkins, Herty (2), Hines, Horne, Humber, Hunter, Huson, Joseph, Kenan, Knight, Lamar (2), Lane, Leverette, Little, McComb, McCullar, McCullough, McIntosh, McKinley, Mitchell, Moore, Myrick (2), Newell, Orme, Parks, Pratt, Prince, Rabun, Richardson, Rutherford, Sanford, Scogin, Scott, Shinholser, Singleton, Stembridge, Stovall, Torrance, Tucker, Vinson, Waller, Whitaker, White, Wiedenman, Williams, and Williamson.

History *of the* Baptist Denomination *in* Georgia *with* Biographical Compendium *and* Portrait Gallery *of* Baptist Ministers *and other* Georgia Baptists. By: Samuel Boykin, Pub. 1881, reprinted 2022, 906 pages, Index, soft cover, ISBN #0-89308-038-1.
GA 8 $68.50

A book of excellent source material for early Georgia families, as it contains biographical sketches of some 628 Georgia Baptist Ministers and Georgia Baptists. These biographical sketches will carry some of these individuals and their families well back into the middle to late 1700's. ***See website for a list of surnames of biographees.***

Bartow County, Georgia, History of. By: Lucy Cunyus, Pub. 1933, Reprinted 2017, 463 pages, Index, ISBN #0-89308-005-5.
GA 44 $45.00

Bartow County was formed in 1832 from Cherokee County. This book has 100 sketches of pioneers, lists of officials of Cass County, Biographies of its famous citizens, lists of early churches, Land Grants, Pioneer settlers 1830-1860, Militia and early marriages 1837-1843.

Bibb County, Georgia Inferior Court Minutes, 1824-1831 (2 Volumes). By: Michael A. Ports, Pub. 2019, soft cover.

Vol. #1, 1814-1827: 380 pages, Index, ISBN #0-89308-992-3.
GA 130 $42.50

Vol. #2, 1826-1831: 316 pages, ndex, ISBN #0-89308-993-1.
GA 131 $35.00

Bibb County was created in 1822 from Jones, Monroe, Houston and Twiggs counties. It is located in the center of the state with city of Macon being the county seat. The Inferior Court tried any civil case except those involving title to land. The court had jurisdiction over county business matters, such as care for the poor, building and maintaining the courthouse, jails, roads bridges and ferries, issuing liquor licenses, nominating justices of the peace, performing naturalization's, appointing guardians, authorizing apprenticeships & indentures, maintaining a register of wills and administering county funds. The Clerk of the Inferior Court kept minutes of the foregoing proceedings--every one of which places individuals in Franklin County at a particular point in time

Bibb County, Georgia Superior Court Minutes, 1823-1839, (7 Volumes). By: Michael A. Ports, Pub. 2018.

Vol. #1, 1823-1826: 452 pages, Index, ISBN #0-89308-982-6.
GA 97 $20.00

Vol. #2, 1825-1828: 452 pages, Index, ISBN #0-89308-982-6.
GA 98 $45.00

Vol. #3, 1828-1831: 428 pages, Index, ISBN #0-89308-983-4.
GA 99 $45.00

Vol. #4, 1831-1835, part 1: 432 pages, Index, ISBN #0-89308-984-2.
GA 124 $45.00

Vol. #5, 1831-1835, part 2: 366 pages, Index, ISBN #0-89308-999-0.
GA 125 $38.50

Vol. #6, 1835-1839, part 1: 432 pages, Index, ISBN #0-89308-987-7.
GA 126 $45.00

Vol. #7, 1835-1839, part 2: 450 pages, Index, ISBN #0-89308-998-5.
GA 127 $45.00

Bibb County was created in 1822 from Jones, Monroe, Houston and Twiggs counties. It is located in the center of the state with city of Macon being the county seat. The Superior Court of the county had jurisdiction over all criminal matters, civil cases involving title to land, appeals from Inferior Court decisions and Justice's Courts, divorces, grand juries, naturalization, and registration of land deeds.

Biographical Souvenior of the States of

Georgia & Florida. By: F.A. Battle & Company, Pub. 1880, Reprinted 2017, 880 pages, Index, Hard Cover, ISBN #0-89308-040-3.

GA 1 $75.00

This volume is perhaps the RAREST of all books of biographical sketches of persons located within Georgia and Florida. It is so rare that are only 6 original copies known to exist in the Public Libraries of Georgia. This book contains 1,000 biographical histories of individuals living in 1889. That means that these genealogies will carry the reader back several generations going as far back as the mid 1700's. This book should be considered a Statewide reference book for both states. This book should be a welcome addition to the library of anyone who is researching in Georgia & Florida. ***See our website for a list of names of biographies.***

Brooks County, Georgia, 1858-1948, The History *of.* By: Folks Huxford, Pub. 1943, reprinted 2021, 702 pages, Index, soft cover, ISBN #978-1-63914-030-5.

GA 64 $60.00

Brooks county is located in the southern portion of the state while sharing a border with Florida. This are of Georgia is often times referred to as the Wiregrass Region. This monumental history of an area with rich and varied heritage begins with the creation of the Irwin County from Indian lands ceded to Georgia in 1818. From Irwin emerged Lowndes and Thomas counties and ultimately Brooks County in 1858. The book contains vivid accounts of the Indian wars and is replete with lists of early settlers. A complete U.S. census for Brooks County in 1860 is given, as well as portions of earlier census reports for the parent counties. Extensive treatment of the Civil War period includes muster rolls of every unit from Brooks in the Confederate or State service and deaths of individual soldiers are indicated. Military units of the Spanish-American War and World War I and II are provided. Topics discussed include professional life, agriculture, religious and fraternal organizations, educational and cultural activities, and the development of Quitman and county industries. This volume contains extensive lists of county officers, residents and soldiers. It concludes with approximately 200 pages of family history covering 65 Brooks County families and their connections: Allbritton, Avera, Baum, Bennett (2), Bower, Branch, Brice, Clower, Creech, Davidson, Davis, Denmark, Dukes, Duncan, Edmondson, Gaulden, Groover-Gruber, Harrell (2), Harden, Hassell, Hendry, Hitch (3), Hodges, Hunter, Jelks (2), Johnson, King (2), Long, Mabbett, Mizell, Morrison, Morton, McCall, McCardel, McDonald, McIntosh, McMichael, McMullen, McRae, Oglesby (2), Patrick, Perdue, Powers, Ramsey, Robinson-Wade, Rountree, Sheffield, Sinclair, Spain, Tillman (2), Turner, Wade, Walker, Wilson, and Young (3).

Burke County, Georgia, Families *of.* By: Robert Scott Davis & Silas Emmett Lucas, Pub. 1981, Reprinted 2018, 816 pages, Index, ISBN #0-89308-211-2.

GA 43 $52.50

Burke County was created in 1777 as one of the original 7 counties of the state. Information in this volume includes: English Crown Grants in St. George Parish in GA 1755-1775; Landowners of St. George Parish, GA; State Land Grants in Burke, Jefferson and Screven Counties, GA; Remnant of the 1798 Federal Direct Tax Digest of Burke County, GA; Land Lottery Records of Burke County, GA 1805-1832; 1820, 1830, 1840 & 1850 Federal Census of Burke County; 1820 Burke County Manufacturers Census; 1840 Schedules of Mines, Agriculture, Commerce, Manufacturers; 1850 Lists of 6 schedules for the 1850 Census; Legend for 1850 Free Schedule; 1850 Slave Schedule of Burke County; 1850 Mortality Schedule of Burke County; 1850 Social Statistics of Burke County; 1850 Agricultural Schedule of Burke County; and 1855 Federal Tax Digest of Burke County.

Camden County, Georgia Inferior Court Minutes, 1794-1815. By: Michael A. Ports, Pub. 2018, 270 pages, Index, soft cover, ISBN #0-89308-981-8.

GA 52 $32.50

Camden County was one the original 7 counties of the state. It was created in 1777 and is located in southeastern corner of the state boarding the Atlantice Ocean. The Inferior Court tried any civil case except those involving title to land. The court had jurisdiction over county business matters, such as care for the poor, building and maintaining the courthouse, jails, roads and bridges, issuing liquor licenses, nominating justices of the peace, performing naturalizations, appointing guardians, authorizing indentures, and maintaining a register of wills. The Clerk of the Inferior Court kept minutes of the foregoing proceedings--every one of which places individuals in Camden County at a particular point in time

Camden County, Georgia Superior Court Minutes, 1797-1809. By: Michael A. Ports, Pub. 2018, 404 pages, Index, soft cover, ISBN #0-89308-938-9.

GA 53 $42.50

Camden County was one the original 7 counties of the state. It was created in 1777 and is located in southeastern corner of the state boarding the Atlantic Ocean. The Superior Court of the county had jurisdiction over all criminal matters, civil cases involving title to land, appeals from Inferior Court decisions, divorces, grand juries, and registration of land deeds.

Chattahoochee County, Georgia, History *of.* By: N.K. Rogers, Pub. 1933, Reprinted 2010, 402 pages, hard cover, New Index, ISBN #0-89308-032-2.

GA 36 $45.00

Located on the Chattahoochee River in southwestern Georgia, Chattahoochee County was carved out of present day counties of Muscogee, Marion, Stewart, Talbot, and Webster Counties, Georgia and on the west across the Chattahoochee River by Russell County, Alabama. The family historian / genealogist will find this book to be a gold mine of information for this and surrounding counties. There are many lists given: road overseers for 1845, road commissioners for 1848 & 1913, Representatives of the State Legislature 1854, Senators 1861, and lists of county officials such as Sheriffs, tax collectors, surveyors, coroners, justices of the peace, and many other types of county officials. There are also lists of marriages from 1854-1889, seven rosters of troops that were organized and recruited from Chattahoochee County, and even the 1st Tax Digest for 1857 is given. The author even includes some church records of which there are church rolls & memberships from various churches covering the time period 1837-1870 and even tombstone inscriptions from the County Line Church. There are also abstracts from the Court of Ordinary from 1854-1865, along with abstracts of the Wills from the county covering 1853-1883. Another interesting aspect of this book are the land transfers that occurred in both Muscogee and Chattahoochee counties that start in 1833 and go well into the 1860's. The major bulk of this book (230 pages) is devoted to family genealogies / biographical sketches of its early residents.

Cherokee County, Georgia, History of. By: Rev. Lloyd G. Marlin, Pub. 1932, reprinted 2023, 303 pages, soft cover, ISBN #978-1-63914-118-0.

GA 15 $30.00

Cherokee County was created in 1831 out of lands that were ceded from the Cherokee Indians as part of the 1832 Cherokee Land Lottery. This book is broken in to two main sections. The first is a historical account of the county with topics as: creation of the county, Indians, Boundaries and divisions, early settlers, Land Lotteries, Land Grants, Militia, Civil War involvement, towns, education, religion, commerce along with other things all important to growth and development to the county. The second section is devoted to biographical sketches of these early residents. Surnames: Anderson, Bearden, Blanton, Bobo, Brady, Burtz, Cagle, Carpenter, Chapman (6), Cline (3), Coker, Collins (2), Covington, Cox, Crisler (2), Day, Dean, Dial, Dobbs, Doss (2), Dowda, DuPree, Edwards, Elliott, Epperson, Erwin, Faulkner, Field, Fincher (4), Galt (2), Garrett, Gramling, Groover, Groves, Harbin, Harmon, Hillhouse, Hogan, Holcomb, Hughes, Johnson, Johnston (3), Jones (6), Knox, Landrum, Lathem, Lewis, McCanless (3), McClure (2), McWhorter, Mahan, Moore (2), Moss, Perry, Pettis, Ponder, Power (2), Redd, Richardson, Roberts (3), Rudasill, Sharp, Simpson, Spears, Stone, Tate, Teasley, Thomas, Thomason, Timmons, Vandivier, Wood (3), Worley and Wright.

Clarke County, Georgia Records, 1801-1892. By: Robert Davis, Jr., Pub. 1993, 264 pages, Hard Cover, Index, ISBN #0-89308-485-9.

GA 19 $35.00

This book contains the names of approximately 21,000 individuals found in these records. This book is divided into four (4) major sections as follows: PART 1 - which contains Loose Original Records: Inventory of Estate Records, 1801-1823; Lost Court Files of the Inferior Court, 1805-1895; A Listing and Description of Miscellaneous Files, 1800-1925. PART 2 - Abstracts from the Miscellaneous Files: 1. Misc. Records such as a Poor List, 1832 & 1837; Estray Declarations and Records, 1820, 1837-1873; 2. Confederate Records, 1862-1892, such as Guardians of Orphan Children of deceased soldiers; Cripple soldiers for life; Soldiers Widows; Dependents on Soldiers for Support, vis: wives and widows and children of Confederate Soldiers; 3. Militia records, 1804-1831; 4. Poor School Records, 1823. PART 3 - Original Marriage Records, 1804-1850's. PART 4 - Inventory of county records of Georgia Archives, viz: 1. Probate Court Records; Superior Court Records including index to Deeds and Mortgages and Superior Court Minutes; 2. Private records on microfilm, such as family histories, journals, family collections; 3. Militia Records from Duke University, 1804-1823; 4. Appendix, containing a missing page from the 1840 census and Land Court Minutes, 1803-1832.

Clarke County, Georgia, History *of* Athens *and.* By: H.J. Rowe, Printed 1999, 180 pages plus New Index, Hard Cover, ISBN #0-89308-412-3.

GA 11 $30.00

Clarke County was created from Jackson County in 1801, and Jackson County had been cut off from Franklin County in 1796. This whole area is a pivotal point of migration into, as settlers were moving westward from South Carolina and was a springboard into areas further west. This book discusses the development of the city of Athens as well as the county of Clarke through discussions of religious, educational, political, and economic affairs that occurred during this time. The researcher will be delighted to find over 145 biographical sketches located throughout the book. These sketches of these early settlers had a wide variety professions ranging from: clergymen, teachers, doctors, politicians, businessmen and etc....

The Colonial Clergy *of* Maryland, Delaware *and* Georgia, 1629-1776. By: Frederick Lewis Weis, Pub. 1950, Reprinted 2021, 104 pages, soft cover, ISBN #978-1-63914-025-1.

MD 5 $17.50

This book is alphabetical list of approximately 700 colonial clergymen from 1629-1776 who settled in Maryland, Delaware, and Georgia. These annotations furnish such useful genealogical data as date & place of birth, date & place of death, names of parents, college of matriculation, date of ordination, denomination, names of parishes, dates in which tenure was held, and a variety of other similar data.

Coffee County Georgia 1755-1855, Ward's History of. By: Warren P. Ward, Pub. 1930, Reprint 2018, 410 pages, New Index, soft cover, 0-89308-976-1.

GA 24 $38.50

Coffee County was created in 1854 from Clinch, Ware, Telfair, & Irwin counties. This book covers the early Indians who lived in the area, the natural environment of the county, the economic and social side of Coffee's history, the Civil War, educational development, churches, newspapers, pioneer families, and railroads. Marriage records from Coffee County in the 1870's are listed.

Columbia County, Georgia Early Court Records, 1792-1840. By: Mrs. F.F. Baker, printed 2013, 156 pages, soft cover, Index, ISBN #0-89308-679-7.

GA 39 $20.00

Columbia County was created in 1790 from Richmond County. These court records contain such things as: Deeds of Gift, Bill of Sale, Powers of Attorney (many of which are from Revolutionary Soldiers, asking that their bounty lands and pensions in other states be obtained for them), and other Legal Oddments.

Cowetta County, Chronicles. By: Mary G. Jones and Lily Reynolds, Pub. 1928, Reprint 2019, 888 pages, maps, Index, 0-89308-016-0.

GA 6 $62.50

Cowetta County was formed in the 1827 Land Lottery. It lies in the western central portion of the state and is considered part of the current Metro Atlana area. The contents of this book: early histories of churches, bisiness, county officials, schools, Lists of first settlers by districts, Revolutionary War Soldiers who died in Cowetta, Marriages from 1827-1838, records of Cowetta County men in the Confederate Army, 163 family genealogies. This book is a MUST for for persons whose families migrated Westward into Central Georgia towards Alabama. For a list Genealogical sketches see the out website.

Effingham County, Georgia 1786-1860, Records of. By: Caroline P. Wilson, Judge Huxford & Rev. S.E. Lucas, Jr., Pub. 1976, Reprinted 2017, 416 pages, New Index, ISBN #0-89308-019-5.

GA 21 $40.00

This book is the joining together of two separate works: "Annals of Georgia Vol. #2" and various legal records that appeared within the Georgia Genealogical Magazine between 1961-1975 that covered Effingham County. Records within this book are: Effingham County Deeds 1767-1806; Marriages 1757-1857; Wills 1826-1854; Court minutes 1827-1850; Miscellaneous Records from Ordinary's Office 1791-1834 & 1850-1865, these records contain such things as: administrations, wills, guardianships, deeds of gifts, gifts of personal property and other proceedings; and lists of residents who drew land in the 1805, 1807, 1820 & 1821 Land Lotteries. Other records covering surrounding areas: Alachua County, FL wills 1836-1858; Duval County, FL. marriages 1825-1859; Bulloch Count, GA. marriages 1795-1842; Camden County, GA. marriages 1819-1842; Columbia County, GA. marriages 1806-1812; Screven County, GA. Wills 1808-1850 and Screven County, GA. marriages 1835-1860.

Elbert County, Georgia, 1790-1935, History of. By: John H. McIntoh, Pub. 1940, Reprint 2019, 676 pages, Index, 0-89308-871-4.

GA 57 $52.50

Elbert County was formed in 1790 from Wilkes County. It lies in the Northeastern portion of the state along the Savannah River just across from Anderson and Abbeville Counties, South Carolina. The first settlers started arriving in the area from Virginia and the Carolinas and continued on as land grants were being issued from service in the Revolutionary War. The first third of this book is a traditional history of the era with topics such as: Indians, creation of the county, politics, religion, involvement in various Wars, Commerce, and etc... But the genealogists will savior over the next two thirds of this book with such things as: Lists of early residents, abstracts of Deeds, Lists of original Land Warrants, Lists of Revolutionary soldiers and their widows, Muster Rolls of Confederate soldiers from Elbert County, Lists of soldiers who died from Elbert County in the Civil War, Lists of Old Graves in Elbert County, abstracts of early Wills and Administrations, and Marriage records 1803-1850. The author has also included Biographical Sketches on: Adams, Allen, Allgood, Alston, Arnold, Banks, Barnett, Blackwell, Brewer, Brown, Butler, Cade, Carpenter, Carlton, Carter (2), Christian, Clark/Clarke (2), Cleveland, Crawford, Conwell, Darden, Deadwyler, DuBose, Eberhardt, Eavenson, Fortson, Goolsby, Hailey/Haley, Hall, Hammond, Hansard, Haynes, Heard, Henry, Herndon, Higginbotham, Hudson, Hunt, Jones, Key, Lanier, LeGrand, marks, Mathews, Maxwell, McIntosh/Mackintosh, McMillan, Middleton, Oliver, Rice, Stark, Swift, Thornton, Wall, Walthall, Webb, Wilhite, Willis, Woolridge, Worley, and Wyche. The Index that was completed for this reprint contains names of over 16,500 individuals.

Elbert County, Georgia, Records of. By: Grace Gillam Davidson, Pub. 1930, Reprinted 2020, 354 pages, Index, ISBN #0-89308-008-X.

GA 17 $35.00

Elbert County was formed in 1790 from Wilkes County. It lies in the Northeastern portion of the state along the Savannah River just across from Anderson and Abbeville Counties, South Carolina. The first settlers started arriving in the area from Virginia and the Carolina's and continued on as land grants were being issued from service in the Revolutionary War. This volume was originally published as Volume III of the Historical Collection of the Georgia Chapters National Society Daughters of the American Revolution. Contents of this book: Wills 1791-1831, Wills Record Book 1830-1835, Index to Will Book 1829-1860, returns of Administrators and Guardians 1791-1838, Minutes of Inferior Court 1791-1830, Deed Books 1789-1797, Land Court Records 1791-1822, Land Lotteries 1806, 1821-1827, & 1832, Tombstone records and Marriages 1806-1834.

Elbert County, Georgia, 1820-1860 *and* Wilkes County, Georgia, 1850, The Census Records of. By: Irene S. Wilcox, Pub. 1979, reprinted, 2020,146 pages, ISBN #0-898308-155-8.

GA 13 $20.00

Wilkes County was created in 1777 from the northern part of St. Paul's Parish. This land was acquired from the Creek & Cherokee Indians in payment for debts owed to Indian Traders. It is the parent county, in whole or part, for: Elbert, Greene, Hart, Lincoln, Madison, Oglethorpe, Taliaferro and Warren. Elbert County was formed in 1790 from Wilkes County. It lies in the Northeastern portion of the state along the Savannah River just across from Anderson and Abbeville Counties, South Carolina. The first settlers started arriving in the area from Virginia and the Carolina's and continued on as land grants were being issued from service in the Revolution War. The 1820 census lists 1078 Heads of household; the 1830 some 1080; the 1840 some 961; the 1850 some 1180 and the 1860 census a total of 911 Heads of household in Elbert County. The 1850 Wilkes County Census has some 734 Heads of Household.

Elbert County, Georgia Court of Ordinary, Record of Apprentices, 1867-1903 (2 Volumes). By: Michael A. Ports, Pub. 2020, 222 pages, Index, soft cover, ISBN #0-89308-030-6.

Vol. #1: 222 pages, Index, ISBN #0-89308-030-6.
GA 111 $27.50

Vol. #2: 252 pages, ndex, ISBN #0-89308-552-9
GA 112 $30.00

Elbert County was formed in 1790 from Wilkes County. It lies in the Northeasern portion of the state along the Savannah River just across from Anderson and Abbeville Counties, South Carolina. The first settlers started arriving in the area from Virgina and the Carolinas and continued on as land grants were being issued from service in the Revolutionary War. These records primarily consist of copies of the indentures of apprenticeship, essentially the contracts binding the apprentice to the master. The indentures provide the date and term of the apprenticeship, and the names of the apprentice, the master, the person authorizing the indenture, usually a parent, guardian, next of kin, the ordinary, or judge, as well as witnesses. The indentures also specify the duties and responsibilities of both the apprentice and master.

Elbert County, Georgia Inferior Court Minutes, 1800-1850. (5 Volumes), By: Michael A. Ports, Pub. 2020, soft cover.

Vol. #2, 1800-1804: 332 pages, Index, ISBN #0-89308-973-7.
GA 105 $38.50

Vol. #3, 1800-1804: 324 pages, Index, ISBN #0-89308-974-5.
GA 106 $37.50

Vol. #5, 1807-1815: 326 pages, Index, ISBN #0-89308-999-0.
GA 108 $37.50

Vol. #6, 1810-1812: 138 pages, Index, ISBN #0-89308-410-7.
GA 109 $20.00

The Inferior Court tried any civil case except those involving title to land. The court had jurisdiction over county business matters, such as care for the poor, building and maintaining the courthouse, jails, roads bridges and ferries, issuing liquor licenses, nominating justices of the peace, performing naturalization's, appointing guardians, authorizing apprenticeships & indentures, maintaining a register of wills and administering county funds. The Clerk of the Inferior Court kept minutes of the foregoing proceedings--every one of which places individuals in Elbert County at a particular point in time

Vol. #7, 1809-1850: 220 pages, Index, ISBN #0-89308-420-4.
GA 110 $27.50

Contrary to the microfilm heading, the records in this volume #7 are NOT court minutes; but rather are the records concerning roads and bridges. The records include the orders appointing road commissioners and overseers, petitions to construct new roads and bridges or alter existing ones, and the reports of commissioners regarding the efficacy and public utility of newly proposed roads and bridges or alterations or repairs to existing ones.

Franklin County, Georgia Inferior Court Minutes, 1794-1812. (Volumes 1 & 2). By: Michael A. Ports, Pub. 2018, Index, 364 pages, soft cover, Index, ISBN #0-89308-991-5.
GA 128 $40.00

Franklin County was created in 1784 and was considered the 8th county of the state. It is located in the north eastern portion of the state boarding South Carolina along the Savannah River. The Inferior Court tried any civil case except those involving title to land. The court had jurisdiction over county business matters, such as care for the poor, building and maintaining the courthouse, jails, roads bridges and ferries, issuing liquor licenses, nominating justices of the peace, performing naturalizations, appointing guardians, authorizing apprenticeships & indentures, maintaining a register of wills and administering county funds. The Clerk of the Inferior Court kept minutes of the foregoing proceedings--every one of which places individuals in Franklin County at a particular point in time.

Franklin County, Georgia Superior Court Loose Papers, 1797-1860. By: Michael A. Ports, Pub. 2018, Index, 348 pages, soft Cover, Index, ISBN #0-89308-989-3.
GA 12 $40.00

Franklin County was created in 1784 and was considered the 8th county of the state. It is located in the northeastern portion of the state boarding South Carolina along the Savannah River. These records include bills of complaint, petitions, bonds, subpoenas, arrest warrants and other court orders, concerning both civil and criminal cases. In addition, these papers include election returns, lists of voters, juror panels, paupers and two declarations made to establish eligibility for a Revolutionary pension. one naming wife and children and listing property owned.

Franklin County, Georgia Superior Court Minutes, 1814-1834. (4 Volumes). By: Michael A. Ports, Pub. 2018, soft cover.

Vol. #1, 1814-1818: 196 pages, Index, ISBN #0-89308-929-X.
GA 120 $25.00

Vol. #2, 1821-1824: 186 pages, Index, ISBN #0-89308-930-3.
GA 121 $25.00

Vol. #3, 1825-1829: 270 pages, Index, ISBN #0-89308-931-1.
GA 122 $32.50

Vol. #4, 1830-1834: 264 pages, Index, ISBN #0-89308-932-X.
GA 123 $25.00

Franklin County was created in 1784 and was considered the 8th county of the state. It is located in the north eastern portion of the state boarding South Carolina along the Savannah River. The Superior Court of the county had jurisdiction over all criminal matters, civil cases involving title to land, appeals from Inferior Court decisions, divorces, grand juries, and registration of land deeds.

(Gordon County) Climb *the* Hills *of* Gordon. By: Jewell Reeve, Pub. 1962, 2nd Reprinting 1997, 320 pages, Hard Cover, Index, ISBN #0-89308-128-0.
GA 37 $25.00

A long out-of-print book filled with stories about the people who made Gordon County, their businesses and many little known facts about this county and its people. It is truly a refreshing history covering the period from 1857-1957.

Gwinnett County, Georgia, 1818-1943, History *of.* (Volume #1). By: James C. Flanigan, Pub. 1943, Reprint 2019, 446 pages, 0-89308-977-X.
GA 51 $40.00

Gwinnett County was created in 1818 from Jackson County and lands gained through the cession of Creek Indian lands. It lies in the north-central part of the state. This book is similar to other books of the era, discussing such topics as: Indians, Creation of the county, commerce, education, geography, politics and etc. But the reader will discover very useful things interspersed throughout this book such as: Muster rolls of Militia from 1813-1814; Lists of First Taxpayers 1820; Census of 1820; Lists of Lottery Drawers in Gwinnett for the 4th, 5th, 6th and 7th Districts; along with Gwinnett citizens who drew lots in Monroe and Houston Counties; Lists of First Settlers; Early Court Records 1821-1850; list of Gwinnett citizens who drew land in the 1832 Cherokee Land Lottery; List of 1835 & 1840 Pensioners; Lists of owners of Slaves 1820, 1840, 1850, & 1860; Lists of Plantation owners who owned more than 500 acre, and Names of Gwinnett County citizens who served in various Companies during the Civil War along with data on the ones who died during service. The author has also included biographical sketches of some early residents of the county: Adair (2), Anthony, Arnold, Baugh, Beasley, Berry, Bracewell, Brown, Camp, Chester, Cupp, Garmany, Gordon, Hale, Hall, Hawthorne, Hopkins, Howell, Hudson, Hutchins, Jackson, King, Laurence, Liddell (2), Lietch, Loveless, Malthie, Martin, Nesbit, Pruett, Rambo, Richardson, Rogers, Russell, Sammon, Save, Smith, Spencer, Stuart, Thomas, Whitworth (2), Williams, and Wilson.

Hancock County, Georgia, Land Deed Genealogy of. By: Helen & Tim Marsh, Pub. 1997, 348 pages, Hard Cover, Index, ISBN #0-89308-662-2.
GA 47 $38.50

Hancock County was created in 1793 from Greene and Washington Counties. It is surrounded by present day counties of: Baldwin, Greene, Glascock, Putnam, Taliaferro, Warren, and Washington. This book contains abstracts of Deed Books A-E which covers the years 1794-1802. This book should be quite useful as all federal census for Georgia were lost from 1790-1820.

Hancock County, Georgia Inferior Court Minutes, 1800-1808. (Volume #1). By: Michael A. Ports, Pub. 2018, 194 pages, Index, soft cover, ISBN #0-89308-835-8.
GA 37 $25.00

Hancock County was created in 1793 from Greene and Washington Counties. It is surrounded by present day counties of: Baldwin, Greene, Glascock, Putnam, Taliaferro, Warren, and Washington. The Inferior Court tried any civil case except those involving title to land. The court had jurisdiction over county business matters, such as care for the poor, building and maintaining the courthouse, jails, roads bridges and ferries, issuing liquor licenses, nominating justices of the peace, performing naturalization's, appointing guardians, authorizing apprenticeships & indentures, maintaining a register of wills and administering county funds. The Clerk of the Inferior Court kept minutes of the foregoing proceedings--every one of which places individuals in Hancock County at a particular point in time

Hancock County, Georgia Superior Court Minutes, 1794-1805. (2 Volumes). By: Michael A. Ports, Pub. 2019.

Vol. #1, 1794-1805, part 1: 348 pages, Index, ISBN #0-89308-757-2.
GA 58 $38.50

Vol. #2, 1794-1805, part 2: 348 pages, Index, ISBN #0-89308-768-8
GA 59 $38.50

Hancock County was created in 1793 from Greene and Washington Counties. It is surrounded by present day counties of: Baldwin, Greene, Glascock, Putnam, Taliaferro, Warren, and Washington. The Superior Court of the county had jurisdiction over all criminal matters, civil cases, appeals from Inferior Court decisions and Justice's Courts, divorces, grand juries, naturalizations, and registration of land deeds.

Hancock County, Georgia, 1806-1850, Marriages *of.* By: Martha Lou Houston, Pub. 1947, reprinted 2022, 84 pages, soft cover, ISBN #978-1-63914-060-2.
GA 137 $15.00

Hancock County was created in 1793 from Greene and Washington Counties. It is surrounded by present day counties of: Baldwin, Greene, Glascock, Putnam, Taliaferro, Warren, and Washington. These marriages are listed by Groom in alphabetical order.

Hart County, Georgia, History of. By: John W. Baker, Pub. 1935, Reprint 2019, 440 pages, Index, 0-89308-933-8.
GA 61 $40.00

Hart County was created in 1853 from Franklin and Elbert Counties. It lies in the Northeastern portion of the state. It sits on the Savannah River that separates Georgia from Old 96 and Abbeville Districts, South Carolina. Contents of this book start out with a detailed pre-formation of the county and its formation going into such things as: Militia Districts, towns, transportation, religion, politics, lists of Muster Rolls from the C.S.A and other items important to the development of the county. But more importantly, approximately 2/3rds of this book are devoted to genealogies of the following families or individuals: Ayers, Bailey, Barron, Benson, Black, Bobo, Bowers, Brown (3), Burton, Carnes, Carter, Chandler, Chapman, Cleveland, Cobb, Cornog, Craft, Dooley, Dyar, Fisher, Flemming (2), Gibson, Glover, Gordon, Hall, Harbour, Hart, Haynes, Herndon, Hodges (2), Holland, Hunt, Jackson, Johnson, Jones, Kay, Ledbetter (2), Looney, Magill, Maret, Matheson, McCurry (4), McDonald, McMullen, Myers (2), O'Barr, Parker (8), Patterson, Pearman, Peek (2), Poole, Redwine, Richardson, Sadler, Sanders (3), Skelton (2), Stephenson, Stowers (2), Teasley, Thornton, Tyler, Vernon, White (2), Williams, and Wright.

Jackson County, Georgia Inferior Court Minutes, 1796-1802. By: Michael A. Ports, Pub. 2019, 116 pages, Index, soft cover, ISBN #0-89308-088-8.

GA 129 $20.00

Jackson County was created in 1796 from Franklin County. It was the parent county in part or whole to Banks, Barrow, Clarke, Gwinnett, Hall, Madison and Walton Counties. Many of her first settlers came from nearby Effingham County. The Inferior Court tried any civil case except those involving title to land. The court had jurisdiction over county business matters, such as care for the poor, building and maintaining the courthouse, jails, roads bridges and ferries, issuing liquor licenses, nominating justices of the peace, performing naturalization's, appointing guardians, authorizing apprenticeships & indentures, maintaining a register of wills and administering county funds. The Clerk of the Inferior Court kept minutes of the foregoing proceedings--every one of which places individuals in Jackson County at a particular point in time

Jasper County, Georgia 1802-1922, Records of. By: Robert Scott Davis, Orig. Pub. 1990, reprinted 2015, 485 pages, soft cover Index, ISBN #0-89308-626-6

GA 91 $48.50

This book contains: Marriage records 1816-1914, wills 1809-1907, estate files 1809-1907, Misc. pension records 1812-1920, superior court cases 1809-1922, county court files 1860-1913, justice of the peace court case files 1802-1935, Poney Homestad (debt & tax exemptions) records 1867-1907, land grant records 1799-1823, deeds 1808-1903, and miscellaneous unbound records 1808-1935.

Jones County, Georgia, History of. By: Carolyn White Williams Pub. 1957, Reprint 2020, 1128 pages, Index, Hard Cover, 0-89308-872-2.

GA 60 $85.00

Jones County was created in 1807 from Baldwin County. It is located in the center of the state. Originally known for its farmlands before the Civil War, it suffered destruction during the Civil War as Sherman's march to the sea passing through the county due to it cotton gin factor being retrofitted to produce pistols for the Confederate Army. This book is similar to other history books of the era with such topics being discussed: preformation of the county, formation of the county, Indians, early settlers, involvement in the War of 1812, education, religion/churches, towns, roads/trails, and considerable amount of discussion of its involvement in the Civil War. The author has included inscriptions from 40 cemeteries from around the county. She has also included the history of 22 ante-bellum homes located in Jones County and often times giving a biographical sketch of its owner: Clinton, Gordon-Bowen-Blount, Comer, Small, Newton, Peyton, Pitts, Cabaniss, Day-Barron, Barron, Glawson, Lancaster, Greene, White, Roberts, Moughon, Tomotavia, Johnson, and Lowther. But more importantly are the 80 plus genealogies of persons from the county. The reader will also discover an appendix filled with genealogical data: 1811 Tax Digest, 1820 Census, 1826 Land Lottery Draws, Marriage Bonds 1811-1890, Slave Deed Records 1791-1865, Index of Wills 1808-1890, Abstracts of Wills 1808-1810, List of Revolutionary Soldiers and Widows of Soldiers, Roster of Confederate Soldiers, WWI and WWII, Index to 1850 Census, and List of Garnd Jurors 1808-1810.

Laurens County, Georgia History of. By: Bertha S. Hart, Pub. 1941, Reprinted 2018, 612 pages, Index, ISBN #0-89308-888-9.

GA 42 $48.50

Laurens County was created in 1807 from Wilkinson County. This book covers the early Indians who lived in the area, the natural environment of the county, the economic and social side of Coffee's history, the Civil War, educational development, churches, newspapers, pioneer families, and railroads. A particular useful feature of this book is the extensive last half of the book which covers the marriages of the county 1809-1848, Wills 1808-1869 and genealogies of some 130 persons........

Lincoln County, Georgia, History of. By: Clinton J. Perryman, Pub. 1933, reprinted 2021, 224 pages, Index, ISBN #978-1-63914-005-3.

GA 62 $25.00

Lincoln County was created 1796 from Wilkes County. This book is not too different from other county history books of this era. With such topics as formation of county, trade and transportation, labor, farming, religion, towns and involvement in Revolutionary & Civil War - all important in the development of the county - are carefully discussed. This type of county history book can help one develop ideas or paths to those missing ancestors by showing the customs and traditions of the local residents. A particular useful feature of this book is the extensive biographical information included. Almost a third of this book is devoted to biographical sketches for: Ashmore (2), Boykin, Clarke, Crawford (2), Curry, Dooly (3), Dunaway, Florence, Hogan (3), Hudson, Humphreys, Lamar (2), Lyon, Murray, Perryman, Smalley, Strother, Tutt, Ward, Ware and Zellars.

Macon County, Georgia, History of. By: Louise F. Hays, Pub. 1935, reprinted 2023, 803 pages, Index, soft cover, ISBN #089308-776-9.

GA 51 $62.50

Macon County was created in 1837 from Houston and Marion Counties. It is the parent to Peach and Taylor counties. Many of its the early settlers migrated from Newberry and Orangeburg Counties, South Carolina. This book begins with an account of the original inhabitants, the Muscogee, Euchee and Creek Indians, of the region. The book describes the rapid settlement of the area after the land between the Flint and Ocmulgee Rivers was secured by treaty and then disposed of by Lottery. A section of the book is devoted to lists of early settlers holding land grants in what was to become Macon County. The Civil War is given extensive coverage in chapters made up of excerpts from letters, unpublished stories, official documents, and personal reminiscences along with a chapter on Andersonville Prision which was located in the southern part of the county. Interwoven in and around the narrative is a vast amount of genealogical source material, such as lists of land lottery winners, county officials with dates of service, scores of Bible records and cemetery transcriptions, the Macon County tax list of 1838, marriage and will abstracts from 1858 to 1909. A Civil War Roster and a World War I veterans lit contain thousands of names. The genealogist of family historian will be delighted in the section entitled Families, it is approximately 178 pages of genealogies prepared by kinsfolk of the following Macon County families: Baldwin, Barksdale, Brown, Carmichael, Collins, Cornwell, Crocker, DeVaughn, Williams-Dawson, Derrick, DuPree, Dykes, Easterlin, Edwards, Edgeworth, Elsmore, English, Epting, Felton, Fokes, Frederick, Gardner, Greer, Griffin, Guerry, Haslam, Hays, Hall, Hamilton, Harrison, Harp, Haugabook, Hicks, Higgins, Hill, Johnson, Keen, King, Kleckley, Lewis, Lovejoy, Marshall, Massey, Maxwell, McCaskill, McKellar, McKenzie, Meadows, Moncrief, Montfort, Murray, Murph, Niles, Nixon, Osborne, Patrick, Peacock, Perry, Rice, Richardson, Robinson, Shealy, Slappey, Solomon, Smith, Sperry, Stubbs, Veal, Walker, Walters, Ware, Watts, Wicker, and Williams.

Men *of* Mark *in* GEORGIA, (7 Volumes). By: William J. Northern, Pub. 1912, reprinted 2023, 460 pages, Index, soft cover, ISBN #978-1-63914-118-0.

This 7-volume set of books is a cover-to-cover set of biographical sketches of men from Georgia. No other single publication contains so much biographical material relating to the early men of Georgia during this time period. ***Go to our website to see a complete list of surnames of individuals to be found with the following books.***

Vol. #1: 471 pages, Index, ISBN #978-1-63914-111-1.

GA 80 $50.00

The first volume contains the biographies of nearly a hundred of the leaders prior to 1800, covering the colonial, revolutionary and formative periods of Georgia History

Vol. #2: 514 pages, Index, ISBN #978-1-63914-112-8.

GA 81 $50.00

The second volume contains the biographies of nearly a hundred fifty sturdy men, who, from 1800 till the War between the States, raised Georgia from a condition of struggling poverty to a position of great material wealth and prosperity

Vol. #3: 662 pages, Index, ISBN #978-1-63914-113-5

GA 83 $60.00

The third volume is considered the war volume as it contains the biographies of nearly a hundred fifty men from 1733 to 1911.

Vol. #4: 534 pages, Index, ISBN #978-1-63914-114-2.

GA 85 $50.00

The fourth volume contains the biographies of nearly a hundred fifty men's stories since the war as illustrated by the men who have been, and are, the leaders of the State's political, professional and industrial life.

Vol. #5: 568 pages, Index, ISBN #978-1-63914-115-9

GA 89 $50.00

The fifth volume contains the biographies of nearly a hundred twenty men's stories since the war as illustrated by the men who have been, and are, the leaders of the State's political, professional and industrial life.

Vol. #6: ??? pages, Index, ISBN #978-1-63914-116-6.

GA 90 $50.00

The sixth volume contains the biographies of nearly a hundred fifty men's stories since the war as illustrated by the men who have been, and are, the leaders of the State's political, professional and industrial life.

Vol. #7: ??? pages, Index, ISBN #978-1-63914-117-3

GA 103 $50.00

The Seventh volume contains the biographies of nearly a hundred fifty men's stories from 1733 to 1911, as illustrated by the men who have been, and are, the leaders of the State's political, professional and industrial life.

Muscogee County, Georgia Superior Court Minutes, 1838-1841. (2 Volumes in 5 parts) By: Michael A. Ports, Pub. 2021, soft cover.

Vol. #1 - part 1, 1838-1840, 328 pages, Index, ISBN #978-1-63914-010-7.
GA 132 $37.50

Vol. #1 - part 2, 1838-1840: 350 pages, Index, ISBN #978-1-63914-011-4.
GA 133 $40.00

Vol. #1 - part 3, 1838-1840: 326 pages, Index, ISBN #978-1-63914-012-1
GA 134 $40.00

Vol. #2 - part 1, 1840-1841: 388 pages, Index, ISBN #978-1-63914-041-1.
GA 135 $42.50

Vol. #2- part 2, 1840-1841: 368 pages, Index, ISBN #978-1-63914-042-8
GA 136 $42.50

Muscogee County was created in 1826 from lands ceded by the Creek Indians. It lies on the western boundary of the state boarding Alabama along the Chattahoochee River. The Superior Court of the county had jurisdiction over all criminal matters, civil cases involving title to land, appeals from Inferior Court decisions and Justice's Courts, divorces, grand juries, naturalizations, and registration of land deeds.

Oglethorpe County, Georgia Superior Court Minutes, 1794-1799. (Volume #1). By: Michael A. Ports, Pub. 2019, 178 pages, soft Cover, Index, ISBN #0-89308-838-2.

GA 49 $23.50

Oglethorpe County was created from Wilkes County in 1793 and later became the parent county to Madison County. The Superior Court of the county had jurisdiction over all criminal matters, civil cases involving title to land, appeals from Inferior Court decisions and Justice's Courts, divorces, grand juries, naturalization's, and registration of land deeds.

Pulaski and Bleckley Counties, Georgia, 1808-1956, History of. By: Mrs. Wallace Leigh Harris, Pub. 1957, Reprint 2019, 1120 pages, 0-89308-948-6.

GA 48 $68.50

Pulaski County was created in 1808 from Portions of Laurens and Washington counties. Bleckley county was created in 1912 from Pulaski County. The time frame of this book begins with the creation of Pulaski County and continuing on through the creation of Bleckley County, with such topics as frontier life, Indians, trade & transportation, labor, farming, politics, education, newspapers and religion - all important in the development of the county. These types of HISTORY books can be very helpful in your research. They can help one develop ideas or pathways to those missing ancestors by showing the customs and traditions of local residents. This is very important in trying to figure out what significant factors were prevalent in the county, such as floods, droughts, matters of economic prosperity, matters of governmental intrusion or influence, or one of any number of things that might cause a person to stay or move on. The family researcher will be delighted with the authors 275 pages of some 163 biographical sketches of individuals and families. Mrs. Walker has also included numerous lists: pay rolls & muster rolls of soldiers who served in the War of 1812, lists of jurors from 1805, Pulaski County Marriages 1808-1956, Bleckley County Marriages 1913-1856, Pulaski County Wills 1809-1947, Bleckley County Wills 1913-1956, 1818 Tax Digest Pulaski County, 1827 Land Lottery, Graves of Revolutionary and 1812 Soldiers marked by DAR, and lists of Veteran s from WWI & WWII.

Richmond County Georgia, Records of. By: Grace Gillam Davidson, Pub. 1930, Reprinted 2020, 408 pages, Index, ISBN #0-89308-007-1.

GA 16 $40.00

Richmond County was created in 1777. It is one of the original counties of the state and was formed out of a portion of the colonial Parish of St. Paul. It is the parent county to: Columbia, Glascock, McDuffie and part of Warren Counties. It lies on the eastern side of the state boarding the Savannah River and just across from Edgefield County, South Carolina. This volume was originally published as Volume II of the Historical Collection of the Georgia Chapters National Society Daughters of the American Revolution. Contents of this book: Will 777-1797 7 1798-1840, Index to Will Books 1840-1853, Administration and Guardians Bonds 1777-1830, Marriage Bonds 1785-1830 Marriages 1813-1839, Deeds 1750-1790, Minutes of the Inferior Court 1790-1830 and Walton Family History.

The Salzburgers *and their* Descendants. By: P.A. Strobel, Orig. Pub. 1855, Reprinted 2019, 326 pages, Index, soft cover, ISBN #0-89308-771-8.

GA 40 $28.50

The Georgia Colony was chartered by King George to act as buffer between the Spanish settlement and Native American tribes in Florida and Charles Town in South Carolina. These German exiles started arriving in the New World in the 1730's and slowly started settling up and down the Savannah River. It is estimated that approximately 50% of the population of Effingham & Chatham County areas are directly descended from these early settlers. Since the first immigrants arrived in 1734, as many as 15 generations have followed, many of whom still live on ancestral land.

Salzburgers *and* Allied Families. By: P.R. Gnann & Mrs. LeBey, Orig. Pub. 1956, Reprinted & Revised 2003, approx. 4,000 pages in 4 volumes, Hard Cover, Index, ISBN #0-89308-012-8.

GA 2 $250.00

The Georgia Colony was chartered by King George to act as buffer between the Spanish settlement and Native American tribes in Florida and Charles Town in South Carolina. These German exiles started arriving in the New World in the 1730's and slowly started settling up and down the Savannah River. It is estimated that approx. 50% of the population of Effingham & Chatham County areas are directly descended from these early settlers. Since the first immigrants arrived in 1734, as many as 15 generations have followed, many of whom still live on ancestral land. This book has been completely REVISED & UPDATED since its last printing. It is now in 4 volumes with each volume having approx. 1000 plus pages.

Stewart County, Georgia. History *of.* By: Sara Dixon, Pub. 1958, Reprint 2017, 824 pages, Index, Hard Cover, 0-89308-502-2.

GA 96 $58.50

Stewart County was created in 1830 from Randolph County. But just 5 years earlier it belong to the vast Indian lands in the Western portion of the state that were ceded to the US Government in 1825. Stewart is the parent county in whole and part to: Chatahoochee, Quitman & Webster. Its lands were covered in the 1827 Land Lottery. Contents of this book are: Marriage records 1828-1860, Wills 1837-1847, Deed Book "A", Church & Cemetery Records, Lists of Stewart County Guards 1835-1850, and Over 300 pages of this book are devoted to biographical Sketches of the pioneer families and leading citizens of the county.

Twiggs County, Georgia, History of. By: J. Lanette O. Faulk & Billy Walker Jones, Orig. Pub. 1960, Reprinted 2017, 486 pages, soft Cover, ISBN #0-89308-009-8.

GA 46 $48.50

This long-awaited reprint of this central Georgia county history book should make many a researcher very happy. This book is a genealogical gem of a book. It is filled with a wide variety of information such as: early history, Indian affairs, roster of soldiers from the Civil War, the Revolutionary War, World War I & II, abstracts of tax Digest for 1818-1826-1853, abstracts of deeds 1809-1900, abstracts of deeds from other Index Books to 1901, abstracts of Wills, Newspaper abstracts, Cemeteries inscriptions for some 45 different cemeteries, Land lottery - Wilkinson County 1805 (now Twiggs). The authors did not stop there. They also added biographical sketches / genealogies of approx. 66 early settlers of this important county.

Upson County, Georgia, The Early History *of.* By: C.W. Nottingham & E. Hannah, Orig. Pub. 1930, reprinted 1999, 1122 pages, New Index, Hard Cover, ISBN #0-89308-029-2.

GA 6 $65.00

Upson County was created in 1824 from Crawford and Pike Counties, GA. and was a major seat of migration of settlers moving across Georgia into the southwest part of Georgia and into that lower part of Alabama bordering the Chattahoochee River. The book contains the names of approximately 40,000 individuals. The contents of this book are: early history of the county; a listing of fortunate drawers in the Land Lotteries of 1820, and 1821; persons living in Upson County who drew land in the 1827, 1832 Cherokee and 1832 Gold Lotteries of GA.; the 1830 Census of Upson; some Revolutionary War veterans living in the county; first public roads; Marriage records for the years 1825-1850; brief abstracts of Wills, 1825-1865; some early Deed records; Church histories with memberships and cemetery records and numerous Bible records of early pioneer families; the founding of Thomaston in 1825; the 1850 Census of Upson Co. listing not only the head of household, but each family member, age, place of birth, etc.; lists of Civil War regiments and companies; newspapers; industries and civic leaders; history of medical profession and biographical sketches of many of the early doctors. Also, of very special interest to the genealogists, the author has place numerous biographical sketches within this book of many of the pioneer families of Upson County.

Walker County, Georgia, History of. By: James A. Sartain, Pub. 1932, Reprinted 2019, 570 pages, Index, ISBN #0-89308-887-0.

GA 56 $48.50

Walker County was created in 1833 from Murray County which in turn was created from Cherokee County in 1832 and Cherokee was created in 1832 from Indian lands in the northwestern portion of the state. This history is similar to other history books of the era with discussions of: formation of county, Indians, commerce, religion, education, militia districts, slavery, involvement in various wars, and items all important to the development of the county. The author has given considerable amount of data on the Civil War with such things as Muster Rolls being listed for various companies and he has also included Biographical Sketches of: Anderson, Andrews, Arnold, Bayless, Blackwell, Blaylock, Brothers, Brown, Bryan, Center, Chambers, Chastain, Clarkson, Clements, Conley, Copeland, Coulters, Dickerson, Dunn, Dyer, Fariss, Freeman, Garmany, Graham, Hackney, Hall, Hammond, Haslerig, Hearn, Henderson, Henry, Hixon, Hunter, Jackson, Johnson, Johnston, Jones, Keown, McConnell, McCulloh,

McCutchen, McFarland, Miller, Millican, Moore, Myers, Napier, Park, Parker, Patton, Pickle, Pittman, Ponder, Ransom, Roberts, Sartain, Schmitt, Shattuck, Shaw, Simmons, Sizemore, Spearman, Stansell, Stegall, Suttle, Thurman (2), Tucker (2), Veatch, Weaver, Wheeler, White, Whitlow, Wood (2), and Young. The reader will also discover a chapter devoted to tombstone inscriptions of 54 early public and private cemeteries.

Ware County, Georgia, History of. Mrs. J.L. Walker, pub. 1934, reprinted 2018, 568 pages, soft cover, Index, ISBN #0-89308-034-9.

GA 10 $48.50

Ware County was created in 1824 from Appling County. It sits in the southern portion of the state and was directly influenced by the the 1820 Land Lottery of GA. This book is filled with genealogical and historical materials, viz.: Creek Indian War, Militia Muster Rolls, Approx. 150 biographical sketches/ Family Histories, Officers of Ware Co. from 1824, Civil War Lists, general historical material from the formation of the county until 1934, cemetery inscriptions, and etc.....

Washington County, Georgia, History *of.* By: Ella Mitchell, Orig. pub. 1924, reprinted 2000, 172 pages plus New Index, Hard Cover, ISBN #0-89308-730-0.

GA 82 $28.50

Washington County was created in 1784, for the purpose of rewarding the Patriots in defense of Georgia. These Patriots were not only from Georgia, but the Carolinas, Virginia, and even men direct from Ireland and Scotland. This county was carved out of Liberty County, GA. and was once the parent county of Chandler, Emanuel, Greene, Hancock, Johnson, Laurens, Montgomery, Tattnal, Treutlen, and Toombs counties. This book is not too different from other history books of its kind, as it discusses the usual topics, such as the information of the county, agriculture, education, commerce, slavery, the men who served in various wars, etc.... Of special note, the reader will discover that the author has interspersed this book with numerous biographical sketches of these early settlers.

(Wilkes *and* Burke County) Georgians *in the* Revolution: At Kettle Creek. By: Robert S. Davis, Jr., Orig. pub. 1986, Reprinted 2007, 272 pgs, Hard Cover, Index, ISBN #0-89308-350-X.

GA 45 $38.50

This book contains the names of 4,000 men who served in this area of Georgia during the Revolution. This book is divided into 2 parts with the first dealing with the persons & events that pertain to Wilkes County. There is a complete and detailed account of the battle that took place at Kettle Creek on Feb. 14, 1779. Also included are the Loyalists trials of Ninety-Six in 1779 and the prisoner list of Ninety-Six Jail in 1779. There is a Full documented list of soldiers so far known to have been in Kettle Creek, both patriot & loyalists. The second part of this book deals with Burke County's participation in the Revolution. The author has included lengthy articles on colonial St. George Parish, Burke County, in the American Revolution, the battle of Burke County Jail, documents about the militia, the war in South Carolina fought by Burke Countians, the Battle of Briar Creek, John Twiggs, John Jones, John Thomas, John Dooley, Col. Leonard Marbury, the Burke County Jail, a chronology of the war in Georgia and much, much more.

The Wilkes County Papers, 1777-1833. By: Robert S. Davis, Pub. 1979, reprinted 2019, 338 pages, Soft Cover, Index, ISBN #0-89308-170-1.

GA 67 $38.50

Wilkes County is Georgia's oldest county, being the first of the original eight created by the first state constitution in 1777. The Federal Census of 1790 revealed that one-third of the population of Georgia was living in Wilkes County. Since 1790, lands that once were part of Wilkes County have been used to create all or parts of present-day Elbert, Hall, Lincoln, Madison, McDuffie, Oglethorpe, Taliferro, and Warren. This book is a collection of never-before-published abstracts of collections of Wilkes County loose marriages, estates, poor school, military, land, court, state, and other records from libraries and archives throughout the South. NONE of these original papers abstracted here were available to Grace G. Davidson in compiling her famous: Early Records of Georgia, Wilkes County". Most of these papers were removed from Wilkes County by private individuals and were "Lost" to researchers until they turned up in manuscript collections throughout the South.

Wilkes County Papers, 1773-1889, The Supplement *to*: By: Robert S. Davis, Pub. 1999, reprinted 2013, 164 pages, soft cover, Index, ISBN #0-89308-411-5.

GA 68 $20.00

This new book by Robert S. Davis is also a collection of never-before-published abstracts of collections of Wilkes County. Material contained within this volume: Estate Records, Inferior Court Cases, Justice of the Peace Case Files, Land Court Minutes, Lists of soldiers who fought at the Battle of Kettle Creek 1779, Records of Ceded Lands of Original Wilkes County, Early Settlers, Superior Court Minutes, Tax Digest 1785, and more Loose Wilkes County, Georgia records.

(Wilkes County) Early Records *of* Georgia. (Vols. 1 & 2). By: Grace Gilliam Davidson, Pub. 1933, Reprinted 2017, 844 pages, Index, Hard Cover, ISBN #0-89308-006-3.

GA 14 $65.00

Wilkes County was created in 1777 from the northern part of St. Paul's Parish. This land was acquired from the Creek & Cheokee Indians in payment for debts owed to Indian Traders. It is the parent county, in whole or part, for: Elbert, Greene, Hart, Lincoln, Madison, Oglethorpe, Taliaferro and Warren Contents of Volume 1 (409 pages): Ceded Lands, 1773-1775; Mixed Records, Wills, 1777-1819, 1819-1836; Inventories and Appraisements, 1784-1812; Minutes of Inferior Court; Returns of Administrations and Guardians Book 1, 1809-1816; Remnant of Oldest Deed Book, 1784-1785; Deed Books, 1785-1790; Land Court Records, 1786-1792; Land Lotteries, 1805, 1807, 1820, 1821, 1827, 1832; Paschal family Bible Record; Index. Contents of Volume 2 (421 pages): Minutes of First Court; Tax Digest, 1785; Deed Books GG & HH; Will Books, 1819-1836; Index to Will Book II, 1837-1877; Returns of Estates; Returns of Administrators and Guardians; Original Marriage Bonds, 1792-1816; First Marriage Book, 1792-1834; Index These volumes jointly contain the names of over 42,000 individuals.

Worth County, Georgia, History *of.* By: Lillie Martin Grubbs, Pub. 1934, Reprint 2018, 612 pages, Index, 0-89308-947-8.

GA 4 $52.50

Worth County was created in 1853 from Dooley and Irwin Counties. This book is not too different from other county history books of this era. With such topics as trade and transportation, labor, farming, politics, and race relations - all important in the development of the county - are carefully discussed. This type of county history book can help one develop ideas or paths to those missing ancestors by showing the customs and traditions of the local residents. A particular useful feature of this book is the extensive biographical information included. This volume contains more than 170 biographical sketches plus information on Confederate soldiers who immigrated to Worth County from other places along with data on Worth County residents who served in the Civil War.

Georgia Land Records and Lotteries

Index *to the* Headright *and* Bounty Grants *in* Georgia *from* 1756-1909, Revised. By: S. Emmett Lucas, Jr., Pub. 1970, reprinted 2006, 786 pages, Hard Cover, ISBN #0-89308-017-9.

GA 23 $55.00

Most of the land in the eastern portion of Georgia was distributed to settlers as Headright grants; the amount of the land given to a person (family) was based upon household size. The act for distributing this land allowed a man to take up to 200 acres upon his own headright, plus an additional 50 acres upon the head of each member of his family and limited any grant to 1000 acres. Based on legislation passed during the Revolutionary War, BOUNTY lands were granted to both veterans and patriots, the later being citizens who had not molested their neighbors families or property, refugees who had served in militia companies outside of the state, militiamen of the state, men who had served in militia companies and to residents who did not leave the state or remove their property in the last eleven months of the Revolution (1781-1782). The information in this index shows: FIRST - the name of the person who received the grant; SECOND - the county in which the grant was located; THIRD - the book in which the grant is recorded; FOURTH - the page in the grant book; FIFTH - the number of acres in the grant, SIXTH - the year the grant was dated. From the information found herein, one can begin to determine the size of an ancestor's family at the date the grant was issued. A BOUNTY grant shows only the words ON BOUNTY written under the grant. It is not proof of military service, since ordinary citizens also received bounties for not leaving the state during the Revolution. In 1909 the Land Office Acts were repealed and the state granted no more land. This long awaited out-of-print volume contains the names of over 61,000 persons who received grants of land between 1756 and 1909. This reprint includes over 1,000 names that had been omitted from the original manuscript of 1970.

1807 Land Lottery *of* Georgia. By: Silas Emmett Lucas, Jr., Orig. pub. 1968, reprinted 2019, 170 pages, map, Soft Cover, ISBN #0-89308-020-9.

GA 25 $27.50

The original 1968 edition was arranged alphabetically by counties, and then alphabetically by surname, making it extremely difficult to use when searching a given individual or surname. Southern Historical Press has completely revised this book, arranging all persons listed in alphabetical order by surname, making this book now much easier to use. It contains the names of approximately 12,000 fortunate drawers.

1820 Land Lottery *of* Georgia. By: S. Emmett Lucas, Jr., Pub. 1968, reprinted 2005, 382 pages, Hard Cover, Index, ISBN #0-89308-585-5.

GA 26 $40.00

Unlike other Land Lottery books on Georgia, this

one "the 1820" is NOT and will not be available for reviewing on the internet. If you want it, you will need to buy it here in book format. This Lottery created 8 new counties: Appling, Early, Gwinnett, Habersham, Hall, Irwin, Raburn and Walton, which in later years have been further divided into some 48 other counties. This book is arranged in alphabetical order by surname. This book lists 30,000 fortunate drawers. In general, the researcher will be able to gleam many different types of information from the Georgia's Land Lotteries. The eligibility requirements of each of the Lotteries offer genealogists legal evidence of citizenship, residence in Georgia, age, family, and material status, physical infirmities, and possibly service in the Revolutionary War, the War of 1812 or Indian Wars.

1821 Land Lottery *of* Georgia. By: Silas E. Lucas, Jr., Orig. Pub. 1973, Revised & Reprinted 1986, 262 pages, Hard Cover, ISBN #0-89308-586-3.

GA 66 $35.00

The original 1973 edition was arranged alphabetically by counties and then alphabetically by surname, making it extremely difficult to use when searching a given individual or surname. We have completely revised this book, arranging all persons listed in alphabetical order by surname, making this book now much easier to use. This Lottery created 5 new counties of which they are: Dooly, Fayette, Henry, Houston, and Moore. This book is arranged in alphabetical order, containing approximately 15,000 names.

1827 Land Lottery *of* Georgia. By: Martha Lou Houston, Orig. pub. 1928, reprinted 2015 with a NEW Index, 326 pages, soft cover, ISBN #0-89308-015-2.

GA 27 $38.50

It contains the names of approximately 41,000 fortunate drawers who received land in this Indian country that became Carroll, Coweta, Troup, Muscogee, and Lee counties and which land today comprises part of Harrolson, Carroll, Douglas, Heard, Cowetta, Troup, Meriwether, Harris, Talbot, Taylor, Chattachoochee, Marion, Schley, Stewart, Webster, Sumter, Quitman, Clay, Randolph, Terrell, and Lee.

1832 Cherokee Land Lottery *of* Georgia. By: James F. Smith, Pub. 1838, Reprinted 2016, 504 pages, maps, New Index, ISBN #0-89308-033-0.

GA 29 $45.00

This is the sixth of the land lottery held in Georgia. This land lottery divided up the land of hte former Cherokee Indian country in 1832. This land area was divided into the present counties of Cass (renamed Bartow in 1861), Cherokee, Cobb, Floyd, Forsyth, Gilmer, Lumpkin, Murray, Paulding and Union. This volume contains the names of over 27,000 fortunate drawers or persons who drew land in these counties, together with their county of residence at the time of said lottery. There are some 60 maps showing each county and district, helping a person to better locate the exact location of an ancestor's land.

1832 Gold Lottery *of* Georgia. By: Silas Emmett Lucas, Jr.,1976, reprinted & revised 2015, 568 pages, soft cover, Index, ISBN #0-89308-638-X.

GA 28 $45.00

The original 1976 edition was arranged alphabetically by counties and then alphabetically by surname, making it extremely difficult to use when searching a given individual or surname. Southern Historical Press has completely revised this book, arranging all persons listed in alphabetical order by surname, making this book now much easier to use. The gold lots are found in present-day Union, Lumpkin, Forsyth, Cherokee, Cobb, Paulding, Cass, and Floyd counties. It contains the names of approximately 41,000 fortunate drawers.

1833 Land Lottery *of* Georgia. By: Robert S. Davis, Pub. 1991, Reprinted 2016, 74 pages, Index, ISBN #0-89308-005-5.

GA 33 $15.00

Farris Cadle, author of an upcoming book on the history of Georgia land grants and surveys, discovered a Georgia law of 1833 that ordered the fractional (less then 40 acres) land lots of the 1832 Georgia Gold Lot Lottery to be dispensed in a special 1833 land lottery. The winners were to be drawn from the remaining (losing) tickets of the two 1832 land lotteries.

A search of the Georgia Surveyor General Department has turned up the list of some 1,500 Georgia citizens who won the lots dispensed in the forgotten 1833 land lottery. Reproduced are the names and other information on those land lots and their winners. The original of this list is the last document on microfilm reel 286/49 at the Georgia Department of Archives and History. Also given away in this land lottery were a handful of lots left over from previous land lotteries. For information on abbreviations used in designating participants in the 1832 land lotteries, see James F. Smith, The 1832 Cherokee Land Lottery.

Also included in the list are more than thirty land lots omitted from the original drawing of the 1820 Georgia Land lottery. These lots are designated with "1820 LL". This list appears at the end of the list of Houston County land lots on Microfilm reel 286/47 at the Georgia Dept. of Archives & History. These lots were drawn for and given to participants in the 1820 land lottery.

The Loose Land Lottery Papers *of* Georgia, 1805-1914. By: Silas Emmett Lucas, Jr. & Robert S. Davis, Orig. pub. 1979, reprinted 2014, 366 pages, soft cover, Index, ISBN #0-89308-156-6.

GA 30 $38.50

This book is a compilation of the loose petitions, oaths, letters, and other papers of the winners in ALL SEVEN of Georgia's Land Lotteries. These petitions do not appear in the Land Lottery Books of their corresponding year. These were petitions that were found loose/separate within the basement of the archives. Let it be understood, these land lotteries do not appear in any other land lottery book except for this one. This book should have been called The Loose land Lottery Papers. These are the records of some of the winners and / or their heirs and include valuable family information. They contain more than 3,000 individuals.

Research Aids

1850 Georgia Mortality Schedules *or* Census. By: Aurora Shaw, Orig. Pub. 1970, reprinted 1982, 87 pages, soft cover, Index, ISBN #0-89308-214-7.

GA 38 $17.50

This mortality schedule gives the name, age, sex, state of birth, and other data for every white person (approximately 4,500) who died in Georgia between June 1, 1849 and June 1, 1850.

The Georgia Black Book, Vol. #1: Morbid, Macabre, and Disgusting Records of Genealogical Value. By: Robert S. Davis, Jr., Pub. 1982, reprinted 2006, 452 pages, Hard Cover, Index, ISBN #0-89308-291-0.

GA 63 $45.00

The contents of this book include chapters on "Horse Thieves and Other Charming People, 1754-1823"; "Liars, 1810-1938" - the Georgia Land Lottery Fraud Papers; "Convicts, 1817-1850" - Convict Records; "Murders, Murderers and Murder Victims, 1823-1969" - from Governor's Proclamations (issued for offering rewards for killers who had fled justice), 1823-1900; "Convicts, 1851-1871" - which includes prison, number or name and aliases, date entered prison and county in which convicted; "Insane Asylum Inmates, 1853-1870" - which includes the person's number, name and county of residence and when admitted; "Principal Keeper's Reports, 1866-1873, Lists of Convicts to Fill Gaps in (the chapter on Convicts, 1851-1871)"; "Racial Incidents, 1865-1868" - reports of racial violence against blacks in Reconstruction Georgia; "Central register of Convicts, 1867-1879" - this continues the earlier chapters on Murders, Murderers, and Murder Victims; "More Murders, Murderers, and Murder Victims, 1869-1900" - a continuation of the earlier chapter on this subject; "Central register of Convicts, 1872-1897" - a continuation of a listing of convicts... and "Other Sources Equally Disgusting". This volume contains the names of over 13,500 persons.

The Georgia Black Book, Vol. #2: More Morbid, Macabre, and Sometimes Disgusting Records of Genealogical Value - Just When You Thought It Was Safe to Get Back Into Genealogy. By: Robert S. Davis, Jr., Pub. 1987, reprinted 2008, 435 pages, Hard Cover, Index, ISBN #0-89308-600-2.

GA 78 $45.00

Here are more unique and little known records from the Georgia Archives to fill in gaps on your family tree and answer question that have nagged you for years. This book includes How To Research Asylum, Prison, and Murder Record in Georgia; Divorces Found in Georgia Acts 1793-1868; name Changes of Illegitimate and Adopts in Acts of the Georgia Legislature, 1800-1856 (by John E. Moseley); Federal Direct Tax Defaulters in Georgia, 1812; Georgia Widows and Orphans of the War of 1812; First Book of the Georgia Insane Asylum, 1842-1853; Georgia Civil War Depredations; Artificial Limbs Given to Georgia Civil War veterans; Racial Violence in Georgia, 1868-1871; the Georgia Widows and Orphans of the Civil War Lottery, 1866-1876; Prison Records, 1877-1886; Petitions for Pardons and Paroles, 1858-1942, Contains the names of approximately 12,000 persons.

A Researcher's Library *of* Georgia History, Genealogy, *and* Records Sources, Vol. #1. By: Robert S. Davis, Jr., Pub. 1987, reprinted 2005, 552 pages, Hard Cover, Index, ISBN #0-89308-535-9.

GA 70 $50.00

Bob Davis has compiled into one indexed volume his MOST significant articles on and abstracts of Georgia records. More than half of this book, A Researchers Library, however is new material spanning virtually all Georgia for all of her more than 250 years. This is some of the best genealogical material to be found in one reference book encompassing the years from colonial times down through the Civil War. Chapters included in this book are on Georgia's First Settlers; Lost Colonial Georgia Plats; Records from the Peter Force papers; The Georgia Provincial Rangers; Land Grants under the Trustees, 1733-1739; a Medical Miracle Worker; Lost Georgia Land Grants under the Trustees 1775 and 1778; Revolutionary War Soldiers in the American State Papers; Bounty Script to Soldiers and their heirs, 1833-1870; Officer index to Saffell's records of the Revolutionary War; Death dates of Revolutionary War Officers in the South; 1840 Federal Pension list for Georgia; Supplement to

Knight's Roster; Supplement to Georgia Citizen and Soldiers; persons who may not have received Bounty Grants; Headright Caveats, 1777-1868; Dr. Newton's medical log, 1789; Some records from the Cuyler Collection; the Walton War - A Supplement; Indian depredation; 1810 Federal Census of Putnam County; Militia Roster, 1812-1815; Georgia's Roster of the War of 1812. Also chapters on Birth States of Georgia Federal Employees 1816 and 1819; Persons exempted to be allowed to be tested before the Bar; Missing page of the 1820 Census of Madison County; Applicants before Georgia's Board of Physicians, 1826-1881; Paddlers Licenses, 1825-1843; the Georgia battalion in the Texas Revolution; St. George Parish - Burke County; Gleaning from Georgia Newspapers; First settlers of Northeast Georgia; White men with families in the Cherokee Nation, 1830; Voters lists, 1834-1838; Counties in Georgia and Carolinas - an 1835 map; Enlistment oaths, 1861; Georgia Battalion, US Army, Confederate Pensioners, 1894; some Civil War memoirs; and Confederate Veterans at Bowden College. The Index mentions approximately 30,000 names.

A Researcher's Library *of* Georgia History, Genealogy, *and* Records Sources, Vol. #2. By: Robert S. Davis, Jr., Pub. 1991, reprinted 2006, 516 pages, Hard Cover, Index, ISBN #089309-683-5.

GA 87 $50.00

Bob Davis is known for his vast knowledge in Georgia History & Genealogical Research and here in volume 2 of his planned 3 book series, he has complied into one indexed volume, his Favorite Tricks in Georgia Research. Now these tricks do not work every time but when they do, you will be extremely thankful that you have this book in your possession. This book along with its companion volume #1 should be in the library of anyone who is doing genealogy research in Georgia. Chapters included in this volume are: Did you know; Question and answers about Georgia research; the First Georgians and their records, 1733-1783; Records of the Georgia Surveyor General Dept.; the Ceded lands are the Original Wilkes County, GA.; Going to and Gone from Georgia; Migration records; Civil War research in Georgia; some Cherokee and Georgia Indian records - an Addendum; Places in GA.; Sources for local history; Fort files in the John H. Goff Collection; Place name cards in the Leon Hollingsworth Collection; Georgia suppliers to the Confederacy; Georgians - Misc. Colonial Georgia records; Colonial Georgia Records; records in the Cuyler Collection; Index to Governor's Papers - Cuyler Collection 1756-1786; Misc. Revolutionary War records; 2500 Georgians in the Sheftall Papers; Settlers from Old 96 Dist. S.C. to GA. and beyond; Early GA. Congressmen; list of Georgia doctors before 1830; settlers of the Georgia Indian border, 1829-1833; Georgians at Sanlacinto; some GA. Bounty Land Grants, 1854-1856; 600 Georgia Rebels (biographies); Confederate Dead; Civil War pardons and Amnesty records; Biographical Sketches of the GA. Legislature 1871; some Spanish American War veterans; GA. Confederate Soldiers home; names in county records; Orig. County records at GA. Archives; Obits. from the Milledgeville Area; Butts County Taxable's 1828; some Chatham County registrants for the land lottery 1827; some families of old Cherokee County; 1850 Census of Clinch (East Lanier) County; Missing pages from the 1801 Elbert County Tax Digest; records of Franklin County; some Hancock County records; some Jackson County Estates 1796-1813; some Loose Liberty and McIntosh County records 1771-1854; Morgan County Yankees 1877; Twiggs County records 1820 and 1866-1901; Whitfield County Politian's 1868; some Wilkinson County 1827 land lottery registrants.

RESEARCH *in* GEORGIA - With a Special Emphasis Upon the Georgia Department of Archives & History. By: Robert S. Davis, Jr., Pub. 1981, reprinted 2002, 268 pages, maps, soft cover, Index, ISBN #0-89308-199-X.

GA 41 $32.50

This is one of the most comprehensive guides to research sources in Georgia and especially the Georgia Department of Archives and History. Mr. Davis has painstakingly surveyed the records and their locations and compiled a book that is a watershed for Georgia historians and genealogists. It is written as a guide, leading him or her step-by-step to the records - many of which are unknown to even the most experienced researcher due to long years of neglect. The inclusion of an outline to the county material on microfilm can help many a traveler to realize that a trip to the archives is more useful than one to the county courthouse. I can think of no better book with which people can use as a beginning tool for research in Georgia - Ken Thomas, Genealogy, The Atlanta Constitution. Outline of Contents: General Subject and County Index: Department guide explaining the various records and their potential genealogical value. Other Resources: periodicals, listing titles and addresses of over 35 genealogical and historical periodicals of specific interest, maps. County Records: an inventory. Basic lists by county of microfilmed records with indications for particular time periods when particular records are not available, with date of creation of each county and its number in order of creation and the name of the county it was formed from. Tax Digests: Basic discussion of the specific usefulness of tax records, with a lists of those on microfilm at the archives. Census Records: census records that are available at the Archives on microfilm for Georgia by year, as well as other states. County Histories: Bibliography of histories with specific genealogical references of approximately 1,000 titles. Land Lotteries & Colonial Records: comprehensive inventory of colonial books or records and loose documents, with reel numbers specifying their location in the Archives Microfilm Library, plus an extensive list of publications in which printed copies of these may be found in abstracted form.

Some Georgia County Records, Volume #1. By: Silas Emmett Lucas, Jr., Pub. 1977, reprinted 1994, 432 pages, Hard Cover, Index, ISBN #0-89308-044-6

GA 31 $40.00

This book contains abstracts of legal records for Columbia, Hancock, Jefferson, and Warren counties, Georgia. It contains the names of more than 40,000 persons listed in these records.

Some Georgia County Records, Volume #2. By: Silas Emmett Lucas, Jr., Pub. 1977, reprinted 2019, 488 pages, soft cover, Index, ISBN #0-89308-057-8.

GA 32 $40.00

This book contains abstracts of legal records for: Clarke, Greene, Jasper, Morgan, Oglethorpe, and Putnam counties. These records are: Clarke County Wills 1803-1842, Clarke County Administrators Bonds 1801-1827, Clarke County Admin. & Guardians Bonds 1811-1825, Clarke County Marriages 1807-1820, Jasper County Ordinary Court Minutes & Wills 1812-1823, Jasper / Randolph County Estate records 1810-1814, Morgan County Marriages 1808-1818, Putnam County Wills 1808-1857, Oglethorpe County Wills 1793-1807, Greene County Deeds 1785-1802, Greene County Wills 1794-1810, Greene County Miscellaneous Records 1787-1801, Greene County Marriages 1787-1803. It contains the names of more than 40,000 persons listed in the FULL Name Index.

Some Georgia County Records, Volume #3. By: Silas Emmett Lucas, Jr., Pub. 1978, reprinted 2019, 368 pages, Soft Cover, Index, ISBN #0-89308-058-6.

GA 33 $40.00

This book contains abstracts of legal records for Bibb, Butts, Fayette, Henry, Monroe, and Newton counties. It contains the names of more then 40,000 persons listed in these records.

Some Georgia County Records, Volume 4. By: S. Emmett Lucas, Jr., Pub. 1991, reprinted 2019, 526 pages, soft cover, Index, ISBN #0-89308-685-1.

GA 92 $45.00

This book contains abstracts of legal records for Burke, Butts, Columbia, Emanuel, Greene, Hancock, Jasper, Morgan, and Richmond counties, Georgia. These records are: Burke County residents 1786-1819, Burke County Militia 1819, Burke County residents 1820, Burke County War of 1812 Roster, Burke County Index to the 1820, 1830, & 1840 Census, Burke County Index to the 1850 Mortality Census, Burke County Marriages 1855-1869, Butts County Deeds 1829-1845, Columbia County Wills 1803-1824, Emanuel County Marriages 1817-1879, Emanuel County Tax Digest 1841, Greene County Deeds 1793-1802, Greene County Marriages 1787-1875, Hancock County Wills & Estates 1798-1804, Jasper County Loose Wills 1809-1907, Jasper County Loose Estate papers 1809-1907, Jasper County Deeds 1808-1810, Morgan County Wills 1806-1829, Richmond County marriages 1785-1869. It contains the names of more than 35,000 persons listed in FULL Name Index.

Some Georgia County Records, Volume #5. By: S. Emmett Lucas, Jr., Pub. 1991, 326 pgs, Hard Cover, Index, ISBN #0-89308-686-X.

GA 93 $45.00

This book contains abstracts of legal records for Baker, Bibb, Early, Jones, Monroe, Marion, Morgan, Randolph, and Talbot counties. It contains the names of more than 25,000 persons listed in these records.

Some Georgia County Records, Volume #6. By: Silas Emmett Lucas, Jr., Pub. 1993, 500 pages, Hard Cover, Index, ISBN #0-89308-687-8.

GA 94 $45.00

This book contains abstracts of legal records for Cherokee, Cobb, Dawson, Forsyth, Gordon, Gwinnett, Gilmer, Hall, Lumpkin, Murray, Pickens, Rabun, Walton, Whitfield counties. It contains the names of more than 40,000 persons listed in these records.

Some Georgia County Records, Volume #7. By: Silas Emmett Lucas, Jr., Pub. 1993, 475 pages, Hard Cover, Index, ISBN #0-89308-486-7.

GA 95 $45.00

This book contains abstracts of legal records for Clarke, Franklin, Habersham, Lincoln, Oglethorpe. It contains the names of more than 38,000 persons listed in these records.

Some Georgia County Records, Volume #8. By: Silas Emmett Lucas, Jr., Pub. 2019, 492 pages, Soft Cover, Index, ISBN #0-89308-661-4.

GA 100 $45.00

This book contains abstracts of legal records for Burke, Chatham, Montgomery, Murray, Oglethorpe, and Washington Counties. Also included are Miscellaneous Bible Records, and a list of the enlisted men in the Georgia Navy for the year 1861. It contains the names of more than 28,000 persons listed in these records.

Some Georgia County Records, Volume #9. By: Ed Van Schaick, Pub. 1997, 487 pages, Hard Cover, Index, ISBN #0-89308-659-2.

GA 101 $45.00

This book contains abstracts of legal records for Effingham, Morgan, and Warren Counties. It contains the names of approximately 30,000 persons listed in these records.

Some Georgia County Records, Volume #10. By: Ed Van Schaick, Pub. 1999, 403 pages, Hard Cover, Index, ISBN #0-89308-565-0.

GA 101 $40.00

This book contains abstracts of legal records for Baldwin, Burke, Cherokee, Jackson, and Richmond Counties. It contains the names of approximately 16,000 persons listed in these records.

Newspaper Notices

Marriages & Obituaries *from* The Macon Messenger, 1818-1865. By: Willard Rocker, Orig. Pub. 1988, 590 pages, Soft Cover, Index, ISBN #0-89308-340-2.

GA 65 $48.50

The marriage & death notices contained in this volume have been abstracted from the Georgia Messenger & the Georgia Journal and Messenger, both published in Macon, GA. The 5,000 obituaries listed here are not localized for just the Macon area, but are much comprehensive. Because of the centrality of the city of Macon in the state of Georgia, this newspaper would be a natural focal point for people all over Georgia to have marriages & deaths recorded. There are approximately 14,000 marriages and obituaries for people in the Macon, GA. area and other Georgia counties such as: Bibb, Butts, Chatham, Coweta, Dooley, Greene, Jefferson, Jones, Lee, Lowndes, Monroe, Muscogee, Oglethrope, Pike, Screve, Twiggs, Upson, Walker and Ware as well as other counties throughout the state of Georgia and other states as: Alabama, California, Florida, Indiana, Kansas, New York, North & South Carolina and Tennessee.

Genealogical Material *from* Legal Notices *in* Early Georgia Newspapers. By: Judge Folks Huxford, Pub. 1989, reprinted 2006, 310 pages, Hard Cover, Index, ISBN #0-89308-656-8.

GA 86 $38.50

The types of legal notices found in this book are as follows: Letters of Administration of estates; establishment of lost plats; appointment of Road Commissioners; Grand Jury presentations; advertisements of divorce and separation; notices of Indian depredation of Whites; powers of attorney; lists of deserters; rewards and warrants for arrests; divorce suits; guardianship; notices of application for dowry... and many other such things to locate one's ancestors that would be next to impossible to find from other sources. Legal notices such as the above from the following Georgia newspapers are to be found here: Georgia Gazette (Savannah), Jan.. 11, 1790 to Nov. 21, 1799 and Jan. 2, 1800 to Jan., 1802; The Columbian Museum & Savannah Advertiser, Mar. 31, 1796 to Nov. 26, 1819; The Republican & Savannah Evening Ledger, July 15, 1808 to Nov. 20, 1805; The Southern Patriot (Savannah), Dec. 22, 1804 to Oct. 25, 1805; The Southern Recorder (Milledgeville), Mar. 18, 1824 to Dec. 17, 1844; The Georgia Journal (Milledgeville), Dec. 17, 1809 to Dec. 11, 1816; The Southern Centennial & Universal Gazette (Augusta), July 6, 1793 to Oct. [illegible], 1799 and Jan. 9, 1794 to Oct. 24, 1799; The Augusta Chronicle & Gazette of the State, Nov. 9, 1800 to Mar. 14, 1825 and July 24, 1790 to Nov. 19, 1800 and June 5, 1790 to Nov. 15, 1800; The American Advocate, Jan. 13, 1816 to Oct. 3, 1816; and The Darien Gazette, Oct. 22, 1818 to Mar. 14, 1825.

MARRIAGE *and* OBITUARIES *from* EARLY GEORGIA NEWSPAPERS. By: Judge Folks Huxford, Pub. 1989, reprinted 2005, 464 pages, Hard Cover, Index, ISBN #0-89308-655-X.

GA 84 $48.50

The 18 different newspapers from which these marriage & obituaries come from cover the years 1787-1884 in varying times & formats with no one paper covering the entire time frame. Even though these newspapers come from: Baldwin, Bibb, Chatham, Hancock, Hart, Jefferson, McIntosh and Richmond counties along with 2 newspapers from Washington D.C. and Boston, Mass., this book should be considered a State-Wide reference source. Since these entries do not only pertain to the above mentioned counties but to neighboring ones as well. In the early days of pioneer development of the State, there were very few newspapers in existence. So, the ones that did exist would cover an extremely large area and people would travel far & wide to have their marriages and obituaries put in. On many instances these entries are like mini-biographies, naming several generations of family members, occupations, births, residents, etc.....

Rev. War Records

Georgia Citizen *and* Soldiers *of the* American Revolution. By: Robert S. Davis, Jr., Pub. 1979, reprinted 2020, 266 pages, Soft Cover, Index, ISBN #0-89308-169-8.

GA 20 $32.50

More than 1,700 citizens, 1,000 Patriot soldiers, and 800 Loyalists are included in this volume. Also, records of many Virginians who served in Georgia Continentals; of members of South Carolina Continental units in Georgia; and some South Carolina Loyalists are also included. This book will be a MUST for those looking for Revolutionary War service for a Georgia ancestor since the D.A.R. no longer accepts the undocumented records from McCall's three volumes on Georgia Revolutionary War soldiers and only small portions from Lucian Lamar Knight's volume on Georgia in the Revolution.

Georgia's Roster *of the* Revolution. By: Lucian Lamar Knight, Orig. Pub. 1920, reprinted 1997, 658 pages, Hard Cover,Index, ISBN #0-89308-604-5.

GA 9 $50.00

This is one of the most comprehensive and authoritative published records of Georgia Revolutionary War soldiers. This book is a MUST for those researchers doing work in Georgia during the Revolutionary time period. It should be a companion volume to: A Researcher's Library of Georgia History, Genealogy, and Records, Vol. 1, and Georgia Citizen and Soldiers. Even though Georgia did not furnish a large body of troops to the Revolutionary struggle, it did acquire a vast number of veterans filing for bounty land grants from other states. The reason for this is that it was the youngest of the English colonies with vast amounts of land but a scant population, located on the remote southern frontier. These bounty grants were issued after the war as payment for service rendered and to promote settlement in this the youngest of the colonies.

ILLINOIS

Record *of the* Services *of* Illinois Soldiers *in* The Black Hawk War, 1831-1832, *and in* The Mexican War, 1848-1888. By: Isaac H. Elliott, Pub. 1882, Pub. 2023, 376 pages, Soft Cover, ISBN #978-1-63914-105-0.

IL2 $40.00

This book contains a complete roster of commissioned officers and enlisted men of both wars, taken from the official rolls on file in the War Department in Washington, D.C. with an appendix giving a record of the services of the Illinois Militia, Rangers and Riflemen in protecting the Frontier from the ravages of the Indians from 1810 to 1818.

War *of* 1812 Bounty Lands *in* Illinois. By: James D. Walker, Pub. 1840, reprinted 2021, 666 pages, Index, soft cover, ISBN #978-1-63914-009-1.

IL 1 $52.50

Illinois has had quite the interesting history to statehood in 1818. French Canadian explorers started arriving in the late 1600's via the Mississippi River. They established missions and forts along various rivers before retreating back into what is now Missouri. This allowed the British to take rule over these lands from the French. After the Revolutionary War, settlers began arriving from Kentucky in the 1780's via the Ohio River. In 1812, tensions between these settlers and the Native American came to an impasse. U.S. troops would eventually prevail and 5 million acres of land in this Illinois Territory were set aside to pay for these services. Information to be found within this book: date of patent, its Warrant Number, name of the veteran along with his rank and regiment, description of land including its location, name of the patentee recipient, many time giving his last know city and state of residence, and date of delivery of the patent. By knowing this warrant number, the researcher can then acquire photocopies of the veteran's service records. The amount of information contained in the Bounty Land Warrant Application Files varies greatly. In claims made by their heirs, the Veteran's service, date and place of death, relationship to the veteran, and if appropriate, the date and place of death of remarriage of widow is given. In support of many claims, discharge certificates and various personal documents were submitted to prove marriage and to establish dependency.

INDIANA

Indiana Land Entries. Volume 1: Cincinnati District, 1801-1840. By: Margaret R. Waters, Pub. 1948, reprinted 2023, 253 pages, Index, soft cover, ISBN #978-1-63914-122-7.

IN 1 $28.50

The earliest land records of Indiana Territory go back to 1801, when a land office was established in Cincinnati. Tracts were surveyed according to the rectangular survey system first adopted in Ohio. The earliest tract books, published here, contain the records of the Cincinnati District and extend from April 1801 to August 1840. The area covered is mainly a district known as the "wedge" or "gore," located in the southeastern part of the state and bounded roughly by the Ohio-Indiana state line, the Ohio River, and the Greenville Treaty Line. It comprises all of the present counties of Ohio, Dearborn, Union, and Wayne; most of Switzerland, Fayette, Franklin, and Randolph; and a partial section of Jay. These records give the names of about 10,000 purchasers of land in the Cincinnati District as well as the specific location of their land and the date of the record.

Indiana Land Entries. Volume 2, Part 1: Vincennes District, 1807-1877. By: Margaret R. Waters, Pub. 1948, reprinted 2023, 285 pages, Index, soft cover, ISBN #978-1-63914-123-4.

IN 2 $30.0

The earliest land records of Indiana Territory go back to 1801, when a land office was established in Cincinnati. Tracts were surveyed according to the rectangular survey system first adopted in Ohio. This volume begins in 1807 and continues up to 1877. It covers approximately the central third of the Vincennes District, comprising all of the present counties of Daviess, Gibson, Knox, Martin, and Pike; and over half of Monroe and Lawrence. These records give the names of approximately 12,000 purchasers of land as well as the specific location of their land and the date of the record.

Memoirs *of the* Lower Ohio Valley, Personal and Genealogical. (2 Volumes) By: Federal Publishing Company, Pub. 1905, reprinted 2022, soft cover.

Vol. #1: 404 pages, Index, ISBN #978-1-63914-077-0.

KY 56 $40.00

Vol #2: 400 pages, Index, ISBN #978-1-63914-078-7

KY 57 $40.00

These books contain nothing but biographies' of person from the following counties of KENTUCKY: Boone, Gallatin, Grant, Owen, Henry, Trimble, Oldham, Jefferson, Shelby, Spencer, Bullitt Hardin, Meade, Breckenridge, Hancock, Ohio, Daviess, Henderson, Hopkins, Muhlenberg, Livingston, Union, Caldwell, McCracken, Hickman, Graves, and Calloway; counties of INDIANA: Dearborn, Ohio, Ripley, Switzerland, Jefferson, Jennings, Clark, Scott, Washington, Floyd, Harrison, Crawford, Orange, Perry, Dubois, Spencer, Pike, Gibson, Posey, Warrick, and Vanderburgh; counties of ILLINOIS: Alexander, Gallatin, Hardin, Johnson, Massac, Pope, Pulaski, Saline, and Union. ***See our wesite for a list of biographies.***

KENTUCKY

1790 Census *of* Kentucky. By: Charles B. Heinemann, Pub. 1938, Revised Reprint 2013, 188 pages, soft cover, Index, ISBN #0-89308-479-4.

KY 25 $22.50

In 1790 the present Commonwealth of Kentucky was part of Virginia, although a movement was underway to form a separate state. This resulted in the creation of the Territory of Kentucky in July 1790, and Kentucky was formally admitted to the Union in 1792. The census was to begin in August 1790, and when it was completed the returns were sent to Washington. During the War of 1812, the census of Kentucky was destroyed. The material this (reconstructed) census is based on are the personal property tax lists in the Kentucky Historical Society. The tax lists used in compiling this book were: Bourbon 1790, Fayette 1787, 1788 and 1789, Jefferson 1789, Lincoln 1790, Madison 1789, Mason 1790, Mercer 1789, Nelson 1792, and Woodford 1790. This book contains the names of approximately 9,500 persons found in these tax lists

Biographical Cyclopedia *of the* Commonwealth of Kentucky. By: John M. Gresham, Orig. Pub. 1896, reprinted 2019, 738 pages, NEW INDEX, ISBN #0-89308-192-2.

KY 18 $52.50

This excellent volume contains some 1104 Biographical sketches of Kentuckians and their families with over 10,000 persons listed in the NEW Index. Also to be found are 32 finely executed steel engravings of some of the biographees. Many of the biographies take the families back into the mid 1700's. ***See website for list of biographies.***

Biographical Encyclopedia *of* Kentucky: of the Dead and Living Men *of the* Nineteenth Century. By: J.M. Armstrong Company, Orig. Pub. 1876, Reprinted 2019, 820 pages, NEW INDEX, ISBN #0-89308-193-0.

KY 17 $58.50

Like similar books of the era, this volume is filled with some 1408 Biographical sketches of individuals prominent in Kentucky history, with 78 finely executed steel engravings of some of the biographies. Many of the Biographies have birth dates in the 1790's and early 1800's and hence many family genealogies are carried well back into the 1730's. This book contains the names of over 7,000 persons.

Bourbon, Scott, Harrison *and* Nicholas Counties, Kentucky, History of. By: W.H. Perrin, Orig. Pub. 1882, reprinted 2022, 848 pages, Index, Soft Cover, ISBN #0-89308-142-6.

KY 12 $68.50

This book is devoted to "the Blue Grass Region" of the state of Kentucky. It has been said to have more genealogical information than any other book of its kind. The book is divided into two main topics of interest. The first is a general history of the four above mentioned counties. With the second being of greater interest to the genealogist, this section is devoted to biographical sketches of these early settlers. The index alone references over 8,000 individuals.

Certificate Book *of the* Virginia Land Commission, 1779-1780, The Register for 1923. By: KY Historical Society, Orig. Pub. 1923, reprinted 1992, 344 pages, Index, ISBN #0-89308-207-4.

KY 19 $35.00

The original records of Kentucky County, Virginia, 1776-1780, were lost in a fire in the 19th century which makes this book quite important because it contains the names of most of the pioneer settlers of the state of Kentucky. The Certificate Book comprises most of Vol. 21 (1923) of the Register of the Kentucky Historical Society and gives information about the claims for land made by settlers between 1775 and 1779 who detailed the location of their claim and the date of settlement.

The "Cornstalk" MILITIA *of* Kentucky. By: G. Glenn Clift, Pub. 1957, reprinted 2013, 256 pages, soft cover, Index, ISBN #0-89308-318-6.

KY 22 $30.00

This book is a brief history of the militia and records of commissions of officers in the organization from the beginning of statehood to the commencement of the War of 1812. It has a section on the organization of commissioned officers and regiments by counties. This book contains the names of approximately 9,000 individuals who served in the militia in Kentucky and should be a must for anyone doing Kentucky research during this time span.

Christian County, Kentucky, History of. By: William Henry Perrin, Pub. 1884, Reprinted 2019, 718 pages, Index, Hard Cover, ISBN #0-89308-165-5.

KY 16 $58.50

Christian county was created in 1796 from Logan County, KY. It sits on the southern boarder right across from Montgomery County, TN. This volume printed separately from its companion on Trigg County, contains over 400 Biographical sketches of individuals. Also history of early schools, businesses in some 14 precincts of the county and filled with many interesting stories. The NEW FULL NAME INDEX mentions over 6,000 names of individuals that are found other than the Biographies.

Clark County, Kentucky, History of. (Volume #1): Land *of* Our Fathers. By: A. Goff Bedford, Pub. 1958, reprinted 2019, 582 pages, Index, soft cover, ISBN #0-89308-893-5.

KY 49 $48.50

Original known as Bourbon County, Virginia, Clark County was created in 1785 from Fayette County, KY. It was much larger area than present-day Bourbon County, as its original territory included the counties of: Bracken, Boone, Campbell, Estill, Fleming, Floyd, Greenup, Harrison, Kenton, Mason, Montgomery, Lewis, Nicholas, Pendleton, Powell and Robertson. This book is similar to other history books of the era, but what does set it apart is the extensive section of religion and the churches role in its development. This book is filled with over 6,000 names that helped its development.

Cumberland County, Kentucky, History of. By: J.W. Wells, Pub. 1947, Reprinted 2019, 442 pages, ISBN #0-89308-890-0.

KY 35 $40.00

Cumberland County was created in 1798 from Green County. It sits in along the Kentucky-Tennessee border in the south central portion of the state. Of special note: it sits directly above Smith and Jackson counties, TN, during the time of its creation. This area of Kentucky saw large numbers of persons moving into and through as people were looking for new lands to settle as they were coming around the Appalachian Mountains heading West. Information to be found within this book: Marriages 1799-1817; Tax Lists 1799; Lists of Military Grants in Cumberland County; Lists of Land Grants in Cumberland; Grants by Kentucky in Cumberland County; Death / Inscriptions from 7 cemeteries in the county; Lists of Revolutionary Pensioners; short sketches of some Revolutionary soldiers who were living in Cumberland County; Lists of Cumberland County soldiers who served in the War of 1812, Civil War, and Spanish American War along with the cemetery buried in when known; almost 100 pages is devoted to genealogies of early pioneers. ***See website for list of biographies.***

Fayette County, Kentucky, History of. By: J.H. Battle & Robert Peter, MD, Pub. 1882, Reprinted 2017, 856 pages, hard cover, NEW INDEX, ISBN #0-89308-163-9.

KY 15 $65.00

Fayette County was created in 1780 as one of the first three counties form by the Virginia Legislature in Kentucky Territory. This book is probably one of the MOST sought-after books on Kentucky History/ Genealogy. It is the definitive history on Fayette County, KY. and the city of Lexington. The NEW

FULL NAME INDEX that was produced for this volume mentions approximately 12,000 individuals.

Historic FAMILIES *of* Kentucky. By: Thomas Marshall Green, Pub. 1889, Reprinted 2019, 310 pages, Index, ISBN #0-89308-797-1.

KY 51 $30.00

This book is a basic history of the state, with considerable emphasis on the accomplishments of its pioneer families, including their public service in the nation's struggle for independence. The main emphasis of the book is to trace these pioneer families and their origin within this country while a number of them were of Scotch-Irish extraction whose ancestors immigrated to America in the early 18th century and became pioneers of the Valley of Virginia. Descendants of these families of the Valley were among the early pioneers of Kentucky. Families for which biographical Sketches are found within: Alexander, Allen Anderson, Andrews, Ball, Barbour, Bell, Benton, Birney, Blair, Bowman, Brashear, Breckindridge, Brown, Buford, Bulitt, Burden, Butler, Campbell, Carlisle, Carrington, Caron, Caruthers, Carthrae, Chrisman, Christian, Clarke, Clay, Crittenden, Cummings, Dickson, Drake, Duke, Fontaine, Frogg, Hall, Harbeson, Hardin, Harvey, Harvie, Hawkins, Helm, Innes, Irvine, Gordon, Jones, Keith, Kirk, Le Grand, Lewis, Logan, Luke, Lyle, Madison, Marshall, McAlpine, McClure, McClarty, McClung, McDowell, McKnight, McPheeters, Metcalfe, Miller, Moffett, Monroe, Montgomery, Moore, Murray, Neil, Newton, Patton, Parker, Paxton, Pepper, Pickett, Preston, Price, Randolph, Reade, Reed, Reid, Smith, Starling, Stuart, Strother, Taylor, Thornton, Todd, Venable, Warner, Washington, Woodson, Wallace.

Jessamine County, Kentucky, A History of. By: Bennett H. Young, Pub. 1898, reprinted 2020, 288 pages, Index, ISBN #0-89308-102-7.

KY 45 $30.00

Jessamine County was created in 1798 form Fayette County. It lies in the center of the state. Most of her early settlers were from North Carolina and Virginia. These pioneers crossed into Kentucky after the Revolutionary War in search of new lands. This book is not too different from other county history books of this era. With such topics as trade and transportation, labor, farming, politics, and race relations - all important in the development of the county - are carefully discussed. This type of county history book can help one develop ideas or paths to those missing ancestors by showing the customs and traditions of the local residents. But the genealogist will love that approximately 1/3 of the book is devoted to biographical sketches of these early pioneer.

Johnson County, Kentucky: A History of the County and Genealogy of Its People Up to the Year 1927. By: Mitchell Hall, Pub. 1928, reprinted 2021, 556 pages, soft cover, ISBN #978-1-63914-044-2.

KY 36 $38.50

Located within the Big Sandy Valley, Johnson County was formed in 1844 from: Floyd, Lawrence and Mason Counties. This book is similar to other history books of the era with such topics being discussed: English colonists, early settlement, government, local customs, geology, education, religion, industrial and etc.... The author has loaded this book with wide variety of genealogical information such as: 1925 & 1890 Tax List; 1837 Tax List of Floyd County; A list of early residents from 1844 to 1848 which were pulled from the 1st court order book; 1793 Tax List of Mason County; a map of pioneer trails from the Carolinas and Virginia into the Big Sandy Valley; Kentucky Land Grants and Entries affecting Eastern Kentucky and Johnson County, various lists of county officials and men serving in WWI; a list of Revolutionary soldiers from Mason, Floyd & Johnson counties showing name, date of pension, number of court order book, along with page number; and other items of interest.

Kentucky Land Warrants for the French, Indian and Revolutionary Wars. By: Phillip Fall Taylor and Samuel M. Wilson, 2 Volumes in one, Pub. 1917 and 1913, reprinted 2006, 200 pages, Hard Cover, New Index, ISBN #0-89308-499-9.

KY 26 $32.50

A Calendar for Warrants for Land in Kentucky, Granted for service in the French and Indian Wars; and Land Bounty Land Warrants Granted for Military Service in the War for Independence. This section of Land Bounty Warrants is taken from the 1913 Year Book of the Kentucky Society of the SAR and contains the names of approximately 6,075 men who served in the Revolution from Virginia. The name of the soldier or officer is given; number of acres he received; rank; department of service, i.e., Continental or State Line of Virginia State Navy; Number of years service and the date of the warrant. The earliest surveys of land in Kentucky taken from the 1917 Yearbook of the Society of Colonial Wars in Kentucky were military surveys made in Fincastle County which in 1773 comprised all of the state of Kentucky, Fayette, Jefferson, and Lincoln Counties. Information contained in these surveys are the name of the person drawing the land; rank; acres surveyed; location of land often giving water courses and adjacent neighbors. These surveys begin in 1774 and continue through 1789 and contain the names of approximately 1,000 persons. By combining the materials from the two above books, the researcher for both Kentucky and Virginia is given a much needed new source of information on these early settlers.

Kentucky Pioneer and Court Records. By: Mrs. Harry Kennett McAdams, Orig. Pub. 1929, reprinted 1998, 382 pages, Index, Hard Cover, ISBN #0-89308-475-1.

KY 27 $40.00

Here is one book that no researcher looking for lost relatives in the state of Kentucky can do without. Because the counties that this book covers represented over half of the entire state of Kentucky in the late 1700's. The counties covered in this book are: Anderson, Boyle, Clark, Estill, Fayette, Fleming, Garrard, Harrison, Jessamine, Lincoln, Madison, Mercer, Montgomery, Nicholas, Scott, Wayne, and Woodford. These records begin in the 1700's and go well into the 1800's covering a large range of topics, such as: abstracts of Wills, Deeds, Marriages, and even church/religious records are covered (Old Bible, Churches, Graveyards, and Cemeteries).

Kentucky Soldiers *of the* War of 1812. By: Adj. General State of KY, Orig. Pub. 1891, reprinted 2006, 465 pages, Hard Cover, New Index, ISBN #0-89308-481-6.

KY 24 $45.00

When the War of 1812 began, Kentucky had a total population of only 400,000, and out of this total furnished 40 regiments of volunteer militia, as well as a number of battalions and companies -i.e., more than 25,000 men between 1812-1815. Of the 1,876 Americans killed during the war, some 1,200 or about 64% were Kentuckians. The military records of Kentuckians who did serve in the War of 1812 are incomplete and scattered, and the rosters preserved in this volume represent those extant and available to the Adj. General in 1890/1, and since few lists have been discovered since this original report, this volume must stand as the primary source for data on soldiers from Kentucky in that war. When this book was done in 1890, the legislature authorized a maximum of 350 copies to be printed, so this edition will indeed be a valuable tool for Kentucky research. This book contains the names of approximately 25,126 men who served from Kentucky.

Lawyer and Lawmakers of Kentucky. By: H. Levin, editor; Pub. 1897, reprinted 1982, 808 pages, Hard Cover, New Index, ISBN #0-89308-319-4.

KY 21 $65.00

This is probably the rarest of all the biographical sketch books ever done on Kentuckians, having been published in 1897. The book covers all of the prominent lawyers, as well as those who were not so prominent. This is a MUST book for every Library shelf. It contains biographical sketches of approx. 700 individuals and finely executed steel engravings of 121 biographies. There are approx. 10,500 names of individuals listed besides those of the biographies.

Marshall County, Kentucky, Lemon's Hand Book of. By: J.R. Lemon, Pub. 1894, reprinted 2021, 186 pages, New Index, soft cover, ISBN #978-1-63914-043-5.

KY 55 $25.00

Marshall County was formed in 1842 from Calloway County. It lies in the far Western portion of the state surrounded by Calloway, Graves, McCracken, Trigg, Lyon and Livingston counties along with being a stone's throw from the Ohio and Tennessee Rivers. Due to its geography, settlers began showing up in this area around 1818, just after the Jackson Purchase of these lands from the Chickasaw Indians. The citizens of the county were sympatric to the Confederate side during the Civil War. Many of her residents belonged to the famous Kentucky Orphan Brigade. This book has many of the usual topics being discussed: early history, creation of the county, early settlements, government, churches, economics, early hangings and etc.. Over half of the book is devoted to biographical sketches of these early residents of the county.

Mason County, Kentucky, History of Maysville *and*. By: G. Glenn Clift, Pub. 1936, Reprinted 2019, 472 pages, Index, soft cover, ISBN #0-89308-572-3.

KY 38 $42.50

Mason County was created in 1788 as one of the nine counties from the Kentucky District. It was taken from Bourbon County in 1788 and lies in the northeastern corner of the state bordering Ohio. This book is a traditional county history book that covers the usual topics. It also has considerable material bearing on the history of Washington, the early county seat, and Maysville, or Limestone as it was known in pioneer days. Approximately 1/3 of this book is devoted to county records and pension papers of soldiers who served in the Revolutionary War, Indian Wars, War of 1812; A list of men who served in the War of 1812 and wills of these pioneers settlers from 1791-1810.

Memoirs *of the* Lower Ohio Valley, Personal *and* Genealogical. (2 Volumes) By: Federal Publishing Company, Pub. 1905, reprinted 2022, soft cover.

Vol. #1: 404 pages, Index, ISBN #978-1-63914-077-0.

KY 56 $40.00

Vol #2: 400 pages, Index, ISBN #978-1-63914-078-7

KY 57 $40.00

These books contain nothing but biographies' of

person from the following counties of KENTUCKY: Boone, Gallatin, Grant, Owen, Henry, Trimble, Oldham, Jefferson, Shelby, Spencer, Bullitt Hardin, Meade, Breckenridge, Hancock, Ohio, Daviess, Henderson, Hopkins, Muhlenberg, Livingston, Union, Caldwell, McCracken, Hickman, Graves, and Calloway; counties of INDIANA: Dearborn, Ohio, Ripley, Switzerland, Jefferson, Jennings, Clark, Scott, Washington, Floyd, Harrison, Crawford, Orange, Perry, Dubois, Spencer, Pike, Gibson, Posey, Warrick, and Vanderburgh; counties of ILLINOIS: Alexander, Gallatin, Hardin, Johnson, Massac, Pope, Pulaski, Saline, and Union. ***See our wesite for a list of biographies.***

Ohio County, Kentucky in the Olden Days. By: Harrison D. Taylor, Pub. 1926, Reprinted 2019, 224 pages, Index, ISBN #0-89308-903-6.

KY 39 $20.00

Ohio County was created in 1798 from Hardin County. It sits in the western portion of the state with its northern boundary being the Ohio River for which it received its name but in 1829 was divided to create the counties of Davies and Hancock. The reader will discover genealogical data on early families, data concerning Ohio county in the War of 1812, early land titles, biographies of early citizens and approximately 2,500 marriage records prior to 1840.

Perry County, Kentucky, History of. By: Eunice T. Johnson, Pub. 1953, reprinted 2016, 286 pages, Index, ISBN #0-89308-919-2.

KY 42 $28.50

Perry County was created 1820 from Clay and Floyd Counties. It in turn was carved up to create in part and whole the counties of: Breathitt, Harlan, Knott, Letcher, and Leslie. This is the story of one of the most colorful communities in the Appalachian Mountains. Located on the north fork of the Kentucky River, It sits in the southeastern corner of the state bordering Virginia. This book covers the whole story from the time the first hardy pioneers moved across the mountains from Virginia to build cabins, stake out land claims, and subdivide this part of Kentucky into a county. The author has also included a section of the book entitled "Early Perry County Families": Baker, Begley, Boling, Brashear, Campbell, Combs, Cope, Cornett, Davidson, Duff, Eversole, Francis, Fugate, Grigsby, Gross, Hall, Holliday, Ison, Johnson, Lusk, Morgan, Napier, Noble, Ritchie, Smith, Stamper, Webb and a list of individuals from the counties First Tax Book, 1821-1822.

Pioneer Families *of* Eastern & Southeastern Kentucky. By: Wiliam C. Kozee Pub. 1957, reprinted 2018, 284 pages, soft cover, ISBN #0-89308-927-3.

KY 52 $58.50

This book is basically a source book of genealogical data rather than a collection of family histories. Genealogical information on each county is uniform and is arranged in the following manner: 1) the boundary line and establishment by law of each county, 2) a synopsis of the earliest court records pertaining to the county, 3) a list of pioneering families according to the 1810 federal census, and various county Tax Lists, 4) finally Marriage Records of various southeastern KY counties. There are additional sections that cover lists of Revolutionary, War of 1812 and Civil War soldiers.

Pulaski County, KY. Court Orders, 1804-1810. By: Karen Tracey, printed 2016, 320 pages, Index, ISBN #0-89308-892-7.

KY 28 $35.00

This Never Before published book makes for a great research tool for those persons researching in Kentucky. Pulaski County was created in 1799 from Lincoln and Green Counties. Its importance to genealogy is in the fact that it sits in what is called the Cumberland Gap. This area saw a large number of persons migrating from the east and the south in search of lands to the west.

Pulaski County, KY., History of. By: Alma O. Tibbals, Pub. 1952, Reprinted 2016, 292 pages, Index, ISBN #0-89308-889-7.

KY 33 $32.50

Pulaski County was formed in 1799 from Lincoln and Green Counties, KY. History books of this era provide clues via local customs and traditions of the residents. The usual topics are discussed, such as: formation of the county, early towns, religion, commerce, education, agriculture, and politics. The researcher will delight in the section on family genealogies of early settlers. You will also discover that the author has included: Tax Lists 1799, 1800, 1804, 1806; Lists of persons with military service in The Revolutionary War, War of 1812, Mexican War (1847), and The Civil War.

Revolutionary Soldiers *in* Kentucky, also a Roster *of the* Virginia Navy. By: Anderson Chanault Quisenbury, Pub. 1896, Reprinted 1992, 248 pages, Hard Cover, New Index, ISBN #0-89308-480-8.

KY 23 $30.00

This volume contains a roll of the officers of the Virginia Line who received Land Bounty Grants; a roll of the revolutionary Pensioners in Kentucky; a list of the Illinois Regiment who served under General George Rogers Clark in N.W. Campaign. Found in this book are those citizens of Kentucky who were granted Revolutionary Pensions to the year 1835 as registered by the Secretary of War. To this list has been appended a list of names of many persons to whom the state of Virginia granted lands on account of Revolutionary services; and also rolls of the soldiers of General George Rogers Clark's "Illinois Regiment" nearly all of whom settled in Kentucky; and of the Virginia Revolutionary Navy, many of whom also settled there and other descendants of whom are living in the state. The Revolutionary War pensions in Kentucky numbered about 3,000. Some names, but not many (except widows), were added to the list before 1835. Some of the additional names are preserved in Collins' HISTORY of KENTUCKY, in two volumes, which contains a list of nearly 900 who were still living in the state in 1840.

Todd County, Kentucky, History of. By: J.H. Battle, Pub. 1884, Reprinted 2017, 404 pages, NEW INDEX, ISBN #0-89308-162-0.

KY 13 $38.50

Todd county was created in 1819 from Christian and Logan counties. It too is located in the Southwestern portion of the State along the Kentucky-Tennessee border. This volume contains over 200 Biographical Sketches and the NEW FULL NAME INDEX that was produced for this volume mentions the names of over 4482 other individuals are found herein.

Trigg County, Kentucky, History of. By: J.H. Battle, Pub. 1884, Reprinted 2017, 311 pages, NEW INDEX, ISBN #0-89308-164-7.

KY 14 $30.00

Trigg county was created in 1820 from Christian and Caldwell counties. It too is located in the Southwestern portion of the State along the Kentucky-Tennessee border. This volume contains over 185 Biographical Sketches and the NEW FULL NAME INDEX that was produced for this volume mentions the names of over 1200 other individuals are found herein.

TRIGG County, Kentucky, 1790-1900, Statistical Handbook *of*. By: Eurie Pearl Wilford Neel, pub.1961, reprinted 2020, 726 pages, Index, ISBN #0-89308-678-9.

KY 52 $58.50

Trigg County was created in 1820 from Christian and Caldwell counties. It too is located in the Southwestern portion of the State along the Kentucky-Tennessee border. Records within this book are: Logan County Marriage Bonds 1790-1797, Christian County Census 1820, 1830 & 1840, Christian County Marriage Bonds 1797-1820, Livingston County Census 1810, Livingston County Tax Lists 1804 & 1811, Livingston County Marriage Bonds 1799-1810, Caldwell County Tax Lists 1810, Caldwell County Marriage Bonds 1809-1820, Caldwell and Trigg County Militia Roll, Trigg County Census 1820, 1850 & 1880, Trigg County Poll Books 1826, 1827, 1829, 1840-1842, 1850, 1853, 1856, 1859-1861, 1864, 1867, 1868 & 1890, Trigg County Order Book "A" 1820-1825, Trigg County Vital Statistics 1851-1853, Trigg County Marriage Bonds 1820-1900, Trigg County lists of Graves of Veterans, Cemetery Records for all counties, Hopkins and Todd County data, Militia and Muster Rolls.

Union County, Kentucky, History of. By: Evansville Bindery, Pub. 1886, Reprinted 2019, 920 pages, Index, ISBN #0-89308-896-X.

KY 37 $28.50

Union County was created in 1811 from Henderson County, KY. It lies in the western portion of the state bordering Gallatin County, Illinois and Posey County, Indiana along the Ohio River. This book is similar to other books of this era as it discusses the same topics such as: commerce, agriculture, transportation, education and religion. All of which are important to the development of the county. But the genealogists will find extremely exciting are the early marriages 1811-1825, Lists of Ex-Confederate soldiers, lists of ex-Union Soldiers and the hundreds of biographical sketches of these earlier citizens that are interspersed throughout the book. ***See website for list of biographies.***

Wayne County, Kentucky, 1800-1900, A Century of. By: Augusta Phillips Johnson, Pub. 1939, Reprinted 2019, 308 pages, Index, ISBN #0-89308-739-4.

KY 34 $28.50

Wayne County was created in 1800 from Pulaski and Cumberland Counties. It sits in the southern portion of the state along the Walker Line boarding Tennessee. Of special note: it sits directly above Smith and Jackson counties, TN, during the time of its creation. The first settlers began arriving along the Cumberland river in the 1770's. Revolutionary War veterans also began arriving in the 1790's prior to the establishment of the county. All subjects in the development of the county are discussed along with Marriages 1801-1813; Biographical, Genealogical and Miscellaneous Notes on: Bartleson, Berry, Buster, Carter, Chrisman, Duncan, Ewing, Gholson, Hardin, Hendrick, Ingram, Jones, Kendrick, Kennedy, Lanier, McBeath, McDowell, Miller, Oatts, Phillips, Ramsey, Sallee, Saunders, Shearer, Tate, Todhunter, Warden, West, Woods, and Worsham. The Index has approximately 3,000 entries.

Western Kentucky, Memorial Record *of*. (Volumes 1 and 2). By: The Lewis Publishing Company, Pub. 1904, reprinted 2023, 860 pages, Index, ISBN #0-89308-

247-3.

KY 58 $65.00

The Western portion of the great commonwealth of Kentucky has produced many grand men and women, whose carriers have shed lustre not only on the history of the community in which they lived, but also on that of their state and nation. The entire make up of this book is biographical sketches of men and women of person living in western Kentucky. These biographical sketches were collected largely by interviews. The New Index references approximately 7,000 persons within this book. Surnames of the biography's: Akin, Allen (2), Allensworth, Anderson (4), Arnold, Atkins, Atwood, Baker, Ballowe, Barber, Barry, Bauer, Becker, Beeler (3), Bell (2), Bennett, Berry, Bethshares, Beyer, Bishop, Blakey, Blane, Bloomfield, Blue, Blythe, Boli, Bone (2), Boone, Boyd (2), Bradley, Bradshaw, Brasher, Braswell, Breathitt (3), Brewer, Briggs, Brooks (2), Brothers, Brown, Bryant, Buchanan, Bugg (2), Bullock, Burch, Burchard, Burgess, Burnett (2), Burton, Bush, Butler (2), Caldwell, (2), Campbell (3), Carrico, Carter (2), case, Catlett, Choice, Chowning, Clark (2), Clay, Coleman (2), Colley (2), Collins, Conant, Cook, Cooper, Corbett, Coulter, Coyle, Crawford, Creedle, Crockett, Crossland (3) Crouch, Crumbaugh, Cummins, Curd, Crutchfield, Curtsinger, Dabney, Dalton, Daniel, Darby (2), Davis (6), Day, Dean, Deboe, Dickey, Dismukes, Dorsey, Douthit, Downer, Dreyfuss, Driskill, Dunn, Dycus, Eager, Eaton, Elliott (2), Elliston, Elmore, Elsey (2), Eubanks, Faith, Farabough, Farley (2), Farrell, Finch, Finley, Fisher (4), Flatt, Flourney, Foster, Fowler (3), Friedman (2), Futrell, Galloway (3), Gardner (2), Garnett (3), Garrett, George, Gilbert (2), Glenn, Gordon (2), Grace, Graham, Grant, Graves, Gray, Greer (2), Gresham, Griffin (2), Grifith, Groom, Gunn, Guthrie, Hale (2), Hall, Happy, Harrison, Hazelwood, Henderson, Henry, Herndon, Hicks, Hilliard, Hobbs, Hobson, Hodge, Hodges, Hogancamp, Holloway, Hostetter, Housman, Howard, Hubbard, Huey, Hughes (2), Husbands (2), Jackson (3), James (3), Jeffrey, Johnson (2), Jones, Kane, Kelley, Kevil, Kirkpatrick, Klapp (2), Koltiusky, Lackey (2), Landes, Landrum, Lawson, Leavell, Lee, Leech (2), Lemon, Lenihan, Leonard (2), Lightfoot, Ligon, Linn, Lisanby, Little, Loeb, Lovelace (2), Lyon, Major, Mantle, Marble (2), Martin (2), Mason, Mathews, Maxon, McAlister, McCarroll, McClain, Meacham, Merritt, Miller, Mizell, Molloy (2), Moore (5), Moorman, Moreman, Morehead (2), Morgan (2), Morris, Morton, Mosby, Moss (4), Myatt, Nance (3), Newberry, Newman, Nichols, Ogilvie (3), Oliver, Owen (2), Payne (2), Peal, Perryman, Petree, Petrie, Pettit, Phillips, Pierceall, Polivick, Pollard, Pool, Potter, Powell (2), Pritchett, Prowse, Pryor, Pullen, Purdy, Puryear, Quiqley (3), Randle, Ratliff, Ray (2), Reddick, Reed (2), Reeves, Reynolds, Rich, Richmond, Riglesberger, Rivers, Robb, Robbins (2), Robertson, Rock, Rodgers, Rogers, Rozzell, Randolph, Samuels, Sanderson, Saunders, Schmidt, Scott, Shacklett, Shelbourne, Shelton (2), Sherrell, Sights, Sleeth (2), Smith (5), Spalding (2), Spicer (2), Spink, Stanfield, Stanley, Starr, Steele, Stevens, Stone, Sublett, Sullivan, Tartt, Taylor, Templeman, Terrell (2), Tharp, Thompson (3), Todd, Torian, Travis, Trimble, Troutman, Turk, Turner (2), Underwood, Utley, Utterback, Vaughn, Via, Walker, Wallace (2), Waller, Wasbam, Watkins (2), Webb, Whayne, Wheeler, White (3), Whitlow, Wickliffe, Wiley, Williams, Williamson, Willingham (3), Wisdom, Witty, Woelfle, Wood (2), Wray, Wright, Wyatt, Yates (2), Yeiser (2), and Young.

Research Aids

Old Kentucky Entries *and* Deeds, 1779-1853.

By: Willard Rouse Jillson, Pub. 1926, Reprinted 2018, 582 pages, Index, soft cover, ISBN #0-89308-949-4.

KY 48 $48.50

This is a complete index to the earliest land records of Kentucky alphabetically arranged under the names of the grantees, giving the number of acres, dates, locations, and page references in the original records.

The bulk of the work is devoted to the early Fayette, Lincoln, and Jefferson County records which were turned over to Kentucky by Virginia in 1792. Also included are Military Warrants 1782-1793, Court of Appeals Deeds-Grantees 1783-1909, Court of Appeals Deeds-Grantors 1783-1909, Court of Appeals Deeds-Wills 1769-1850, and Court of Appeals Deeds-Power of Attorneys 1781-1853.

Kentucky Court *and other* Records, Volume #1.

By: Mrs. William Breckenridge Ardery, Pub. 1932, Reprinted 2018, 206 pages, Index, soft cover, ISBN #0-89308-718-1.

KY 32 $20.00

The records within this volume are all from original court entries. They include such things as: Wills, Marriages, Old Bibles and Tombstone Inscriptions for the counties of Barren, Bath, Bourbon, Clark, Daviess, Fayette, Harrison, Jessamine, Lincoln, Madison, Mason, Montgomery, Nelson, Nicholas, Ohio, Scott, and Shelby.

Kentucky Court *and other* Records, Vol.#2.

By: Mrs. William Breckenridge Ardery, Pub. 1932, Reprinted 2018, 256 pages, Index, soft cover, ISBN #0-89308-782-3.

KY 47 $25.00

The records within this volume are all from original court entries. They include such things as: Wills, Deeds, Orders, Suites, Church Minutes, Marriages, Old Bibles and Tombstone Inscriptions for the counties of Bath, Bourbon, Bracken, Clark, Fayette, Fleming, Hardin, Harrison, Jefferson, Jessamine, Lincoln, Madison, Mason, Montgomery, Nicholas, Oldham, Scott, Warren and Woodford.

Kentucky Marriages, 1797-1865.

By: G. Glenn Clift, Pub. 1938-40, reprinted 2020, 210 pages plus New Index, ISBN #0-89308-906-0.

KY 30 $28.50

These marriage notices are listed in chronological order. Data to be found within each entry gives: the name of the bride and the groom, the date of marriage, the place of residence and names of parents when known. The author has also included the source of the information for each entry. The new index that was created for this book mentions approximately 8,000 persons.

Kentucky Obituaries, 1787-1854.

By: G. Glenn Clift, Pub. 1941-43, reprinted 2020, 294 pages, New Index, ISBN #0-89308-917-6.

KY 31 $30.00

This book was created as a companion volume to a book entitled Kentucky Marriages, 1797-1865 by the G. Glenn Clift. The 5,000 plus obituary notices were extracted from six early Kentucky newspapers and published in The Register of the Kentucky Historical Society. The Newspapers from which they were abstracted from: the Observer & Reporter, the Kentucky Gazette, the Reporter, the Kentucky Reporter, the Observer, the Argus of Western America and . Most entries give the name of the deceased, place of residence, name of spouse, names of parents and other survivors, date of death, and other genealogical data. The new Index that was created for this book mentions approximately 7,000 persons.

Early Kentucky Wills *and* Inventories, 1780-1842.

By: J. Estelle Stewart King, Pub. 1933, Reprinted 2019, 304 pages, Index, ISBN #0-89308-747-5.

KY 43 $27.50

The will and inventories that have been abstracted cover the time frame 1780 and 1842. This book should be considered a statewide resource with the exception of Crittenden County. The information found within includes dates of instrument and probate, names of wife and children, and names of witnesses. The arrangement is county by county, each with its own index, with a general index at the rear of the book containing all the names mentioned in the text. Counties being covered are: Barren, Bourbon, Bullitt, Caldwell, Christian, Clark, Crittenden, Daviess, Fayette, Franklin, Gallatin, Garrard, Greene, Hardin, Harrison, Henderson, Henry, Hopkins, Jefferson, Jessamine, Knox, Lincoln, Livingston, Logan, Madison, McCracken, Mercer, Muhlenberg, Nelson, Nicholas, Ohio, Scott, Shelby, Spencer, Todd, Warren, Washington, and Woodford.

Petitions *of the* Early Inhabitants *of* Kentucky *to the* General Assembly *of* Virginia, 1769-1792.

By: James R. Robertson & John F. Dorman, Pub. 1914, Reprinted 2019, 326 pages, Index, ISBN #0-89308-206-6.

KY 20 $30.00

Robertson's petitions are verbatim transcripts of the text of 110 petitions between 1769 and 1831 relating to the earliest settlers, together with a list of the persons who signed the petitions keyed to the petition number. An index covers names and subjects mentioned in the petitions. A 44-page addendum section containing additional petitions of Kentuckians to the Virginia Legislature has been included. This additional section was taken from "The Kentucky Genealogists" and prepared by Mr. John Frederick Dorman, F.A.S.G.. The NEW FULL NAME INDEX that was produced for this addendum section mentions approximately 2,250 individuals.

Miscellaneous Records

(Rare 9 Volume Series)

These are probably the RAREST and MOST VALUABLE set of books ever published on early Kentucky families. Confusion has long existed concerning these titles because the authors referred to each Volume as an "Edition", causing many to believe that each "Edition" carried more than one Volume per "Edition". Only nine "Editions" (volumes) were published with two being labeled Edition No. 8. In this catalog, this Publisher is referring to the two No. 8's as 8-A and 8-B to distinguish between them. Like most works of this kind, each Edition contains first, a History of the State with its ties to early Virginia; these are followed by varying appendixes one of which contains a listing of both Federal and Confederate Troops in service from Kentucky. Following these come the very important biographical sketches of individuals and their families, many going well back into the early to mid 1700's. Unlike a contemporary, partial and rearranged edition of this series, the Publisher is following the original Perrin, Battle, and Kniffin editions as originally done, EXCEPT that the History of Kentucky and Appendixes will be separated from the sections of biographical sketches, and will appear as a separate volume. Each Edition has had a new full-name index prepared and included to assist the reader in their research.

The General History: By: W. H. Perrin, J.H. Battle, and G.C. Kniffin, Pub. 1885, Reprinted 2019, 692 pages, NEW FULL NAME Index, ISBN #0-89308-132-9.

KY 2 $52.50

This is the general or historical portion of probably the Rarest and MOST VALUABLE set of books ever published on the state of Kentucky and its early families. Like most works of this kind, this edition contains a history of the state with its ties to early Virginia; these are followed by varying appendices one of which contains a listing of both Federal and Confederate troops in service from Kentucky. This is an extremely detailed and complete history of the state covering such things as: Origin and Development of the First Colony in Virginia, Virginia as a Dependency of the Crown, Beyond the Alleghenies - Virginia's conquest in the West, Exploration and First settlement of Kentucky, the Colonization of Kentucky, Kentucky's part in the Revolutionary War, the Pioneers and Pioneer Days, Indians, early Politics and and extension of Frontier lines, Kentucky's involvement with the Annexation of Texas and the War with Mexico, considerable amounts of information and data on Kentucky's involvement in the Civil War, Genealogy of the Boone Family, First Platt of Louisville, Names of First Settlers, Indian Grants to Whites, Boonesborough, the Girty Family; Land Titles, and etc....... The NEW FULL NAME Index for this reprint has approximately 7,000 entries.

The First Edition: By: Perrin, Kniffen & Battle, Pub. 1885, Reprinted 2017, 478 pages, soft cover, Index, ISBN #0-89308-133-7.

KY 3 $48.50

This book contains the Precinct histories of the seven counties in the Jackson Purchase, (which originally were Indian lands located in the extreme southwestern corner of the state bordering Missouri, Tennessee and Illinois) and 740 biographical sketches of individuals in the following counties: Ballard, Calloway, Fulton, Graves, Hickman, McCracken and Marshall. The index mentioned approximately 14,500 persons.

The Second Edition: By: Perrin, Kniffen & Battle, Pub. 1885, Reprinted 2018, 542 pages, Index, soft cover, ISBN #0-89308-134-5.

KY 4 $52.50

Contains Biographical sketches from the following counties: Butler, Caldwell, Crittenden, Hancock, Hopkins, Livingston, Logan, Lyon, McLean, Muhlenburg, Ohio, Union, and Webster. The NEW FULL NAME INDEX that was produced for this volume mentions approximately 18,500 individuals.

The Third Edition: By: Perrin, Kniffen & Battle, Pub. 1885, Reprinted 1999, 613 pages, Index, Hard Cover, ISBN #0-89308-135-3

KY 5 $48.50

Contains 1,172 biographical sketches of individuals from the following counties: Allen Barren, Breckenridge, Edmondson, Grayson, Hardin, Hart, Larue, Meade, Metcalfe, Monroe, Simpson, and Warren. The index mentions approx. 23,000 persons.

The Fourth Edition: By: Perrin, Battle & Kniffin, Orig. Pub. 1885, reprinted 1999, 613 pages, Hard Cover, New Index, ISBN #0-89308-135-3.

KY 6 $40.00

Contains 613 biographical sketches of individuals from the following counties: Adair, Boyle, Casey, Cumberland, Garrard, Green, Lincoln, Madison, Marion, Mercer, Nelson, Taylor, Trigg, and Washington. The index mentions approx. 15,000 persons.

The Fifth Edition: By: Perrin, Battle & Kniffin, Orig. Pub. 1886, reprinted 2014, 164 pages, soft cover, New Index, ISBN #0-89308-137-X.

KY 7 $25.00

This volume contains 385 biographical sketches of individuals from the following counties: Anderson, Franklin, Jessamine, and Woodford. The index mentions approximately 6,000 persons.

The Sixth Edition: By: Perrin, Battle & Kniffin, Orig. Pub. 1885, reprinted 2014, 184 pages, Hard Cover, New Index, ISBN #0-89308-138-8.

KY 8 $25.00

This volume contains 465 biographical sketches of individuals from the following counties: Henry, Oldham, Shelby, Spencer, and Trimble. The index mentions approximately 7,000 persons.

The Seventh Edition: By: Perrin, Kniffen & Battle, Pub. 1885, Reprinted 2017, 214 pages, soft cover, Index, ISBN #0-89308-139-6.

KY 9 $25.00

Contains Biographical sketches on individuals from the following counties: Boone, Campbell, Gallatin, Grant, Kenton, Owen, and Pendleton. The NEW FULL NAME INDEX that was produced for this volume mentions approximately 4,000 individuals.

The Eidth Edition (8-A): By: Perrin, Battle & Kniffin, Orig. Pub. 1888, reprinted 2013, 210 pages, soft cover, New Index, ISBN #0-89308-140-X.

KY 10 $27.50

Jefferson County was created in 1780. It was one of the first 3 counties created in Kentucky of which the other two were Fayette & Lincoln. Jefferson County was created from Kentucky County, VA., which in turn was created from Fincastle County, VA. Jefferson County is located along the Ohio River in North Central portion of the state. It is the parent county in whole or part of: Anderson, Bullett, Carroll, Franklin, Henry, Shelby, Spencer, Trimble counties. Even though this book does not have any general history of the county, the reader will be delighted to find that this volume contains 210 biographical sketches of individuals from Jefferson County. The index mentions approx. 2,000 persons.

The Eidth Edition (8-B): By: Perrin, Kniffen & Battle, Pub. 1885, Reprinted 2015, 311 pages, Index, ISBN #0-89308-141-8.

KY 11 $32.50

The biographical sketches of individuals and their families in this book go back into the early to mid 1700's. Contains Biographical sketches on individuals from the following counties: Bath, Bracken, Breathitt, Cater, Clark, Clay, Estill, Flemming, Floyd, Greenup, Johnson, Knox, Laurel, Lawrence, Lee, Letcher, Lewis, Mogoffin, Mason, Montgomery, Morgan, Owsley, Pike, Pulaski, Robertson, Rockcastle, Russell, Wayne, and Whitley. The NEW FULL NAME INDEX that was produced for this volume mentions approximately 7,500 individuals.

(Rare 2 Volume Series)

History *of* Kentucky. (2 Volumes). By: Lewis Collins, Orig. Pub. 1874, reprinted 2019, 734 pages & 870 pages, Index, Hard Cover, ISBN #0-89308-166-3.

KY 1 $125.00

These two volumes by father and son are the most valued, accurate and complete history of Kentucky to be found in print and for many generations were the textbooks for the study of Kentucky history. The Index to this set of books mentions over 25,000 persons.

Vol. I contains: A list of Revolutionary soldiers in Kentucky; soldiers of the county of Kentucky when Kentucky County was still a part of Virginia. The Annals from 1774-1874; an outline or chronological history of Kentucky; and a section of miscellaneous statistics on the state such as: Governors, Representatives, organizations before statehood and much other valuable data.

Vol. II contains a revised and up-dated version of Lewis Collins original 1847 history of Kentucky's 116 counties at this date and approximately 500 sketches of individuals prominent in their formation and settlement, together with their families. A very detailed genealogy of the family of Daniel Boone is given in Volume #2.

LOUISIANA

Land Claims *in the* Eastern District *of the* Orleans Territory. By: Walter Lowrie, Editor, Orig. Pub. 1834, reprinted 1986, 160 pages, Index. ISBN #0-89308-582-0.

LA 1 $27.50

When the Louisiana Purchase took place in 1803, only two territories were immediately formed - the Louisiana and Orleans territories. An act of congress in 1812 provided that the territory heretofore called Louisiana should hereafter be called Missouri. The southern portion of the territory of Missouri became the Territory of Arkansas in 1819, and the northern portion became the state of Missouri in 1821. The Territory of Orleans became the state of Louisiana in 1812. In these records the original proprietor is named, by whom the land is presently being claimed, reason for change of title (purchase or inheritance), nature and extent of claim, and, if the claim was disallowed, the reasons for disallowance.

Old Louisiana Plantations *and* Family Trees, Volume #1. By: Herman de Bachelle Seebold, Pub. 1941, reprinted 2020, Vol. #1: 562 pages, Index, ISBN #0-89308-010-1.

LA 4 $48.50

This set of books is the definitive guide to the important plantation homes of Louisiana, along with the socially prominent families who owned them. These books are filled with rare photos of historically significant town homes, plantations and outbuildings that are no longer extant and provide detailed genealogical and anecdotal information on a genteel society and lavish lifestyle that is now only a memory. These families and plantations cover the entire state from: Ascension, Assumption, East & West Baton Rouge, East & West Feliciana, Iberville, Jefferson, Madison, Natchitoches, New Orleans, Pointe Coupee, Rapides, St. Charles, St. James, St. John, St. Martins, St. Mary, Terrebonne, and Washington Parishes.

Old Louisiana Plantations *and* Family Trees, Volume #2. By: Herman de Bachelle Seebold, Pub. 1941, reprinted 2020, Vol. #2: 428 pages, Index, ISBN #0-89308-011-X.

LA 5 $40.00

This set of books is the definitive guide to the important plantation homes of Louisiana, along with the socially prominent families who owned them. These books are filled with rare photos of historically significant town homes, plantations and outbuildings that are no longer extant and provide detailed genealogical and anecdotal information on a genteel society and lavish lifestyle that is now only a memory. These families and plantations cover the entire state from: Ascension, Assumption, East & West Baton Rouge, East & West Feliciana, Iberville, Jefferson, Madison, Natchitoches, New Orleans, Pointe Coupee, Rapides, St. Charles, St. James, St. John, St. Martins, St. Mary, Terrebonne, and Washington Parishes.

Biographical & Historical Memoirs *of* Northwest Louisiana. By: Southern Publishing Co., Orig. Pub. 1890, Reprinted 2016, 776 pgs, Hard Cover, New Index, ISBN #0-89308-778-5.

LA 3 $68.50

Here is one very, very rare book that is so hard to find that until now many persons were not even aware of its existence. This book is a MUST for persons doing research in the state of Louisiana (with particular interest in the Northern Half of the state), East Texas, and Southern Arkansas. Parish that are cover: Avoyelles, Bienville, Bossier, Caddo, Caliborne, DeSoto, Grant, Natchotoches, Rapides, Red River, Sabine, Webster and Winn. This book is broken down by the parish, with the general history being discuss. Many different things of use can be found in this section of the book: such as the establishment of the parish itself, transportation, newspapers, agriculture, education, cities within the parish, early land buyers, slave owners, political notes, military affairs, lists of soldiers, transactions of the Police Jury, and many, many other useful tidbits of information. But what the genealogists will savor, are the biographical sketches that fill this book. Approximately 2/3rds of this book is devoted to biographical sketches of these early settlers. Until now if you could even locate a book, it was extremely difficult to use due to its lack of an index. Due to this problem, we have completed a brand NEW every name index which mentions over 26,000 individuals.

Southwest Louisiana Biographical *and* Historical. By: William Henry Perrin, Pub. 1891, Reprinted 2018, 802 pages, Index, Hard Cover, ISBN #0-89308-764-5.

LA 2 $65.00

This book is a MUST for persons doing research in the state of Louisiana (with particular interest in the Southern Half of the state). Parish that are cover: Acadia, Calcasieu, Camron, Iberia, Lafayette, St. Landry, St. Martin, St. Mary, and Vermilion.

This book is broken down by the parish, with the general history being discuss. Many different things of use can be found in this section of the book: such as the establishment of the parish itself, transportation, newspapers, agriculture, education, cities within the parish, early land buyers, slave owners, political notes, military affairs, lists of soldiers, transactions of the Police Jury, and many, many other useful tidbits of information. But what the genealogists will savor, are the biographical sketches that fill this book. Approximately 1/2 of this book is devoted to biographical sketches of these early settlers.

MARYLAND

(War *of* 1812) The British Invasion *of* Maryland. By: William M. Marine, Reprinted 2016, 528 pages, Index, ISBN #0-89308-449-2.

MD 2 $52.50

This is comprehensive history of Maryland in the war of 1812. However, the bulk of this work (over 300 pages) is an exhaustive register of 11,000 Marylanders who served in the war. The names of the soldiers, sailors, and citizens are arranged alphabetically with references to rank, company, regiment, and occasionally additional information.

The Colonial Clergy *of* Maryland, Delaware *and* Georgia, 1629-1776. By: Frederick Lewis Weis, Pub. 1950, Reprinted 2021, 104 pages, soft cover, ISBN #978-1-63914-025-1.

MD 5 $17.50

This book is alphabetical list of approximately 700 colonial clergymen from 1629-1776 who settled in Maryland, Delaware, and Georgia. These annotations furnish such useful genealogical data as date & place of birth, date & place of death, names of parents, college of matriculation, date of ordination, denomination, names of parishes, dates in which tenure was held, and a variety of other similar data.

Muster Rolls *and* Other Records *of* Service *of* Maryland Troops *in the* American Revolution, 1775-1783. By: Maryland Historical Society, Pub. 1900, reprinted 2022, 736 pages, Index, ISBN #978-1-63914-051-0.

MD 7 $62.50

This book is derived from impeccable sources of authority for Continental service during the American Revolution. The records used to complete this book come from muster rolls, payrolls and Land Office records. The researcher will discover lists from: the Flying Camp, Maryland Troop Musters, the German Regiment, Artillery Rolls, Rolls of Men in Lee's Dragoons and Pulaski's and Armand's Legions, Naval Rolls, Invalid Returns, and Rolls of Escaped and Exchanged Prisoners. The data of 20,000 plus soldiers serving under the colonial flag of Maryland will include various information depending upon his command. Typical entries will include full name, rank, dates of enlistment and discharge, and miscellaneous remarks such as whether wounded, killed, or missing. The reader will discover that additional information such as: birthplace, age, height, and comments on personal appearance can be found on numerous soldiers too.

Proceedings *of the* Maryland Court *of* Appeals, 1695-1729. By: Carol T. Bond, Pub. 1933, reprinted, 2022, 724 pages, Index, soft cover, ISBN #978-1-63914-049-7.

MD 6 $58.50

This book is a MUST for those doing research in the state of Maryland during this colonial time. The records within this book cover the entire state. The reader will be enlightened to the number of judicial records left by these early Maryland colonists, and the amount of judicial business recorded in them. What makes this so important, is that many of these early records of the state from this Provincial Court era may not have survived in any form except from the court of errors and appeals.

Maryland Revolutionary Records. By: Harry Wright Newman, Pub. 1938, Reprinted 2018, 155 pages, soft cover, ISBN #0-89308-772-6.

MD 3 $20.00

This extremely useful work derives from an examination of more than 3,000 Revolutionary War Pension Claims and bounty land applications. Coverage includes Maryland Revolutionary Pensioners, Maryland Federal Bounty Land Grants, Maryland soldiers whose service has been established through other records, a list of marriages proved through Maryland pension applications and a list of Maryland soldiers whose Revolutionary service was in other states.

Index *of* Maryland Colonial Wills, 1634-1777. By: James M. Magruder, Jr., Pub. 1933, Reprinted 2019, 548 pages, Index, ISBN #0-89308-025-X.

MD 1 $42.50

This book is staple in Maryland Genealogical research. This book is an alphabetical listing of all the Wills of colonial Maryland as found in Will Book 1-41 at the old Land Office in Annapolis, now in file in the Hall of Records. This Index contains the names of approximately 16,000 testators. Information to be found within: Name of testator, year of probate, name of the county, and the volume and page number where the complete Will is recorded.

MISSISSIPPI

1820 Census *of* Mississippi. By: Irene S. & Norman Gillis, 154 pages, Hard Cover, ISBN #0-89308-596-0.

MS 5 $32.50

This book is an alphabetically arrangement of the head of household. This census takes place back when there were only 16 counties. Of special value to those interested in the earliest Mississippi families, this listing, names some 7,350 Family Heads with county of residence, number of white males in each of 6 age groups, white females in each of five age groups, this being as censuses were taken in 1820.

Adams County, Mississippi Minutes *of the* County Court, 1802-1804. By: Works Progress Administration, 1942, Reprinted 2017, 150 pages, Index, ISBN #0-89308-421-2.

MS 22 $20.00

The Mississippi Territory was created in 1798 and shortly thereafter Adams County was created in 1802. It lies in the Southwestern corner of the state boarding Louisiana and Florida, and is referred to as the Natchez District. It is the parent county for: Amite, Franklin, and Wilkinson.

Amite County, Mississippi, 1699-1896. (Vol. #2). By: Albert E. Casey, Pub. 1950, reprinted 2001, 704 pages, Hard Cover, Index, ISBN #0-89308-755-6.

MS 8 $60.00

Amite county was created in 1809. It is located in the famed Natchez District of Mississippi which was considered one of the first outpost in the Southwest. The major portion of this book is devoted to abstracts of Minutes from the original books of the Baptists and Presbyterian Churches located within Amite County, MS.

Amite County, Mississippi, 1699-1890. (Vol. #3). By: Albert E. Casey, Pub. 1957, reprinted 2002, 758 pages, Hard Cover, Index, ISBN #0-89308-756-4.

MS 9 $60.00

Information contained within this volume: 1) Marriages - Adams Co., MS. 1799-1821; Wilkinson Co., MS. 1802-1924; Amite Co., MS. 1820-1890; Franklin Co., MS. 1817-1868; Pike Co., MS. 1815-1876; St. Helena Parish, LA. 1813-1875; East Feliciana Parish, LA. 1813-1875; 2) Estate Papers of Amite Co., MS. 1809-1866; 3) Amite County Soldiers - Revolutionary (inc. Loyalists), Creek, 1812, Mexican & Civil Wars; 4) Amite County - teachers, merchants, carpenters, brick masons, mechanics, lawyers, civil officers, etc... 5) Genealogies on some 25 different families.....

Copiah County, Mississippi 1844-1849,

Marriages of. By: Mary E Thomas, Pub. 1958, Reprinted 2017, 128 pages, Index, ISBN #0-89308-660-6.

MS 19 $20.00

Copiah County was created in 1823 out of Hinds County, Mississippi. It is located in the center of the state and was originally purchased from the Choctaw Indians.

Grenada County, Mississippi, History of. By: H.C.J. Hathorn, Pub, 1968, reprinted 2015, 260 pages, New Index, soft cover, ISBN #0-89308-425-5.

MS 17 $30.00

Grenada County was created from lands ceded from the Choctaw Indians in 1833, even though the county was not officially created until the 1870's. It sits in the North Central portion of the State and is surrounded by the counties of: Calhoun, Carroll, Leflore, Montgomery, Sumner/Webster, Tallahatchie, and Yalobusha. The scarcity of this book alone should make this book a MUST for anyone who is interested in or who has family connections to the State of Mississippi.

Land Claims *in the* Mississippi Territory. By: Walter Lowrie, Editor, Orig. Pub. 1834, reprinted 2021, 304 pages, Soft Cover, Index, ISBN #0-89308-583-9.

MS 3 $32.50

Mississippi was formed from land ceded to the United States by South Carolina and Georgia. Part of the British Province of West Florida and part of the land ceded by the French made up the rest of the Territory of Mississippi in 1798. The Territory of Alabama was formed from the Territory of Mississippi in 1817. In 1817, statehood was granted to Mississippi. In these records the original proprietor is named, by whom the land is presently being claimed, reason for change of title (purchase of inheritance), nature and extent of claim, and, if the claim was disallowed, the reason for disallowance. Contains the names of Approximately 5,000 persons.

Marion Co., Mississippi, Miscellaneous Records. By: E. Russ Williams, Orig. Pub. 1962, Revised 1985, reprinted 2002, 376 pages, Hard Cover, Index, ISBN #0-89308-341-0.

MS 2 $38.50

This volume contains orphan court records, wills and estates, 1812-1859; deeds 1812-1840; Territorial and Federal census records and mortality schedules; old road books; 1813 Lawrence County tax lists.

Mississippi Court Records, 1799-1835. By: J. Estelle King, Pub. 1936, Reprinted 2017, 192 pages, Index, ISBN #0-89308-886-2.

MS 12 $20.00

Records within this volume are: Adams County Wills & Marriages, Amite County Wills, Claiborne County Wills, Marriages & Tax Lists, Hinds County Wills & Marriages, Warren County Wills & Marriages, Yalobusha County Tax Lists, Court Records, and Revolutionary Soldiers.

Mississippi Court Records, from the files of the High Court of Errors and Appeals, 1799-1859. By: Mary L. Hendrix, 446 pages, Hard Cover, Index, ISBN #0-89308-529-4.

MS 4 $42.50

This book is a MUST for those doing research in the state of Mississippi. Considering the very limited amount of research data in printed form on the state, makes this one very sought out research tool. The records within this book cover the entire state, and not just the burned counties. The cases herein indexed and abstracted pertain to Will, Administration, Property Settlement, Guardianship, and Divorce cases. What makes this book so important is that: as shown by the chart included in this book, many records were destroyed in courthouse fires. Except for the data contained in the files of the High Court sent up from the Probate Courts of these counties, there is nothing left of these early records. The wills included in this volume, filed with High Court, are copies of the original wills and, in many instances, constitute the only existing evidence of family connections and relationships.

Mississippi Rifles. A Muster of all known Mississippi Soldiers, Sailors, and Marines who served in the Mexican War, 1846-1848. By: H. Grady Howell, Jr., Pub. 2004, 288 pages, Index, ISBN #0-89308-801-3.

MS 16 $35.00

This book is filled with ALL known persons that served under the State of Mississippi in the Mexican War. The author gives a detailed overview of the units and their battles along with an alphabetical listing of Mississippi Soldiers. Mr. Howell even gives a complete listing by Company and a complete listing of Mississippi Mexican War Pensions. He even devotes a chapter to: "How to access pension files". If this was not enough, gives a complete list of all known grave locations/registrations of these soldiers.

Natchez District, Early Inhabitants *of the*. By: Irene S. & Norman Gillis, 158 pages, Hard Cover, ISBN #89308-566-9.

MS 6 $32.50

This book consists of 6 main areas of interest. 1) a Historical background of the state of Mississippi. 2) English Land Grants, 1768-1779, this lists contains the names of grantee, date of grant and number of acres in the grant. 3) Spanish Census of the Natchez District, 1792, this list gives English spelling, of name as recorded and location of individual within the district. 4) Inhabitants of the Natchez District: 1810 (except Wilkinson County, which is for 1805), this list gives the head of household, county located in, and the number of white males & females over and under 21 years of age, and the number of free men of color and number of slaves within a household. 5) Inhabitants of Natchez District: 1816, this list gives name of head of household and county located in. 6) Inhabitants of the Mississippi Territory: 1816, this list gives name of head of household and county located in (except for Natchez Dist. which was reviewed in section #5).

The Natchez Court Records, 1767-1805. By: May Wilson McBee, Pub. 1953, Reprinted 2020, 645 pages, Index, ISBN #0-89308-023-3.

MS 11 $52.50

The Natchez District covers the Mississippi counties of: Adams, Amite, Clairborne, Franklin, Jefferson, Warren, and Wilkinson. In 1799 when Spain took over the rule of this area from the British, the Louisiana parishes of: Carroll, Concordia, Madison and Tensas were added. Two years later, the Spanish commandant commenced to record all matters involving these British inhabitants. This book is broken into two main parts. The first part covers the records of: sureties, bills of sale for land and slaves, inventories, appraisals, wills, etc. The second part of the work, Land Claims, 1767-1805, deals with British land grants in the Natchez District and is based on abstracts of land titles submitted to the United States for confirmation of land ownership. The index mentions approximately 10,000 persons.

Pike County, Mississippi, 1798-1910, Source Records from. By: E. Russ Williams & Luke W. Conerly, Pub. 1909, reprinted with New material 2015, 588 pages, soft cover, New Index, ISBN #0-89308-104-3.

MS 1 $50.00

This old as well as new book contains a reprint of "Pike County, Mississippi, 1798-1876; Pioneer Families and Confederate Soldiers," by the late Luke W. Conerly. Also considerable NEW MATERIAL has been added, viz: Roster of Soldiers of War 1812 (with a select group of Veteran Pension Files); 1816 Territorial Census; 1820 Federal Census; Membership of Bogue Chitto (now Crain's Creek) Baptist Church: 1824, 1827, and 1834; membership of New Zion Baptist: 1823, 1830, and 1866; Obituaries from the minutes of Bogue Chitto Baptist Assoc. Minutes, 1872-1910 (includes some obituaries from Lincoln County); Select group of Pike County Obituaries from the New Orleans Christian Advocate, 1851-1910; Correction to Conerly's original Pike County text plus additional genealogical sketches of pioneer Pike County families, such as: Albritton, Alford, Bacot, Bickham, Brumfield, Coney, Connerly, Dillion/Stallings, Ellis, Ellzey, Felder, Holmes, Kemp/Carter, Lee, Morgan, Newsom, Pierce, Pound/Pounds, Rhodus/Hughe.

MISSOURI

Andrew & Dekalb Counties, Missouri, The History of. By: Goodspeed Publishing Company, Orig. Pub. 1888, reprinted 1997, approx. 591 pages, Hard Cover, New Index, ISBN #0-89308-671-1.

MO 6 $48.50

This volume contains the history of the above-mentioned counties along with Biographical Sketches of some 181 individuals. Genealogical data is to be found on approximately 9,800 other individuals / family members.

Callaway County, Missouri, History of. By: National Historical Company, Pub. 1884, Reprinted 2018, 1030 pages, New Index, Hard Cover, ISBN #0-89308-916-8.

MO 50 $75.00

In 1803, the Missouri Territory became a part of the United States through the Louisiana Purchase. Callaway County was created in 1820 from Montgomery County and the following year Missouri officially became the 24th State of the Union. Callaway County is considered one of the first five counties that laid the foundation upon which Missouri the Mother-State of the Great West was built. This book is broken down in three main sections. The first is a detailed history of the state of Missouri while the second section is a complete and through history of the county broken down through the various townships. The third section is what all family historians will be excited over. This section contains biographical sketches of some 450 individuals and genealogical data on some 4,000 other families / individuals. The New Full name index that was prepared for this reprint contains over 5,000 entries.

Cole, Moniteau, Morgan, Benton, Miller, Maries, and Osage Counties., History of. By: Goodspeed Publishing Company, Pub. 1888, Reprinted 2018, 1068 pages, NEW INDEX, Hard Cover, ISBN #0-89308-105-1.

MO 1 $75.00

This book is broken up into two sections. The first is a detailed history of the above-mentioned counties.

While the second section, covers biographical sketches on some 716 individuals of these counties and genealogical data on approximately 2400 other persons/family members. The NEW INDEX that was produced for this reprint contains the names of approximately 20,000 individuals.

Cooper County, Missouri, History of. By: Henry C. Levens & Nathaniel M. Drake, Pub. 1876, Reprinted 2017, 249 pages, soft cover, New Index, ISBN #0-89308-895-1.

MO 35 $30.00

Cooper County was created in 1819 from Indians lands. It sits in the heart or central portion of the state. It is the parent / grandparent county in whole or part to: Bates, Benton, Camden, Cass, Cole, Henry, Jackson, Johnson, Lafayette, Miller, Moniteau, Morgan, Pettis, Saline, & St. Clair. The NEW FULL NAME INDEX that was produced for this volume mentions approximately 2,500 individuals.

Cooper County, Missouri Marriages and Wills, 1819-1879. By: Elizabeth P. Ellsberry, Pub. 1959, Reprinted 2019, 152 pages, Index, soft cover, ISBN #0-89308-894-3.

MO 31 $25.00

Cooper County was created in 1819 from Indians lands. It sits in the heart or central portion of the state. It is the parent / grandparent county in whole or part to: Bates, Benton, Camden, Cass, Cole, Henry, Jackson, Johnson, Lafayette, Miller, Moniteau, Morgan, Pettis, Saline, & St. Clair. The records within cover the Marriages from 1819-1850 and the Wills of 1820-1870.

Death Records of Missouri Men, 1808-1854. By: Lois Stanley, George F. Wilson & Maryhelen Wilson, Pub. 1983, reprinted 2017, 178 pages, soft cover, Index, ISBN #0-89308-440-9

MO 23 $22.50

Approximately 4,000 death notices from 60 newspapers. Some are familiar - Daniel Boone, Alexander McNair - but most were average citizens. Side by side with those who died on the way west, in Indian skirmishes, in explosions or in natural disasters, are the records of the peaceful end of those who died at home, "worthy and respected".

Death Records of Missouri Pioneer Women, 1808-1853. By: Lois Stanley, George F. Wilson & Maryhelen Wilson, Pub. 1983, reprinted 2019, 104 pages, soft cover, Index, ISBN #0-89308-441-7.

MO 24 $17.50

About 1,800 records including many names which never appear in a census - and a variety of information. Mary Thomas, widow of John, 102 when she died in Mercer County, a Methodist for 60 years, Meeky Jamison, wife of David was buried in old Wesleyan Cemetery, now gone; little Mary V. Simond died on the Upper Crossing of the South Platte, age 2 1/2 years. Surviving children, or parent, are frequently mentioned.

Franklin, Jefferson, Washington, Crawford & Gasconade Counties, Missouri, The History of. By: Goodspeed Publishing Company, Orig. Pub. 1888, reprinted 2001, 1000 pages, Hard Cover, New Index, ISBN #0-89308-669-X.

MO 7 $65.00

This volume contains the history of the above-mentioned counties along with Biographical Sketches of over 812 individuals. The New Index that was prepared for this reprint edition has over 23,000 individuals in it.

Hickory, Polk, Cedar, Dade, & Barton Counties, Missouri, The History of. By: Goodspeed Publishing Company, Orig. Pub. 1889, reprinted 2002, 848 pages, Hard Cover, New Index, ISBN #0-89308-779-3.

MO 8 $65.00

This volume contains the history of the above-mentioned counties along with Biographical Sketches of over 600 individuals. The New Index that was prepared for this reprint edition has over 20,000 individuals in it.

More Death Records *from* Missouri Newspapers, 1810-1857. By: Lois Stanley, George F. Wilson & Maryhelen Wilson, Pub. 1983, reprinted 2017, 130 pages, soft cover, Index, ISBN #0-89308-442-5

MO 25 $20.00

These records cover the time frame of 1810-1857 and contains about 2,900 deaths taken from 20 newspapers. This book sequels two previous books from the same author covering the same period (MO23 & MO24). This book differs from the other two volumes in that: some, primarily adults, are from papers not available for the earlier books while the remaining balance of the book deals with children previously omitted due to space limitations. The records cover a long period, from baby Harriet Penrose who died in St. Louis in Feb. 1810 to deaths on both sides of the state (Kansas City, St. Louis) and numerous places between, in 1857. Most of the children and many women could not be found in a census; they were born and died before 1850 or born before 1850 and died young.

Death Records *from* Missouri Newspapers, 1854-1860. (Vol. #1). By: Lois Stanley, George F. Wilson & Maryhelen Wilson, Pub. 1983, reprinted 2018, 280 pages, Index, soft cover, ISBN #0-89308-444-1

MO 27 $32.50

These records cover the time frame of 1854-1860. The records here (there are approximately 5,500) come from all over Missouri, though some areas were not covered by a newspaper. But there were at least 85 newspapers in existence in the state, at one time or another, during the period covered by these records; and very often a death notice appearing in one would be picked up by one or more of the others. So, even when some of the newspapers are lost (and many are) we still have news from their areas. These records, taken from 42 newspapers, include adults and children old enough to have appeared in the 1850 census, together with probate notices for some "burned" counties, notably Chariton, Dallas, and St. Clair. Some records, not available in the initial preparation for the book, are found in the ADDENDA starting on page 261.

Death Records *from* Missouri Newspapers, 1861-1865. (the Civil War Years). By: Lois Stanley, George F. Wilson & Maryhelen Wilson, Pub. 1983, reprinted 2017, 130 pages, soft cover, Index, ISBN #0-89308-442-5

MO 26 $25.00

These records cover the time frame of 1810-1857 and contains about 2,900 deaths taken from 20 newspapers. This book sequels two previous books from the same author covering the same period (MO23 & MO24). This book differs from the other two volumes in that: some, primarily adults, are from papers not available for the earlier books while the remaining balance of the book deals with children previously omitted due to space limitations. The records cover a long period, from baby Harriet Penrose who died in St. Louis in Feb. 1810 to deaths on both sides of the state (Kansas City, St. Louis) and numerous places between, in 1857. Most of the children and many women could not be found in a census; they were born and died before 1850 or born before 1850 and died young.

Death Records *from* Missouri Newspapers, 1866-1870. (Vol. #2). By: Lois Stanley, George F. Wilson & Maryhelen Wilson, Pub. 1983, reprinted 2017, 248 pages, Index, soft cover, ISBN #0-89308-445-X

MO 28 $30.00

Here are reports from 150 newspapers, over a five-year span, which give valuable details about Missouri ancestors. there are notables; there were centenarians; and those who died in unusual ways. But in the main, these 9,000 records provide valuable ordinary details about the ordinary people who were our ancestors - where and when they died, and from what cause, age, birthplace, former residence, number of children, religious and lodge affiliations, maiden name. Estate records from "burned" counties are also included.

Early Missouri Ancestors, 1808-1822. (Vol. #1). By: Lois Stanley, George Wilson & Maryhelen Wilson, Pub. 1985, Reprinted 2012, 184 pages, soft cover, Index, ISBN #0-89308-432-8.

MO 15 $20.00

This book comes from the abstracts of 6 of the oldest newspapers that existed in Missouri from 1808-1822. These newspapers are: The Missouri Gazette, St. Louis 1808-1822; The Enquirer, St. Louis 1819-1822; The Missouri Intelligencer, Franklin 1819-1822; The Missouri Herald, Jackson 1819-1820; The Independent Patriot, Jackson 1820-1822; and The St. Charles Missourian, St. Charles 1820-1822. The index mentions over 4,000 persons, of which lived and died before the First Census. These newspaper records may be the ONLY mention of their lives. Whether they were prosperous or poor, they left names in newspapers - an absorbing account of the lives and times, fortunes and misfortunes, of our earliest Missouri ancestors.

Early Missouri Ancestors, 1823-1832. (Vol. #2). By: Lois Stanley, George Wilson & Maryhelen Wilson, Pub. 1985, Reprinted 2012, 124 pages, soft cover, Index, ISBN #0-89308-433-6.

MO 16 $17.50

This book comes from the abstracts of 6 of the oldest newspapers that existed in Missouri from 1823-1832. These newspapers are: The Missouri Gazette, St. Louis 1823-1832; The Enquirer, St. Louis 1823-1832; The Missouri Intelligencer, Franklin 1823-1832; The Missouri Herald, Jackson 1823-1832; The Independent Patriot, Jackson 1823-1832; and The St. Charles Missourian, St. Charles 1823-1832. The index mentions over 4,000 persons, of which lived and died before the First Census. These newspaper records may be the ONLY mention of their lives. Whether they were prosperous or poor, they left names in newspapers - an absorbing account of the lives and times, fortunes and misfortunes, of our earliest Missouri ancestors.

(The General History) History of Missouri *from the* Earliest Times *to the* Present. By: Goodspeed Publishing Company, Pub. 1888, Reprinted 2022, 202 pages, New Index, soft cover, ISBN #0-89308-477-8.

MO 4 $25.00

This book contains the general history of the state of Missouri covering such areas as Indian Wars, the Civil War, and skirmishes or battles in Missouri, early settlers, organizations of various counties, general history of various churches.... all of which pertain to the state as a whole. These are the first 196 pages which were located in the original 1880's edition of all histories by the Goodspeed Publishing Company on the state of Missouri.

Greene County, Missouri, History of. By: Western Historical Company, Pub. 1883, Reprinted 2018, 1010 pages, Index, Hard Cover, ISBN #0-89308-715-7.

MO 48 $75.00

Located in the Ozark region of the state, Greene County was created in 1833 from Crawford and Wayne Counties. Due to Missouri being a Slave state, settlers began showing up in the area around the 1820's from the Southern states such as: Virginia, North Carolina, Tennessee and Kentucky. This volume contains biographical sketches of some 523 individuals in these counties and genealogical data on some 2,000 other families / individuals. These persons were not only from VA, TN, NC, & KY but also had large numbers of settlers from OH, PA, IN, IL, & MO along with lesser quantities from the states of DE, GA, IA, MA, MD, ME, NJ, NY, VT, WI, & WV. The NEW INDEX for this reprint mentions over 3,000 entries.

Harrison *and* Mercer Counties, Missouri, History of. By: Goodspeed Publishing Company, Pub. 1888, Reprinted 2018, 684 pages, NEW INDEX, Hard Cover, ISBN #0-89308-915-X.

MO 55 $55.00

Harrison County was created in 1845 from Daviess County and Mercer County was created in 1845 from Livington County. Both counties are located in the northwestern portion of the state. Due to Missouri being a Slave state, settlers began showing up around 1837 from the Southern states of Virginia, North Carolina, Tennessee and Kentucky. This volume contains biographical sketches of some 400 individuals in these counties and genealogical data on some 9,000 other families / individuals. These persons were not only from VA, TN, NC, & KY but also had large numbers of settlers from OH, PA, IN, IL, & MO along with lesser quantities from the states of DE, GA, IA, MA, MD, ME, NJ, NY, VT, WI, & WV.

Jasper County, Missouri, History of. By: Mills and Company, Pub. 1883, Reprinted 2018, 1160 pgs, New Index, Hard Cover, ISBN #0-89308-460-3.

MO 42 $85.00

Jasper County was created in 1841 out of Barry County which in turn was carved out of Greene County. It is located in the southwestern corner of the state boarding Kansas. This history is extremely similar to the one's that Goodspeed Publishing produced on the state of Missouri. A very through history of the county is given along with a very large genealogical / biographical sketch section. Until now, using this book for research has been very difficult. We have included a NEW INDEX that makes this reprint an extremely exciting and useful tool for the family historian / genealogists.

Johnson County, Missouri, History of. By: Kansas City Historical Company, Pub. 1881, Reprinted 2018, 999 pages, New Index, Hard Cover, ISBN #0-89308-615-0.

MO 43 $75.00

Johnson County was created in 1834 from Lafayette County. It is located on the western side of the state with the Santa Fe Trail passing right through it. This area of Missouri saw its fair share of pioneer settlers coming from the East in search of new lands and prosperity. Many of whom came from AL, CT, GA, IL, IN, KY, MA, MD, MO, NC, NY, OH, PA, RI, SC, TN, VA, WV, along with the countries of England, Germany, Ireland, Prussia, Scotland & Switzerland. This book is filled with hundreds of Biographical sketches giving such information as marriages, births, deaths, divorces, occupation, military service, education, previous residence, names of siblings, names of parents & grandparents along with their residences current & previous, names of spouse's parents and their residence, in some instances a physical description of the biographies, and many, many other useful tidbits of information that can help the family historian.

Land Claims *in the* Missouri Territory. By: Walter Lowrie, Pub. 1834, Reprint 1986, 232 pages, Hard Cover, Index, ISBN #0-89308-584-7.

MO 3 $35.00

When the Louisiana Purchase took place in 1803, only two territories were immediately formed - the Louisiana and Orleans Territories. An act of Congress in 1812 provided that the Territory hereto called Louisiana should be hereafter called Missouri. The southern portion of the Territory of Missouri became the Territory of Arkansas in 1819 and the northern portion became the state of Missouri in 1821. In these records, the original proprietor is named by whom the land is presently being claimed, reason for change of title (purchase or inheritance), nature and extent of claim, and if the claim was disallowed and the reason for disallowance.

Laclede, Camden, Dallas, Webster, Wright, Texas, Pulaski, Phelps, *and* Dent Counties Missouri, Biographical Memoirs *of*. By: Goodspeed Publishing Company, Pub. 1889, Reprinted 2018; 652 pages, New Index, Soft Cover, ISBN #089308-875-7

MO 10 $52.50

The original book was divided into two main sections, The first being the histories of the various counties while the second section concentrated it efforts onto the biographical sketches of the families of these counties. Our reprint only includes the biographical section with a New 107 pages Index. This book contains more than 794 biographical sketches, including some 4,300 additional family members. Also found in this book are the names of some 12,000 other persons prominent in the early history of these nine counties.

Lincoln County, Missouri, History of. By: Goodspeed Publishing Company, Pub. 1888, Reprinted 2018, 448 pages, NEW INDEX, ISBN #0-89308-908-7.

MO 11 $40.00

Lincoln County Was created in 1820's from St. Charles County. It is located along the Mississippi River just above St. Charles County and is surrounded by Pike, Montgomery and Warren counties. This book is exactly like the other books that Goodspeed Publishing Company published. The book is divided into two main sections. The first is a detailed history of the county while the second covers approx.200 biographical sketches of these earlier settlers. These biographies were recorded in the 1880's, which means that one can expect to find family members dating back into the 1700's.

1,300 Missing Missouri Marriage Records *from* Newspapers, 1812-1853. By: Lois Stanley, George Wilson & Maryhelen Wilson, Pub. 1979, Reprinted 2020, 110 pages, Index, ISBN #0-89308-435-2.

MO 18 $18.50

Newspapers may be the ONLY source of data about marriages missing from civil records, often they reported parents' names, location of the ceremony, minister or Justice of the Peace. Especially valuable marriages of Missourians which took place outside the state, shown in hometown papers.

Early Missouri Marriages *in the* News, 1820-1853. By: Lois Stanley, George F. Wilson, and Maryhelen Wilson, Pub. 1983, Reprinted 2017, 64 pages, soft cover, Index, ISBN #0-89308-437-9.

MO 20 $15.00

Many important details not found in civil records appear in this collection, from about 50 newspapers and covering a wide area. Most identify the Brides's father or a parent - "second daughter to Ezekiel, of Spencer Co., KY.", "daughter of Edwin, deceased", formerly of Hardin Co., TN."

A vital clue often missing in courthouse papers is the "Mrs." preceding the bride's name, many brides were widows. Another useful category are records never found in courthouses because they are from "BURNED" counties or reports of marriages which took place outside of the state. Old newspapers may be the only possible source of such information.

Missouri Marriages *in the* News, 1851-1865. (Vol. #1). By: Lois Stanley, George F. Wilson, and Maryhelen Wilson, Pub. 1984, reprinted 2017, 94 pages, Index, soft cover, ISBN #0-89308-439-5.

MO 21 $15.00

This book contains 1,400 marriages reported from all over the state; about 300 were outside of Missouri, some as close as Illinois and Kansas, others as far away as California. They include a number of odd, interesting and very human sidelights.

Missouri Marriages *in the* News, 1866-1870. (Vol. #2). By: Lois Stanley, George F. Wilson, and Maryhelen Wilson, Pub. 1984, Reprinted 2017, 89 pages, soft cover, Index, ISBN #0-89308-439-5.

MO 22 $17.50

This book contains 1,400 marriages, reported from all over the state; about 300 were outside of Missouri, some as close as Illinois and Kansas, others as far away as California. they include a number of odd, interesting and very human sidelights.

Missouri Taxpayers, 1819-1826. By: Lois Stanley, George Wilson, & Maryhelen Wilson, Pub., 1979, reprinted 2004, 144 pages, soft cover, Index, ISBN #0-89308-434-4.

MO 17 $20.00

This is the First listing ever made of adult male (and some female) residents of Missouri at the time the State entered the Union - about 14,000 names. Virtually a first census from ALL available tax lists, delinquents, miscellaneous taxes from the State Archives plus lists from newspapers showing names found in tax lists.

New Madrid County, Missouri Marriage Records 1847-1881. (2 Volumes). By: Mary Brown & Fay Hedgepath, Pub. 1973, reprinted 2004, soft cover.

Vol. #1, 1847-1874: 116 pages, Index, ISBN #0-89308-803-X.

MO33 $20.00

Vol. #2, 1874-1881: 156 pages, Index, ISBN #0-89308-804-8

MO 34 $25.00

Even though New Madrid was organized in 1805, these marriage records begin with the first two books on file in the office of the county recorder. There is a gap in the marriage records of New Madrid County and is probably accounted for by that at one time the records were kept in various buildings and some of the buildings burned. The researcher will also discover that due to New Madrid's geographical location in the Most Southeastern corner of the State, along the Mississippi River, that you will find some Kentucky and Tennessee marriages being mixed within those of New Madrid County.

Perry County, Missouri Deeds 1821-1844, Abstracts of. By: Bill Eddleman, Pub. 2004, 188 pages, 8 1/2" x 11" soft cover, Index, ISBN #0-89308-800-5.

MO 32 $35.00

Perry County lies in the extreme Eastern portion of the state boarding the Mississippi River. It was created from Ste. Genevieve District in 1821. Many of these early settlers came from the East from such states as: Pennsylvania, Kentucky and North Carolina. Since these families and others arrived here before the Louisiana Purchase, they received large influx of settlers heading West. It is surrounded by the counties of: Bollinger, Cape Girardeau, Madison, Ste. Genevieve and St. Francois. The deeds within this book start with the creation of the county (1821) but many have earlier dates because they were not officially recorded until after it was carved off of Ste. Genevieve.

Pioneer Families of Missouri. Pioneer Families *of* Missouri. By: William Bryan and Robert Rose, Orig. Pub. 1876, Reprint 2018, 590 pages, Index, soft cover, ISBN #0-89308-478-6.

MO 30 $45.00

This book is in 5 parts: The Life of Daniel Boone; Early Days in Missouri; Histories of Families; Biographies and sketches: Anecdote and Adventures. Parts one and three are veritable treasure trove, as part one contains a "Life of Daniel Boone" with important authoritative genealogical and historical data about the BOONE and BRYAN families. Part three contains more or less complete genealogical histories of more than 800 Families which in these FIVE COUNTIES laid the foundation upon which Missouri the Mother-State of the Great West was built. These five counties which this book deals with are: St. Charles, Warren, Montgomery, Callaway, and Audrain. The early settlers of these counties came from VA., PA, CT, MS, KY, VT, NC, TN, WV, GA, LA, NJ, MA, SC, & AL.

Reminiscent History *of the* Ozark Region. By: Goodspeed Publishing Company, Orig. Pub. 1894, Reprinted 1995, 784 pages, Hard Cover, New Index, ISBN #0-89308-106-X.

MO 2 $60.00

It contains the history of 29 Arkansas counties and 26 Missouri counties, as well as some 660 biographical sketches of individuals in this region. Genealogical data is to be found on approximately 2,700 other individuals / families. ARKANSAS COUNTIES are: Baxter, Benton, Boone, Carroll, Cleburne, Crawford, Franklin, Fulton, Garland, Hot Spring, Howard, Izard, Johnson, Logan, Madison, Marion, Montgomery, Newton, Pike, Polk, Pope, Scott, Searcy, Sebastian, Sevier, Stone, Van Buren, Washington, and Yell. MISSOURI COUNTIES are: Barry, Carter, Christian, Dallas, Dent, Douglas, Greene, Howell, Laclede, Iron, Jasper, McDonald, Newton, Oregon, Ozark, Phelps, Polk, Pulaski, Reynolds, Ripley, Shannon, Stone, Taney, Texas, Webster, and Wright.

Southeast Missouri, The History of. Embracing an Historical Account of the Counties of St. Genevieve, St. Francois, Perry, Cape Girardeau, Bollinger, Madison, New Madrid, Pemiscott, Dunklin, Scott, Mississippi, Stoddard, Butler, Wayne, and Iron. By: Goodspeed Publishing Company, Orig. Pub. 1888, reprinted 2022, 1,126 pages, Soft Cover, New Index, ISBN #0-89308-431-X.

MO 13 $75.00

This volume contains the history of the above-mentioned counties along with biographical sketches of 1,878 individuals. Also included in this book are some 11,000 names of additional family members plus 27,000 names of other persons prominent in the early history of these counties.

St. Charles County, Missouri 1805-1844, Marriage Records of. By: Lois Stanley, George F. Wilson, and Maryhelen Wilson, Pub. 1978, Reprinted 1990, 96 pages, soft cover, Index, ISBN #0-89308-436-0.

MO 19 $12.50

A valuable records source: St. Charles was the site of the state's first capital and a cross-section of early population groups - French, "American", and German. Includes Book I and II, never previously published. With brides' index and ministers' list.

Virginia Settlers *in* Missouri. By: Dorothy Ford Wulfeck & A. Maxim Coppeage, Pub. 1960, Reprinted 2018, 158 pages, ISBN #0-89308-651-7.

VA 175 $20.00

This interesting book takes a look at early settlers leaving the East Coast and headed west in search of new lands and new lives. The authors have used various sources such as: Atlases, maps, census records, newspapers, Cemetery Inscriptions and etc., to show the relationship between these early settlers who moved from Virginia to Missouri by showing where they came from and where they have ended up. They have also included 64 mini/biographies various person that have crossed their paths while preforming this research.

NEW JERSEY

Burlington County, New Jersey Marriages, 1681-1913. By: H. Stanley Craig, Pub. 1932, Reprinted 2019, 340 pages, Index, soft cover, ISBN #0-89308-315-1.

NJ 3 $35.00

Burlington County was created in 1694. It is located in the southwestern portion of the state boarding the Delaware River. Records used to compile this book come from: the NJ Archives, County Clerk's records, and Church including some from Quaker Meeting Houses. All marriages are listed in alphabetical order by groom with a bride's index covering the approximately 10,500 marriages.

Camden County, New Jersey Marriages, 1844-1909. By: Stanley Craig, Pub. 1932, Reprinted 2018, 196 pages, Index, soft cover, ISBN #0-89308-303-8.

NJ 4 $20.00

Camden County was created in 1844 from Gloucester. It sits in the southwestern portion of the state boarding the Delaware River. The records used to compile this book come from the County Clerk's Book A & B. All marriages are listed in alphabetical order by groom with a brides index covering the approximately 4,500 marriages.

Cumberland County, New Jersey Marriages, 1742-1878. By: Stanley Craig, Pub. 1932, Reprinted 2018, 334 pages, Index, soft cover, ISBN #0-89308-305-4.

NJ 5 $35.00

Cumberland County was created in 1748 from Salem County. Sources from which this book was compiled from: Marriage Licenses from the NJ Archives, County Clerk's Records -Book A & B, Records from the Justice of Peace dockets, Church records, Journals, and from various genealogies and biographies. The authors have even included numerous marriages that were pulled from various genealogies/biographies that were performed in the 1920's. All marriages are listed in alphabetical order by groom with a bride's index covering the approximately 10,500 marriages.

Genealogical Data *from* Cumberland County Wills, 1747-1861. By: H. Stanley Craig, Pub. 1932, Reprinted 2018, 155 pages, Index, soft cover, ISBN #0-89308-799-8.

NJ 6 $20.00

Cumberland County was created in 1748 from Salem County. The abstracts of these wills cover the years 1747-1861. The author has taken an interesting approach, as he has listed the testators n alphabetical order with an index to cover the rest balance of names.

The Colonial Clergy *of the* Middle Colonies, New York, New Jersey *and* Pennsylvania, 1628-1776. By: Frederick Lewis Weis, Pub. 1957, Reprinted 2021, 188 pages, soft cover, ISBN #978-1-63914-024-4.

PA 30 $22.50

This book is alphabetical list of approximately 1,250 colonial clergymen from 1628-1776 who settled in New York, New Jersey, and Pennsylvania. These annotations furnish such useful genealogical data as date & place of birth, date & place of death, names of parents, college of matriculation, date of ordination, denomination, names of parishes, dates in which tenure was held, and a variety of other similar data.

Old Gloucester County West New Jersey, Sketches *of the* First Emigrant Settlers, Newton Township. By: John Clement, Pub. 1877, reprinted 2022, 446 pages, Index, ISBN #0-89308-037-4.

NJ 18 $40.00

Newton Township is located within Gloucester County which lies on the Delaware River just across from Philadelphia and Delaware Counties, Pennsylvania. This area which was known as West New Jersey received her early emigrants from England into the first townships of Salem, Burlington and Newtown. This book gives a thorough biographical sketch of these earliest of pioneers of this area. Surnames of individuals for which sketches are given: Albertson, Bates, Burroughs, Carpenter, Champion, Clements, Cole, Collins, Cooper, Eastlack, Ellis, Estaugh, Gardiner, Gill, Goldsmith, Graysburys, Hillman, Hinchman, Howell, Hugg, Kaighn, Kay, Lippincotts, Matlack, Mathews, Mickle, Morgan, Newbie, Nicholson, Sharpe, Shivers, Spicer, Stacy, Stokes, Thackara, Tomlinson, Turner, Woods, and Zane. The author has included marriages of various individuals for whom have connections with persons from Newton Township: Burlington County 1679-1794 and Salem 1682-1761. The author has also included several maps showing plats of land ownership within the township.

Hudson County, New Jersey, 1609-1871, History *of the* Land Titles *in*. By: Charles Winfield, Pub. 1872, Pub. 2021, 457 pages, Index, soft cover, ISBN #9787-1-63914-036-7.

NJ 20 $40.00

Hudson County sits along Hudson River just across from New York and Ellis Island in the northern reaches of the state. It was created in 1840 from Bergen County which was established in 1683. The records within this book pre-date the creation of Bergen County and even go back first permanent European settlement (Bergen Township) in the territory of present-day New Jersey. These records cover the time frame of 1609-1871 and not only does it cover the land records of the area but also births, deaths and marriage records. This book has it all for those looking for their relatives in this northern section of New Jersey.

New Jersey Marriage Records, 1665-1800. By: William Nelson, Pub. 1900, Reprinted 2019, 812 pages, soft cover, ISBN #0-89308-313-5.

NJ 1 $75.00

This book should be considered a MUST for researchers working on his mid-Atlantic State. For those researching a marriage, this book is considered the principal authority on early New Jersey marriages. It contains approximately 15,000 marriages, giving place of residence and date of marriage. The bulk of the work derives from marriage bonds and licenses formerly located in the Secretary of State's office. The balance--perhaps an additional 5,000 entries--were extracted from the marriage records of churches and counties in New Jersey. For the sake of simplicity, the marriages are arranged in two alphabets, male and female. In total, there are almost 30,000 entries for the researcher to search.

New Jersey Index *of* Wills *and* Inventories, 1663-1900. (3 Volumes) By: David S. Crater, Pub. 1912-13, Reprinted 2019, soft cover.

Vol. #1, covers the counties of: Atlantic, Bergen, Burlington, Camden, Cape May, Cumberland, and Essex: 516 pages, Index, ISBN #0-89308-813-7.

NJ 10 $45.00

Vol. #2, cover the counties of: Gloucester, Hudson, Hunterdon, Mercer, Middlesex, and Monmouth: 500 pages, Index, ISBN #0-89308-828-5.

NJ 11 $45.00

Vol. #3, covers the counties of: Morris, Ocean, Passaic, Salem, Somerset, Sussex, Union and Warren: 438 pages, Index, ISBN #0-89308-898-6.

NJ 12 $40.00

This must have set of books indexes New Jersey wills and probate records from 1663 through 1900. The 3 volumes together contain more than 185,000 entries, arranged by county with each entry being listed alphabetically under the name of the testator and intestate. Information found within: the number of the will, the year of probate along with references to papers and records connected with them. Special Note: volume three also has alphabetical indexes to the unrecorded wills and New Jersey prerogative wills. All of the wills indexed in this reprint volumes are now in the Bureau of Archives and History in the New Jersey State Library in Trenton, and hence these indexes serve as a valuable guide to further information.

Patents *and* Deeds *and* Other Early Records *of* New Jersey 1664-1703. By: William Nelson, Pub. 1899, Reprinted 2018, 770 pages, Index, soft cover, ISBN #0-89308-312-7.

NJ 2 $68.50

This book contains abstracts of all the known surveys, patents, and deeds of Proprietary New Jersey (1664-1703). There are tens of thousands of documents pertaining to title and transfer of lands are here sorted and calendared, each revealing the names of grantors and grantees, buyers and sellers, relatives and neighbors. These records are arranged under the headings of East and West Jersey. The indexes reference approximately 50,000 persons. Most of these references give a specific place of residence and also a precise description of the survey, including date, location, and acreage. The researcher will discover abstracts of original grants, concessions, and orders of the first Proprietors and Governors. These records describe the circumstances under which the first settlements were made in the Colony, the evolution of the government, along with the origin of the land titles in the Colony.

Genealogical Data, The Salem Tenth *in* West New Jersey. By: H. Stanley Craig, Pub. 1926, reprinted 2022, 100 pages, Index, ISBN #978-1-63914-038-1.

NJ 19 $15.00

The Salem Tenth encompassed approximately 350 square miles in the Southwestern part of the state which includes present day Salem and Cumberland Counties. It was founded by a Quaker named John Fenwick in 1665. This was the first English settlement established in west portion of the state of New Jersey following the English defeat of the Dutch in 1664. It had become the first Quaker colony in North America, predating any settlements in Philadelphia. In 1665, John Fenwick was involved in a financial dispute when acquiring these lands from Lord Berkeley. Lord Berkeley had also sold lands to Edward Billinge in New Jersey. The final outcome of the dispute was that for financial considerations Fenwick was granted a tenth of West Jersey.

Salem County, New Jersey Marriages, 1683-1878. By: Stanley Craig, Pub. 1928, Reprinted 2019, 295 pages, Index, soft cover, ISBN #0-89308-310-0.

NJ 7 $30.00

Salem County was created in 1694 from the Salem Tenth. It is located on the southwestern side of the state boarding the Delaware River. Settlers were showing up to this area from England during the 17th century and settling both sides of the Delaware River. Records used to compile this book come from: the NJ Archives, County Clerk's records, and Church including some from Quaker Meeting Houses. All marriages are listed in alphabetical order by groom with a bride's index covering the approximately 9,500 marriages.

Salem County, New Jersey Wills 1804-1860. (Recorded in the Office of the Surrogate at Salem, New Jersey). By: Stanley Craig, Pub. 1932 Reprinted 2018, soft cover.

Vol. #1, 1804-1830: 214 pages, Index, ISBN #0-89308-311-9.

NJ 8 $25.00

Vol. #2, 1831-1860: 202 pages, Index, ISBN #0-89308-727-0.

NJ 9 $20.00

Salem County was created in 1694 from the Salem Tenth. It is located on the southwestern side of the state boarding the Delaware River. Settlers from England were showing up to this area and settling both sides of the Delaware River as early as the 17th century. Wills are one of the go to records or research tools that the family historian love to get their hands on due to the various family members being mentioned within.

The Records *of the* SWEDISH Lutheran Churches *at* Raccoon *and* Penns Neck, New Jersey, 1713-1786. By: W.P.A. Pub. 1938, Reprinted 2021, 410 pages, Index, ISBN #978-1-63914-021-3.

NJ 16 $40.00

The Swedish Lutheran Churches at Raccoon and Penn Neck were the two most important Swedish churches in New Jersey during the Colonial Period. These two communities are located within Salem County. These records consist of minutes of church meetings, fragments of Pastors' Journals, historical accounts of the churches by early Swedish ministers, official documents and records of baptisms, marriages and deaths.

The SWEDES *and* FINNS *in* New Jersey. By: Works progress Administration, Pub. 1938, reprinted 2021, 177 pages, Index, ISBN #978-1-63914-020-6.

NJ 15 $20.00

This book tells the story of migration of Swedes and Finns in the 17th century from Pennsylvania and Delaware to the creek lands of southern New Jersey. It describes their efforts to preserve their native ways of life and emphasizes the growth of the important Swedish Lutheran Churches at Raccoon and Penns Neck. These two communities are located in Salem County.

NORTH CAROLINA

Old Albemarle *and* Its Absentee Landlords. By: Worth S. Ray, Pub. 1947, Reprinted 2019, 158 pages, Index, soft cover, ISBN #0-89308-899-4

NC 108 $20.00

Albemarle County was created in 1664 and its land mass covered the entire northeastern portion of the state. Six years later, its 4 prescient were created and by 1722 it ceased to function as county. Its land mass was carved up to create in part or whole the counties of: Chowan, Currituck, Pasquotank and Perquimans. This book is a collection of genealogical and historical records covering such things as: Land Grants, Tax records, Birth, Death, and Marriage records for early Albemarle County, the original gateway to the present State of North Carolina. The author has also included Biographical Sketches on: Barrett, Bryan, Cotton, Crudup, Dawson, Edwards, Hardy, Hunt, Lawrence, McKinnie, Marshall, Martin, Robinson, Rogers, Scowen, Sherer, Thomas, West, and Whitfield.

Anson County, North Carolina 1749-1834, Early Records *of*. By: May Wilson McBee, Pub. 1950, Reprinted 2018, 188 pages, Index, soft cover, ISBN #0-89308-980-X.

NC 53 $20.00

Anson County was created in 1750 from Bladen County. Parts of it were carved off to create the counties of: Mecklenburg, Montgomery, Richmond, Rowan, and Union County S.C. The fire of 1868 destroyed most of her records, but some still exists. This book contains List of Land Grants, Abstracts of Land Grant Surveys, Abstracts of Deeds, Abstracts of Court Minutes, Civil Suits in Salisbury District of Superior Court, Abstracts of Wills, Abstracts of Probate Reports, Petitions, List of Major James Cotton's Accounts 1778, Montgomery County Miscellaneous Records, and Richmond County

Miscellaneous Records.

Bladen County, North Carolina 1738-1804, Abstracts *of* Early Deeds. By: Brent Holcomb, Pub. 1979, Reprinted 2018, 88 pages, soft cover, Index, ISBN #0-89308-189-2.

NC 3 $15.00

At is formation in 1734, Bladen encompassed everything west of the present county. Even though many of Bladen's Deeds were lost in the three court house fires, these abstracts are especially informative, with many long chains of title going back to original grants and many references to bordering Craven County, S.C. This book will provide many links which were formerly thought forever lost. Deeds are GREAT source for genealogical research due to the many and varied family members that are mentioned. Not only will the reader find the deed transaction itself, but often times such things as: marriages, relinquishment of dower, divisions of family farms among heirs, remarriages of widows are just a few of the matters you can anticipate finding within records of deeds.

Bladen County, North Carolina, 1734-1900. Abstracts *of* Wills. By: Wanda S. Campbell, Pub. 1962, Reprinted 2018, 168 pages, Index, Soft Cover, ISBN #0-89308-940-0

NC 88 $20.00

At is formation in 1734, Bladen encompassed everything west of the present county. Even though many of Bladen's Records were lost in the two courthouse fires, these abstracts are especially informative, with many long chains of title going back to original grants and many references to bordering Craven County, S.C. This book will provide many links which were formerly thought forever lost.

(Bertie Co.) Colonial Bertie County, North Carolina Deed Books A-H, 1720-1757. By: Mary Best Bell, Orig. Pub. 1963 & 1968, Reprinted 1997, 328 pages, soft cover, Index, ISBN # 0-89308-048-9.

NC 2 $35.00

Bertie Precinct was formed in 1722 and form it were formed the later N.C. counties of Tyrell, Edgecombe, Northampton, Granville, Halifax, Nash, Wilson, Hertford, Martin, Washington, orange, Vance, Franklin, and Warren. This book contains the names of more than 24,000 persons in these deeds.

Buncombe County, North Carolina Births, 1858-1888. By: William D. Bennett, Pub. 1989, reprinted 2022, 112 pages, Index, soft cover 8 1/2" x 11", ISBN #978-1-63914-072-5.

NC 122 $20.00

Buncombe County was formed in 1791 and included what are now the following western North Carolina Counties: Cherokee, Clay, Graham, Haywood, Henderson, Jackson, Macon, Madison, Swain, Transylvania and also parts of Yancey, McDowell, and Polk.

Buncombe County, North Carolina 1783-1850, Index to Deeds. By: James E. Wooley, Pub. 1983, Reprinted 2007, 565 pages, soft cover, Index, ISBN #0-89308-294-5.

NC 11 $40.00

Buncombe County was formed in 1791 and included what are now the following western North Carolina Counties: Cherokee, Clay, Graham, Haywood, Henderson, Jackson, Macon, Madison, Swain, Transylvania and also parts of Yancey, McDowell, and Polk. This deed index includes the date of instrument, grantor, date proven, (except when proved in court), Book #, Page #, and description or the number of acres and water courses when given. The State Grant number is given. The grantees are also indexed, except for the state grants. As there was no 1790 census for the land mentioned in the oldest deeds lies in the state of Tennessee. This book contains the names of more than 40,000 individuals.

Burke County, North Carolina History, Sketches of the Pioneers in. By: Col. Thomas George Walton, Pub. 1984, Reprinted 2016, 96 pages, New Index, ISBN #0-89308-538-3

NC 17 $15.00

The articles comprising the first part of this book, page 5 through 67, were written in 1894 and were published in the old Morganton Herald. Those articles found on pages 68 through 89 were copies from manuscripts of Col. Walton; these are now in the possession of his granddaughter, Mrs. Harry Boggs (1924). This book contains sketches of the following pioneers in Burke County history: Avery, Ballew, Bechter, Bouchelle, Bowman, Bradshaw, Brittain, Caldwell, Carson, Collins, Connelly, Corpening, Dobson, Duckworth, Erwin, Estes, Forney, Graham, Greenlee, Hemphill, Henderson, Herne, Hildebrand (2), Lenoir, McDowell, McEntire, Miller, Morrison, Murphy, Newland, Patton, Perkin, Person, Picken, Rutherford, Stevelies, Tates, Walker, Walton.

Burke County, North Carolina Land Records, 1778. (Vol.#1). By: E.W. Huggins, reprinted 2020, 184 pages, soft cover, Index, ISBN #0-89308-559-6.

NC 24 $23.50

Burke County was formed in 1777 from Rowan, which is bounded by Catawba, Cleveland, Rutherford, McDowell, Avery, and Caldwell counties. More than one third of the book is taken up by the most important year, 1778, when pioneers swarmed into this virgin area to take up new land. These records are of extreme value due to the irreparable destruction of major records being burned/destroyed by the Union Army. Records found in this book are Land Entries 1778; Loose papers and Land Entries, Entry takers' Returns; Land Papers; Plats; land Warrants and Surveys; Land Grants Index; Sample Plat and Warrant and Surveys 1779-1790; an Itinerary of 1777; Commissioners appointed to the Courthouse of Morgans borough 1777-1785; Burke County Officials' Bonds and Tavern Bonds 1784-1800, and Miscellaneous papers.

Burke County, North Carolina Land Records, 1779-1790, Vol. #2, and Important Miscellaneous records, 1777-1800. By: Edith Warren Huggins, Pub. 1981, reprinted 2020, 215 pages, soft cover, Index, ISBN #0-89308-560-X.

NC 25 $25.00

Burke County was formed in 1777 from Rowan, which is bounded by Catawba, Cleveland, Rutherford, McDowell, Avery, and Caldwell counties. This book contains Burke County, N.C. Land Entries 1779-1790; Loose Papers and Land Entries 1779-1798; Entry Takers' Returns 1779-1785; Loose Land papers 1779-1788; Land Entries and Deeds 1779-1809; Deeds, Entries, Poles & Acres 1787-1790; Land Papers and Deeds 1770-1790; Land Plats 1777-1789; Land Warrants and Surveys 1779-1790; An Itinerary of 1777; Commissioners Appointed to Erect Courthouse and Town, Morgans Borough 1777, 1784; Burke County officials Bonds; Tavern Bonds 1784-1800; Apprentice Bonds 1778-1795; Deed of Gift 1772-1777; Power of Attorney 1773-1777; :Tax Records 1782-1793; Lists of Jurors 1788-1793; Road Papers, Petitions, Orders 1787-1795; Burke County Records in Rutherford County Will Books; Land papers and Deeds 1778-1794; Occupation and Professions 1778-1798; Entry Takers Returns 1785-1793; Subpoena Docket for Tories 1782; Enemies Cited to Court 1782; All to be Cited as Tories in January Session 1782; List of Strays Delivered to Samuel Greenlee 1777-1782; Burke County Militia Returns 1780-1782; Revolutionary War Final Settlements, Burke County 1777-1792; Estate Papers 1777-1795; and Some Interesting Civil and Criminal Court Papers, 1773-1790.

(Burke County) Revolutionary War Soldiers of Western N.C. (3 Volumes). By: Emmett R. White, Pub. 1984, reprinted 2017.

The contributions of the Revolutionary War soldiers of Western N.C. during the conflict of 1775-1782 were immense. The rolling hills of the Carolina Piedmont were as much a battleground as those of Pennsylvania and New Jersey. Kings Mountain, Ramsour's Mill, Cowpens, the Indian Wars, and many other conflicts all helped to change the course of American history. Unfortunately, from a historical standpoint, very little written data is available concerning the contributions of the Western N.C. Militiamen. Many of the western counties, though their soldiers contributed greatly to the war effort, are historically "silent". This work is an effort to unravel and to present in a systematic way something about their lives and exploits. The initial two volume will be devoted to Burke County. Each soldier will be written up to his early life (as much as could be made available), his military experiences, his later life, including marriages, children, occupations, etc. Also included will be his land transactions and census locations. Where available, b urial sites will be given as well as pension awards.

Vol. #1, 1784-1787: 340 pages, soft cover, Index, ISBN #0-89308-536-7.

NC 18 $38.50

The ??? genealogies/sketches within this volume pertain to persons from Burke County, NC

Vol. #2, 172 genealogies/sketches: 352 pages, soft cover, Index, ISBN #0-89308-520-0

NC 54 $38.50

The 172 genealogies/sketches within this volume pertain to persons from Burke County, NC.

Vol. #3, : Pub. 2011, 394 pages, Hard Cover, Index, ISBN #0-89308-806-9.

NC 55 $38.50

The bulk of these 166 genealogies/sketches within this volume pertain to persons from Burke County, NC. There are a few of these that cover persons from surrounding counties such as: Rowan, Lincoln, Rutherford and Surry counties.

Catawaba County, North Carolina, A History of. By: Charles Preslar, Pub. 1954, Reprinted 2020, 556 pages, Index, ISBN #0-89308-282-1.

NC 83 $48.50

Catawba County was created from Lincoln County in the 1842. It sits in the western portion of the state. The Catawba River Valley was first settled by Germans and Scotch-Irish settlers who came to this area in the mid-1700's. This book is not too different from other county history books of this era. With such topics as trade and transportation, labor, farming, politics, and race relations - all important in the development of the county - are carefully discussed. This type of county history book can help one develop ideas or paths to those missing ancestors by showing the customs and traditions of the local residents.

Cumberland County, North Carolina Deeds, 1754-1785. (2 Volumes). By: William C. Fields, Pub. 1999.

Vol. #1, 1754-1770: 310 pages, Index, Hard Cover.

NC 84 $35.00

Vol. #2, 1770-1785: 364 pages, Index, Hard Cover

NC 85 $35.00

Cumberland County was formed from Bladen County in 1754 and later became the parent county to Moore County in 1784. These abstracts include Mortgages, Bills of Sale, and Power of Attorney, as well as deeds of sale for land. In short, all transactions recorded in these deed books 1 - 7.

Duplin County, North Carolina Cemetery Records. (Vol. #A). By: Leon H Sikes, Pub. 1983, Reprinted 2017, 132 pages, soft cover, Index, ISBN #0-89308-587-1

NC 34 $17.50

Duplin County was formed in 1750 from New Hanover County, NC. It is located in the Southeastern section of the state and is surrounded by the counties of: Jones, Lenoir, New Hanover, Onslow, Sampson, and Wayne. This book contains inscriptions from graves in the 119 graveyards in the northern portion of the county, along with a few from the southern. There are approximately 2,737 entries.

Duplin County, North Carolina Cemetery Records. (Vol.# B). By: Leon H Sikes, Pub. 1984, Reprinted 2017, 130 pages, soft cover, Index, ISBN #0-89308-594-4

NC 76 $17.50

This book contains inscriptions from graves in 81 graveyards in the eastern portion pf the county. There are approximately 2,800 entries.

Duplin County, North Carolina Cemetery Records. (Vol.# C). By: Leon H Sikes, Pub. 1983, Reprinted 2017, 116 pages, soft cover, Index, ISBN #0-89308-595-2

NC 77 $17.50

This book contains inscriptions from graves in 147 graveyards in the northern portion pf the county. There are approximately 2,083 entries.

Duplin County, N.C. Court of Pleas & Quarter Sessions, 1784-1787. (6 Volumes) By: Leora H. McEachern, Pub. 1978-1980, soft Cover, Index.

Vol. #1, 1784-1787: 118 pages, ISBN #0-89308-808-0.

NC 61 $15.00

Vol. #2, 1788-1791: 116 pages, ISBN #0-89308-809-9.

NC 62 $15.00

Vol. #3, 1791-1795: 116 pages, ISBN #0-89308-810-2.

NC 63 $15.00

Vol. #4, 1795-1798: 124 pages, ISBN #0-89308-846-3.

NC 70 $15.00

Vol. #5, 1798-1803: 118 pages, ISBN #0-89308-847-1

NC 71 $15.00

Vol. #6, 1804-1805: 118 pages, ISBN #0-89308-407-7.

NC 72 $15.00

Duplin County, North Carolina 1749-1868, Marriages of. By: Cora Bass, Pub. 2001, reprinted 2015, 150 pages, soft cover, Index, ISBN #0-89308-521-9

NC 50 $20.00

Even though Duplin County was created in 1749, the marriages from 1749-1754 are missing. The marriage bonds for this book cover the time frame 1755-1868. These bonds were required by the clerk of courts in which the bride-to-be resided in. These bonds were issued before issuing a license to the prospective bridegroom and his bondsman, usually a close friend or relative.

Duplin County, North Carolina Deeds, 1784-1813. By: Eleanor S. Draughton, Orig. Pub. 1983, Reprinted 1986, 256 pages, soft cover, Index, ISBN #0-89308-598-7.

NC 33 $27.50

Duplin County, located in the southeastern section of N.C. was formed in 1750 from New Hanover County. In the year 1800, the county was bounded by the counties of Jones, Lenoir, New Hanover, Onslow, Sampson, and Wayne. Part of New Hanover was annexed to Duplin in 1751, and in 1777 part of Duplin was annexed to Johnston County. A major change involved the formation of Sampson County from Duplin in the year 1784. The county seat of Duplin is Kenansville. The deeds in Book 1A, 3A, and 4A are thoroughly abstracted in this volume. The book is essential for research in the hundreds of families who lived here during the early Federal period before migrating to the west and south. The two indexes include surnames of all persons mentioned in the deeds and the names of slaves. Duplin County residents of the period came for the most part from Virginia Tidewater counties and the Delaware River Valley.

Duplin County, North Carolina Wills, Genealogical Abstracts *from*. By: William L. Murphy, Pub. 1982, Reprinted 1986, 280 pages, soft cover, Index, ISBN #0-89308-597-9.

NC 32 $27.50

This volume contains abstracts of 588 wills and the index has references to 6,030 individuals. The appendix lists wills for the period following: 1861-1900. An index of slave names lists 3,657 individuals. A place name index also is included listing some 410 places.

Edgecombe County, North Carolina, History of. By: Kelly Turner and John Bridgers, Orig. pub. 1920, reprinted 1997, 544 pages, New Index, Hard Cover, ISBN #0-89308-493-X.

NC 43 $48.50

After many years, this book is finally available with a New Index, which makes its use for research at possibility. This book is not too different from other county history books of this era. With such topics as trade and transportation, labor, farming, politics, and race relations - all important in the development of the county - are carefully discussed. This type of county history book can help one develop ideas or paths to those missing ancestors by showing the customs and traditions of the local residents. A particular useful feature of this book is the extensive biographical information included. This volume contains more than 198 biographical sketches, included in which are some 2,000 additional family members. Also found in this nook are the names of some 7,000 other persons prominent in the early history of this county.

(Edgecomb County) Marriages *and* Deaths *from* Tarboro (N.C.) Newspapers, 1824-1865. By: Hugh Buckner Johnson, Pub. 1985, reprinted 2015, 168 pages, soft cover, Index, ISBN #0-89308-558-8

NC 23 $18.50

Tarboro is the county seat of Edgecombe County, which is one of the oldest counties in eastern North Carolina. The newspaper records in this book have references to persons also in the surrounding counties such as: Pitt, Halifax, Nash, Wilson, Wake, Greene, Wayne, and Johnston. Some of the newspapers here are The Southern, The Free Press, The North Carolinian, the North Carolina Press, The North Carolina Free Press, Political Synopsis, The Tarboro Mercury, The Tarboro Press and The Tarboro Scaevola.

Edgecombe County, North Carolina 1777-1868, Marriages *of* Early. By: Williams, Pub. 1958, Reprinted 2018, 336 pages, Index, soft cover, ISBN #0-89308-946-X.

NC 41 $30.00

Edgecombe County was created in 1732 from Bertie County. Edgecombe County was created in 1732 from Bertie County. This book is broken up into two parts. The first part are marriages from the Marriage Bond Book 1732-1867. While the second part includes: marriages proved by Edgecombe County Wills, marriages from the Raleigh Register and North Carolina Gazette 1799-1868, marriages from the Tarboro Free Press 1826-1845, marriages from the Battle Book, marriages from the files of Hugh B. Johnston Jr., marriages proved by records in Halifax County and miscellaneous other sources.

Edgecombe County, North Carolina Wills, 1733-1856, Abstracts *of*. By: Ruth S. Williams and Margarette G. Griffin, Pub. 1956, reprinted 2005, 408 pages, Hard Cover, Index, ISBN #0-89308-830-7.

NC 66 $45.00

Edgecombe County was created in 1741 from Bertie County. Even though these wills begin before the creation of the county, they do begin with the creation of the Edgecombe Precinct. Wills are a wonderful tool for genealogical research, due to the many and varying types of family members that are mentioned within. This book not only contains the wills of the individuals, but also guardians & administrators' bonds, bastardy, apprentices, trustees, sheriffs & treasures bonds, and inventories of estates.

Gates County, North Carolina Deeds, 1776-1833. (5 Volumes). By: Mona A. Taylor, Pub. 1987, reprinted 2006.

Vol. #1, 1776-1803: 280 pages, soft cover, Index, ISBN #0-89308-831-6.

NC 64 $30.00

Vol. #2, 1804-1808: 134 pages, soft cover, Index, ISBN #0-89308-844-7.

NC 65 $15.00

Vol. #3, 1808-1819: 176 pages, soft cover, Index, ISBN #0-89308-845-5.

NC 67 $27.50

Vol. #4, 1819-1828: 186 pages, soft cover, Index, ISBN #0-89308-402-6.

NC 68 $28.50

Vol. #5, 1828-1833: 135 pages, soft cover, Index, ISBN #0-89308-405-0

NC 69 $18.50

Gates County was created in 1778 from Hertford, Chowan and Perquimans counties, N.C. It is located in the Northeastern corner of the state bordering Virginia. It is surrounded by the counties of Camden, Chowan, Hertford, Pasquotank, Perquimans counties N.C. and by Nansemond County, VA. Many inhabitants of the "BURNED" counties of Hertford, N.C. and Nansemond, VA. which adjoin Gates County are mentioned in these early deeds. Deeds are one of favorite research tools of the genealogists due to the wide variety of family connections found within them. Not only will the reader find the deed transaction itself, but often times such things as: marriages, relinquishments of dower, divisions of family farms among heirs, remarriages of widows are just a few of the matters you can anticipate finding within records of deeds.

Granville, County North Carolina 1746-1800, History *and* Genealogies *of* Old. By: Thomas everything, Owen, Pub. 1993, 300 pages, Hard Cover, Index, ISBN #0-89308-487-5.

NC 52 $38.50

Thomas McAdory Owen was at one time Head of the Alabama State Dept. of Archives and History. In an explanatory note to these records, Mr. Owen states that he visited Granville County in 1895 to examine the official records for a genealogy of the Own and Grant families of Grassy Creek, also the Williams family. In the process, he conceived the idea of preparing a history of the county, and the county clerk placed at his disposal 10 of the old "Minute" and "Record" books prior to 1800. He noted that there were some gaps in the records, particularly from May 9, 1776 to Feb. 4, 1777, when apparently No court was held, as pagination was continuous in the Book. He abstracted just about everything, and he listed the documents he did not abstract. This includes wills and inventories, bastardy bonds (lots of these), apprenticeship indentures, marriage bonds etc... Some documents that he considered important he copied in full. His notes start in 1746 and most stopped after the Revolution but he continued the marriage bonds to 1815. The records that this book is taken from are as follows: County court minutes Dec. 2, 1749 through Aug. 6, 1783 and Record Book 1750-1785, and selective Marriage License Bonds, Coroners Inquisitor.

Colonial Granville County, North Carolina *and its* People. By: Worth S. Ray, Pub. 1945, Reprinted 2019, 126 pages, Index, soft cover, ISBN #0-89308-900-1

NC 109 $20.00

Granville County was created in 1746 from Edgecombe County. It was later carved up to help create in part or whole the counties of: Orange, Franklin and Warren. This book is a series of genealogical items and data in a variety of lists, some of the most notable being: Notes from the Records of the Counties of Anson, Buncombe, Caswell, Chatham, Cleveland, Duplin, and Franklin; First and Earliest County Courts of Granville; Muster Roll of the First Residents in Granville County in 1754; Taxpayers of Granville County in 1788; and Marriage Bonds and Records of Caswell, Chatham, Franklin, and Granville Counties. The author has also included biographical sketches of the following families: Bates, Bennett, Boyd, Bullock, Burton, Christmas, Daniel, Eaton, Graves, Harris, Harrison, Hawkins, High, Hill, Hunt, Jones, Knight, Lanier, Morrow, Royster, Satterwhite, Searcy, Sims, Taylor, White, and Williams.

(Guilford County) Founders & Builders of Greensboro, North Carolina. By: Bettie Caldwell, Pub. 1925, Reprinted 2018, 356 pages, Index, ISBN #0-89308-593-6.

NC 79 $35.00

Greensboro lies in the heart of Guilford County, NC. It was created to become the county seat around 1808. This book covers the early history of the area but its main focus details the biographies of 50 of its early citizens. Many of these biographies detail the lives of persons being born prior to its creation with some as early as 1740's. Surnames of biographies': Adams, Albright, Alderman, Benbow, Bumpass, Caldwell, Caruthers, Cone, Cuninggim, Dick (2), Dillard, Doub, Douglas, Eckel, Gillespie, Gilmer (2), Gorrell (2), Gray, Gretter, Hildeshetmer, Humphries, Jones, Lindsay (2), Logan, McIver, Mendenhall, Michaux, Morehead (4), Paisley, Porter, Reece, Scales (2), Schenck, Scott, Settle, Sloan, Smith, Swaim, Walker, Whartton (2), and Wiley.

Guilford County, North Carolina Deeds, 1763-1779. (2 Volumes). By: Wlliam D. Bennett, Pub. 1990, Reprinted 2018.

Vol. #1, 1763-1779: 132 pages, Index, soft cover, ISBN #0-89308-970-2.
NC 105 $18.50

Vol. #2, 1779-1784: 174 pages, Index, soft cover, ISBN #0-89308-971-0.
NC 106 $22.50

Guilford County was formed in 1771 from Orange and Rowan Counties. Many of its early settlers were Scotch-Irish, German Exiles, English Quakers, and even some Welsh. Deeds are one of favorite research tools of the genealogists due to the wide variety of family connections found within them. Not only will the reader find the deed transaction itself, but often times such things as: marriages, relinquishments of dower, divisions of family farms among heirs, remarriages of widows are just a few of the matters you can anticipate finding within records of deeds.

Guilford County, North Carolina Wills, 1771-1841. By: I.B. Webster, Pub. 1979, Reprinted 2005, 190 pages, soft cover, Index, ISBN #0-89308-352-6.

NC 12 $25.00

Guilford County was formed in 1771. It is now bounded on the North by Rockingham County, which was formed Guildford in 1785; on the East by Alamance County; on the South by Randolph County and on the West by Davidson and Forsyth. It contains the names of more than 6,500 persons mentioned in these Wills.

Halifax County, North Carolina, The History *of*. By: W.C. Allen, Pub. 1918, Reprinted 2019, 312 pgs, NEW INDEX, ISBN #0-89308-491-3.

NC 51 $30.00

Halifax County is in the northern part of N.C. within 6 miles of the Virginia line and it adjoins the Tar River and Roanoke River. It borders Martin and Warren counties. Edgecombe County was formed in 1738 and from it a few years later Halifax County was formed in 1758. Part one of this book deals with the information of the county, Revolutionary War activities and general history. Part two is titled "Builders of the County" and is primarily concerned with Biographical sketches of many of the early citizens, namely: Allen, Alston, Ashe, Bradford, Brance, Branch, Burton, Bynum, Conigland, Daniel, Davis, Emry, Haywood, Hill, Hodge, Hogan, Jones, Joyner, Long, Lynch, Moore, Montford, Parker, Potter, Shaw, Smith, Weldon, Whitaker, & many other pioneer settlers...

Haywood County, North Carolina Deeds, 1808-1838, Abstracts of. By: Bill Eddleman, Pub. 2005, 282 pages, Hard Cover, Index, ISBN #0-89308-807-2.

NC 60 $35.00

Haywood County was created in 1808 from Buncombe County, N.C. It was a important migration path for early settlers moving into Tennessee, Georgia and South Carolina. Deeds are GREAT source for genealogical research due to the many and varied family members that are mentioned. Not only will the reader find the deed transaction itself, but often times such things as: marriages, relinquishment of dower, divisions of family farms among heirs, remarriages of widows are just a few of the matters you can anticipate finding within records of deeds. Another very special note, the author has included a slave index to help those persons researching their African-American lines. This book should make a GREAT EDITION to everyone's Library who have family in Western North Carolina.

Haywood County, North Carolina, History of. By: Haywood County Historical Society, Pub. 2009, 504 pages, Index, 8 1/2" x 11" hard cover, ISBN #0-89308-855-2.

BA 7 $40.00

Haywood County was created in 1808 from Buncombe County, N.C. It was a important migration path for early settlers moving into Tennessee, Georgia and South Carolina. These early settlers moving into this area were of Scots-Irish, German and English descent. Even though this book is Brand New and never before published. It has many similarities to other county history books written from much earlier times. With such topics as trade and transportation, labor and industry, farming, politics, legal system, religion, education, natural disasters, and social & community relations - all important in the development of the county - are carefully discussed. This type of county history book can help one develop ideas or paths to those missing ancestors by showing the customs and traditions of the local residents.

Haywood & Jackson Counties, North Carolina, Marriage Bonds of. By: James & Vivian Wooley, Pub. 1979, Reprinted 2015, 324 pages, Index, ISBN #0-89308-107-8.

NC 7 $35.00

These two Western North Carolina counties are important migration paths for early settlers moving into Tennessee, Georgia, and South Carolina. Haywood County was formed in 1808 from Buncombe, while Jackson was formed in 1853 from the middle portions of both Haywood and Macon counties. At one time Jackson County reached from Tennessee boarder south to the South Carolina.

Jones County, North Carolina 1779-1868, Records of. By: Zae Hargett Gwynn, Pub. 1963, Reprinted 2018, 1074 pages, Index, ISBN #0-89308-941-9

NC 89 $68.50

Jones County was created in 1779 from Craven County. It is surrounded by Carteret, Craven, Duplin, Dobbs and Lenoir Counties. The records within this book are: Land Entries 1779-1795, Land Grants 1784-1792, Taxable property records 1779, Deeds 1779-1867, Census records 1786 & 1850, Wills 1778-1868, Inventories settlements & Guardian accounts 1809-1829 and Marriages records 1851-1874.

Macon County, North Carolina Marriages, 1829-1939. By: James Wooley, Pub.

1984, Reprinted 2017, 191 pages, Index, ISBN #0-89308-342-9.

NC 15 $25.00

Macon County was formed in 1828 from Haywood county, and Haywood was formed in 1808 from Buncombe. Macon County is in the Western section of North Carolina and is bounded by the state of Georgia and Clay, Cherokee, Swain and Jackson Counties, N.C. This book contains approximately 7,000 marriages in this 110 years period and is arranged alphabetically by groom. An index of brides is included. Also included are the names of the clerks, registers, justices of the peace and ministers of the gospel who performed these ceremonies. On a marriage bond could be found the names of the groom and his bondsman, the bride, the witness and the date the bond was issued. The marriage may have taken place the same day or a week or more later. In 1868, bonds were discontinued, although marriage licenses and certificates had been issued for many years. Only after 1851 was the J.P. or minister required to return the license to the Clerk of the Court's office. According to the 1868 law, the marriage licenses were to be kept in the Register of Deeds Office, and the age, race, residence, and place of marriage were to be recorded with the other information.

Mecklenburg County, North Carolina Court Minutes, 1774-1780, Book 1.

By: Doris F. Briscoe, Pub. 1966, Reprinted 1997, 336 pages, Index, Hard Cover, ISBN #0-89308-591-X.

NC 9 $35.00

Mecklenburg County was formed from Anson County, N.C. in 1762. It was a pathway of major migration from both Virginia, Pennsylvania and New Jersey as the Scotch-Irish came to the area in huge numbers. Court minutes are considered some of the most important records on the county level. The reason researchers value court minutes so much is because they reflect many areas of activity in the county and the persons involved: estates being settled, persons assigned to jury duty or to work on the roads, lawsuits, wills, probated deeds recorded, apprentices indentured, orphans put under the care of the court, etc. Do not be surprised to find those surnames you have been searching for in other books on this county that you have had no luck with so far.

Mecklenburg County, North Carolina Deed Abstracts, 1763-1779, Books 1-9.

By: Brent Holcomb, Pub. 1979, Reprinted 2018, 280 pages, soft cover, Index, ISBN #0-89308-108-6.

NC 5 $32.50

Mecklenburg county was formed in 1763 from Anson County and in turn Tryon County was formed from Mecklenburg in 1769. This book covers the period when Mecklenburg County also included portions of several South Carolina Counties: Cherokee, Chester, Greenville, Kershaw, Lancaster, Laurens, Newberry, Spartanburg, Union and York. So not only does this book have great significancy for persons researching in this area of N.C. but also for persons who are looking for relatives in the Up-Country of S.C. during the late 1700's.

Mecklenburg County, North Carolina, The History of.

By: J.B. Alexander, Pub. 1902, Reprinted 2018, 504 pages, NEW INDEX, Hard Cover, ISBN #0-89308-490-5.

NC 44 $48.50

This is an excellent history for this county which was a pathway of MAJOR migration from Virginia, Pennsylvania and New Jersey as, the Scotch-Irish came to this area in huge numbers. Besides the regular general history of the county, this book is filled with EXCELLENT genealogical sketches on many of these settlers. Those for whom genealogical sketches are given are: Adrey, Alexander, Avery, Balch, Barringer, Barry, Beard, Brevard, Brown, Bryce, Caldwell, Campbell, Combs, Craighead, Cummings, Davidson, Downs, Dulin, Dunlop, Dunn, Elms, Erwin, Flennikin, Foard, Garrison, Gibbon, Graham, Grier, Happoldt, Harris, Harty, Henderson, Hill, Hunter, Irwin, Jack, Jetton, Johnston, Kennon, Lafferty, Lourie, Lowrie, McCauley, McClure, Maxwell, Miller, Morris, Morrison, Neal, Oates, Orr, Osborne, Pharr, Phifer, Polk, Reese, Robinson, Shipp, Spratt, Strong, Todd, Torrance, Vance, Walker, Wallace, Wallis, Waring, Watson, Williamson, Wilson, Yates and many, many more pioneer settlers. The Roster of 21 Companies furnished by Mecklenburg County in the War of 1861-1865 is also listed. The NEW INDEX that was produced for this reprint mentions approximately 7,000 persons.

Mecklenburg Signers *and their* Neighbors.

By: Worth S. Ray, Pub. 1946, reprinted 2022, 250 pages, Index, ISBN #978-1-63914-053-4.

NC 115 $25.00

Mecklenburg county was formed in 1763 from Anson County and in turn Tryon County was formed from Mecklenburg in 1769. This book is about the persons who settled in the valley between the Yadkin and Catawba rivers more than two hundred years ago. Included among the source records are the various lists of the Signers of the Mecklenburg Declaration; Abstracts of Some Ancient Items from Mecklenburg County Records; Marriage Records and Relationships of Mecklenburg People; List of Public Officials of Mecklenburg County, 1775-1785; First U.S. Census of 1790 by Districts; Tombstone Inscriptions; and Sketches of the Mecklenburg Signers. To make this book more useful, the author has included an index with over 5,000 entries of the persons within.

Nash County, North Carolina, 1777-1868, Abstracts *of* Early Deeds.

By: J.W. Watson, Pub. 1966, Reprinted 2023, 308 pages, Index, Soft Cover, ISBN #978-1-63914-127-2.

NC 119 $35.00

Nash County was created in 1777 from Edgecomb County. It is located in teh Northeastern portion of the state. Deeds are a wonderful source of genealogical information.

Nash County, North Carolina, 1778-1868, Abstracts *of* Wills Book 1.

By: Ruth S. Williams & Margarette G. Griffin, Pub. 1967, Reprinted 2023,183 pages, Index, Soft Cover, ISBN #978-1-63914-128-9..

NC 120 $22.50

Nash County was created in 1777 from Edgecomb County. It is located in teh Northeastern portion of the state. Wills are a wonderful source of genealogical information due to the wide variety of persons mentioned within them.

New Hanover County, North Carolina Inferior Court *of* Pleas *and* Quarter Sessions, 1738-1800.

(2 Volumes). By: Alexander McDonald Walker, Pub. 1960-1962, Reprinted 2019.

Vol. #1, 1738-1785: 262 pages, Index, ISBN #0-89308-936-2

NC 90 $30.00

Vol. #2, 1786-1800: 258 pages, Index, ISBN #0-89308-937-0.

NC 91 $27.50

New Hanover was created in 1729 as New Hanover precent of Bath County which was later dissolved. It is the parent county to Brunswick, Duplin and Pender Counties. It sits on the Atlantic Ocean in the Southeastern portion of the state. It is surrounded by: Brunswick, Bladen, Duplin, Onslow and Sampson Counties. The court was held 4 times a year and heard such cases of assault, batteries, trespass, all breaches of the peace. They held authority of administration in intestate estates and orphans, granted license to build water grist mills, to taverns and ordinaries, and to build and maintain public ferries. The court also appointed Constables and Overseers of Roads, and named the men who lived within the bounds to keep them in repair, as well as recommending three persons to the Governor, of whom one was made Sheriff, as well as imposing taxes for roads, courthouses and goals, appointed all county officers, civil and military, all lists of Jurors and probates of Wills. These records are extremely valuable for the researcher, especially if an ancestor died intestate (without a will), and in some instances a person may be listed in these court records and nowhere else in the county records.

Orange County, North Carolina, 1752-1952.

By: Lefler & Wager, Pub. 1953, Reprinted 2013, 400 pages, ISBN #0-89308-805-6.

NC 74 $40.00

The great migration from Pennsylvania to the Piedmont of the Carolinas came in the middle of the 18th century. Scotch-Irish and German immigrants moved South along the "Great Wagon Road" through the Shenandoah Valley to Carolina, looking for less expensive land and Orange County received a great influx of these immigrants. This book discusses the history of the county from its beginning along with other issues such as: agriculture, education, commerce, Indian affairs, politics, religion, slavery, and war service. But what the family researcher will savior are the biographical sketches of many the early citizens, such as: Andrews, badger, Bettle, Bennehan, Benton, Berry, Bingham, Burke, Butler, Caldwell, Cameron, Caswell, Child, Churton, Corbin, Curtis, Duke, Fanning, Few, Gattis, Graham, Green, Harris, Harrises, Hart, Hawks, Heartt, Henderson, Hogg, Holden, Holt, Hooper, Horton, Howell, Hubbard, Huntington, Husband, Johnston, Jones, Laws, Lloyd, Lynch, Mangum, Martin, Mebane, Micklejohn, Mitchell, Montgomery, Moore, Murphey, Nash, Norwood, Olmsted, Patillo, Phillips, Pool, Rochester, Ruffin, Smith, Spencer, Stanford, Strowd, Strudwick, Swain, Tew, Thackston, Turner, Venable, Waddell, and Watson.

Orange County, North Carolina 1752-1766, Abstracts *of the* Minutes *of the* Court *of* Pleas *and* Quarter Sessions *of.*

By: Ruth H. Shields, Pub. 1965, Reprinted 2005, 182 pages, soft cover, Index, ISBN #0-89308-456-6.

NC 47 $28.50

Orange County was created in 1752 from Granville, Johnston and Bladen Counties with Granville having been formed from Edgecombe County. Rowan County was formed as the western boundary of Orange in 1753. Counties formed from Orange were Guilford and Randolph in 1770 with Rockingham taken from Guilford in 1785, Chatham in 1770 with a small portion of it taken to become part of Wake County in 1770, and in 1771 Caswell County was taken from Orange with Person County taken from Caswell in 1792. The court was held 4 times a year and heard such cases of assault, batteries, trespass, all breaches of the peace. They held authority of administration in intestate estates and orphans, granted license to build water grist mills, to taverns and ordinaries, and to build and maintain public ferries. The court also appointed Constables and Overseers of Roads, and named the men who lived within the bounds to keep them in repair, as well as recommending three persons to the Governor, of whom one was made Sheriff, as well as imposing taxes for roads, courthouses and goals, appointed all county officers, civil and military, all lists of Jurors and probates of Wills. These records are extremely valuable for the researcher, especially if an ancestor died intestate (without a will), and in some instances a person may be listed in these court records and nowhere else in the county records

Orange County, North Carolina 1777-1788, Abstracts *of the* Minutes *of the* Inferior Court *of* Pleas & Quarter Sessions. By: Alma C. Redden, Pub. 1991, Reprinted 2007, 192 pages, Index, ISBN #0-89308-457-3.

NC 48 $28.50

Orange county was formed in 1752 from Granville, Johnston, and Bladen counties with Granville having been formed from Edgecombe County. Rowan County was formed from the western boundary of Orange in 1753. Counties formed from Orange were Guildford in 1785; Chatham in 1770 with a small portion of it taken to become part of Wake County in 1770; and in 1771 Caswell County was taken from Orange with Person County taken from Caswell in 1792.

Granville Proprietary Land Office Records: Orange County, North Carolina. (Volume #1): Loose Papers, 1752-1763. By: William D. Bennett, Pub. 1990, Reprinted 2019, Index, 8 1/2" x 11", soft cover, 94 pages, ISBN #0-89308-994-X.

NC 111 $20.00

In this important volume are abstracts of surviving loose papers from the Granville proprietary Land Office concerning Orange County. These papers include Entries, Warrants to the Surveyor and Surveys. Over a thousand documents concerning land in present Wake, Caswell, Person, Orange, Durham, Alamance, Chatham, Rockingham, Guilford, Randolph, and Stokes Counties have been abstracted. These records cover the period from the formation of Orange County in 1752 until the closing of the Granville Proprietary Land Office in 1763. The information from the papers in the Granville Proprietary Land Office may be the date of entry with a rough description of the land including the waterway and names of neighboring landowners, the warrant, the survey with names of chain bearers, sometimes the date the deed was issued, and any assignment that may have occurred along the way. What this does is place people in a particular place at a particular time up to forty years before the first census and prior to the Revolution. The Index contains more than 1,500 names.

Granville Proprietary Land Office Records: Orange County, North Carolina. (Volume #2): Deeds and Surveys, 1752-1760. By: William D. Bennett, Pub. 1988, Reprinted 2019, 8 1/2" x 11", soft cover, 184 pages, Index, ISBN #0-89308-995-8.

NC 112 $28.50

These are the so-called "Granville Grants" from the Secretary of State Land Grant Office (held by the NC State Archives) for the original Orange County area, including what became Chatham, Caswell, Alamance, Person, and parts of Guilford, Rockingham, Randolph, and Wake Counties. A detailed introduction by George Stevenson, supplemented by the editor's research, explains what the Granville Proprietary was and the records created by its Land Office. In his abstracts of the deeds, Mr. Bennett has included the metes and bounds description, the neighboring landowners, the surveys and plats with the names of the chain bearers and facsimile copies of the signatures of the grantees and the witnesses. This volume provides the at-home researcher with all the information to be found from examination of the original documents. There are 428 of these grants, of which less than 50 appear in surviving Orange County Deed Books. Since this is the one place where the researcher is apt to find his ancestor's signature (many wills and deeds not having survived), it is particularly convenient for the researcher to have a reproduction of the signature with the survey, plat, and abstract of the deed. The author has also included a notation as to the Patent Book and Deed Book where the grant is recorded. The format of this particularly useful book is pleasing. because of its size and location, Orange County is a pivotal county in tracing North Carolina lineages.

Granville Proprietary Land Office Records: Orange County, North Carolina. (Volume #3): Deeds and Surveys, 1761-1763. By: William D. Bennett, Pub. 1989, Reprinted 2019, 8 1/2" x 11", soft cover, 160 pages, Index, ISBN #0-89308-996-6.

NC 113 $28.50

This book continues the publication of metes and bounds descriptions of the original so-called "Granville Grants" fro the Secretary of State Land Grant Office (hel by the NC State Archives) for the original Orange County area, including what later became Chatham, Durham, Caswell, Alamance, Person, and parts of Guilford, Rockingham, and Randolph Counties. Because Mr. Bennett has included the surveys and plats as well as the signatures of grantees and witnesses, the user has at hand all the information from the original. Mr. Bennett has also included, courtesy of the British PRO, the "Plan(that) sheweth part of the Southern Boundary of the Lands Granted the 17th day of September 1744 by his Majesty King George the Second to the Rt. Honble. John Lord Carteret, now Earl Granville, as the same was laid out and marked in the Months of March and April 1746 by Eleazer Allen, Matthew Rowan, William Forbes, and George Gould, Esqrs." One of the fascinating things about this map is that it clearly shows the southern Granville line to have been run as far west as Rocky River in 1746 when all the published histories say the line was not extended taht far west until 1766. Mr. Bennett has presented the deeds and surveys with his usual expertise, and the volume is a MUST for anyone working in the vast are of original Orange County.

Orange County, North Carolina Deed Books 1752-1819. (11 Volumes). By: Wlliam D. Bennett, Pub. 1991, Reprinted 2019.

Orange county was formed in 1752 from Granville, Johnston, and Bladen counties with Granville having been formed from Edgecombe County. Rowan County was formed from the western boundary of Orange in 1753. Counties formed from Orange were Guildford in 1785; Chatham in 1770 with a small portion of it taken to become part of Wake County in 1770; and in 1771 Caswell County was taken from Orange with Person County taken from Caswell in 1792. Deeds are GREAT source for genealogical research due to the many and varied family members that are mentioned. Not only will the reader find the deed transaction itself, but often times such things as: occupations, marriages, relinquishment of dower, divisions of family farms among heirs, current and/or former residences, remarriages of widows are just a few of the matters you can anticipate finding within records of deeds.

Vol. #1, Deed Books 1 & 2, 1752-1786: 184 pages, Index, soft cover, ISBN #0-89308-957-5

NC 92 $25.00

Vol. #2, Deed Book 3, 1752-1786: 172 pages, Index, soft cover, ISBN #0-89308-958-3.

NC 93 $25.00

Vol. #3, Deed Book 4, 1787-1793: 194 pages, Index, soft cover, ISBN #0-89308-959-1.

NC 94 $25.00

Vol. #4, Deed Book 5, 1793-1797: 186 pages, Index, soft cover, ISBN #0-89308-960-5

NC 95 $25.00

Vol. #5, Deed Books 6 and 7, 1797-1799: 156 pages, Index, ISBN #0-89308-961-3.

NC 96 $20.00

Vol. #6, Deed Books 8 and 9, 1799-1802: 162 pages, Index, ISBN #0-89308-962-1

NC 97 $20.00

Vol. #7, Deed Books 10 and 11, 1801-1806: 176 pages, Index, ISBN #0-89308-963-X.

NC 98 $20.00

Vol. #8, Deed Books 12, 1805-1807: 104 pages, Index, ISBN #0-89308-964-8.

NC 99 $20.00

Vol. #9, Deed Books 13, 1808-1811: 172 pages, soft cover, Index, ISBN #0-89308-965-6.

NC 100 $25.00

Vol. #10, Deed Books 14, 1812-1814: 172 pages, soft cover, Index, ISBN #0-89308-???-?.

NC 100 *(out-of-print)*

Vol. #11, Deed Books 15 & 16, 1815-1819: 174 pages, Index, soft cover, ISBN #0-89308-966-4

NC 102 $25.00

Granville Proprietary Land Office Records: Orange County, North Carolina. (Volume #4): Miscellaneous Records. By: William D. Bennett, Pub. 1991, Reprinted 2019, 8 1/2" x 11", soft cover, 96 pages, Index, ISBN #0-89308-997-4.

NC 114 $20.00

This volume completes the remaining Granville papers that concern Orange County, and they help particularly in a pivitol county where all the original deeds have not survived, all deeds were not recorded, and the reconstructed deed books are amazingly incomplete. Facsimiles of surveys and signatures of the grantees and included in the text. Included also in the book are two petitions for the period of c1755, the petitioners living in Orange, Rown, and Anson Counties, some seven pages of names for that early period, previously unpublished.

Orange County, North Carolina Inventories *and* Estates, 1758-1808. By: William Bennett, Pub. 1994, reprinted 2022. (2 Vols)

Vol. #1, 1758-1785: 226 pages, Index, 8 1/2" x 11" soft cover, ISBN #978-1-63914-067-1.

NC 117 $32.50

Vol. #2, 1800-1808: 166 pages, Index, 8 1/2" x 11" soft cover, ISBN #978-1-63914-068-8.

NC 118 $28.50

Orange County was formed in 1752 from Granville, Johnston, and Bladen counties. This transcription of these records provides an accurate description of the industrial and social life in the colony. It provides specific information valuable to the genealogists. For example, the sale of the moveable property of John Andrew dated 11 Oct. 1783 (who, one finds from other records, died intestate) shows many sales to "the widow," not named. The widow, however, signs the account of the sales as Deborah Andrew. The "true inventory of the estate of James McCallister," dated 30 July 1771, shows among other items of personal property, 276 acres of land and was signed by Neil McCallister. Although the minutes of the Court of Pleas & Quater Sessions are missing for this period, we have an approximate date of death for James. Since Neil McCallister's inventory is dated 1 March 1775, we have a time frame for his death; his inventory is signed by Mary McCallister. One learns to wring out every bit of the information in every record. This volume is extremely valuable since it lists many names not found in the surviving court minutes and deed books.

Perquimans County, North Carolina, History of. By: Mrs. Watson Winslow, Pub. 1931, Reprinted 2018, 538 pages, Index, soft cover, ISBN #0-89308-975-3.

NC 57 $48.50

Perquimans county was formed in 1670 as a precinct from Albemarle County. It was considered one of North Carolina's original precincts, with very close ties to Southeastern Virginia counties of: Norfolk, Princess Anne, Nansemond, and Isle of Wight.

This book was designed for the family genealogist in mind. The author has included a wealth of legal records and genealogies for the reader to use that mention approximately 15,000 persons. The records within are: 1792 Tax Lists, 1744 List of House Holders, Rent Rolls prior to 1700, marriages 1669-1856, Petitions 1711-1796, Division of Estates 1770-1811, Deeds 1681-1784, and numerous records concerning the various courts from 1675 to 1754. The family genealogies cover: Albertson, Arnold, Baker, Barrow, Bartlett, Bateman, Beasley, Bentley, Belman, Blanchard, Blitchenden, Blount, Bundy, Calloway, Charles, Chesson, Clare, Cox, Davis, Draper, Durant, Elliott, Fleetwood, Fletcher, Godfrey, Gordon, Granbery, Gregory, Hollowell, Hoskins, Jacocks, Jessop, Jones, Jordan, Lamb, Lawrence, Layden, Leigh, Lillington, Long, Mauldin, McMullen, Mayo, Moore, Morgan, Morris, Newby, Nicholson, Nixon, Pearson, Perry, Phelps, Pierce, Pritlow-Pricklove, Ratcliffe, Scott, Skinner, Snoden, Speight, Spivey, Sutton, Swann, Toms, Tucker, Waite, Williams, Wilson, Winslow, Wood, Woolard and Wright.

Raleigh, North Carolina, Newspapers 1796-1826, Marriage *and* Death Notices from. By: Silas Emmett Lucas Jr., and Brent Holcomb, Pub. 1977, Reprinted 1984, 168 pages, ISBN #0-89308-046-2.

NC 6 $20.00

These marriage and death notices are important because they were from all over North Carolina and adjacent states. There are marriage notices included from counties in which marriage bonds are not extant. These notices are alphabetized by groom. There is also an alphabetized listing of brides. Obituaries are alphabetized by the name of the deceased.

Rockingham County, North Carolina Deeds, 1785-1800. By: Irene B. Webster, Pub. 1973, Reprinted 2017, 122 pages, soft cover, Index, ISBN #0-89308-351-8

NC 13 $17.50

Rockingham County is bordered on the north by Pittsylvania and Henry counties, Virginia; on the east by Caswell County; on the south by Guilford County; and on the west by Stokes. It was formed in 1785 from Guilford County. This book includes Deed Books A - E and contains the names of more than 4,000 persons including grantor, grantee, witness, & etc.

Rockingham *and* Stokes *with* Revolutionary Service, Early Families *of* North Carolina Counties of. (2 Volumes) By: the James Hunter Chapter, NSDSAR of Madison, NC, Pub. 1977, reprinted 2022.

Vol. #1: 184 pages, Index, ISBN #0-89308-672-X.

NC 45 $25.00

Vol. #2: 188 pages, Index, ISBN #0-89308-673-8.

NC 46 $25.00

To complete this book, the publication committee of the James Hunter Chapter NSDAR used information from DAR applications for members of their chapter who descended from soldiers or patriots in this area. Most of the research on the families in this book was based on original records or publications of original records such as estate records, division of land, deeds, court records, cemetery, census, and Bible records, as well as pension applications of Revolutionary War soldiers or their widows. Guilford County from which Rockingham County was formed in 1785 and Surry County from which Stokes County was formed in 1789 were in Salisbury District of North Carolina. To be more specific, they were in that point of Salisbury District called the Upper Salisbury District. Rockingham is bordered by Pittsylvania and Henry Counties, Virginia and Caswell, Guilford, Alamance, and Stokes Counties, NC. Stokes County is bordered by Patrick County, VA and Rockingham, Forsyth and Surry County, NC. This Book has 156 biographical sketches of families/individuals of this area of North Carolina.

Rockingham County, North Carolina Will Abstracts, 1785-1865. By: Irene B. Webster, Pub. 1973, Reprinted 1983, 138 pages, Index, ISBN #0-89308-355-0.

NC 14 $18.50

Rockingham County is bordered on the north by Pittsylvania and Henry counties, Virginia; on the east by Caswell County; on the south by Guilford County; and on the west by Stokes. It was formed in 1785 from Guilford County. This book contains Will Books A-C plus "Old Wills" which were a group of wills discovered in 1957 and were dated prior to 1804.

Rutherford County, North Carolina Wills *and* Miscellaneous Records, 1783-1868. By: James E & Vivian Wooley, Pub. 1984, reprinted 2015, 184 pages, Index, ISBN #0-89308-413-1

NC 16 $25.00

This book containing Books A-E includes not only the wills of Rutherford County, but also powers of attorney, apprenticeships, some estate settlements and some bills of sale, etc. Rutherford was formed in 1779 from Tryon County. It is surrounded by Polk, McDowell, Buncombe, and Lincoln counties and South Carolina state line.

Sampson County, North Carolina Wills, 1784-1895, Abstracts of. By: Cora Bass, Pub. 2015, 176 pages, Index, ISBN #0-89308-897-8.

NC 75 $25.00

Sampson County was created 1784 from Duplin County, NC. It is surrounded by the counties of: Bladen, Cumberland, Duplin, Johnston, New Hanover, and Wayne Counties. This book contains not only the wills of Sampson County, but also powers of attorney, apprenticeships, some estate settlements and some bills of sale, etc.

Stokes County, North Carolina Deeds, 1787-1797. By: W.O. Absher, Pub. 1985, Reprinted 2018, 136 pages, Index, soft cover, ISBN #0-89308-556-1.

NC 21 $22.50

Stokes county was formed in 1789 from Surry County. It is located in the north-central section of the state and is bounded by Rockingham, Forsyth, and Surry counties and the state line of Virginia. In 1849, Forsyth was formed from Stokes County. Deeds are GREAT source for genealogical research due to the many and varied family members that are mentioned. Not only will the reader find the deed transaction itself, but often times such things as: marriages, relinquishment of dower, divisions of family farms among heirs, remarriages of widows are just a few of the matters you can anticipate finding within records of deeds.

Stokes County, North Carolina Wills, 1790-1864. By: W.O. Absher, Pub. 1985, Reprinted 2018, 182 pages, Index, soft cover, ISBN #0-89308-557-X.

NC 22 $22.50

Stokes county was formed in 1789 from Surry County. it is in the north-central section of the state and is bounded by Rockingham, Forsyth and Surry counties and the state line of Virginia. In 1849, Forsyth was formed from Stokes County.

Surry County, North Carolina Court Minutes, 1768-1789, Vols. 1-2. By: Mrs. W.O. Absher, Pub. 1985, reprinted 2011, 168 pages, Index, ISBN #0-89308-554-5.

NC 19 $23.50

Surry County was formed in 1770 from Rowan County. It is in the north-central section of the state and is bounded by the state of Virginia and Stokes, Yadkin, Wilkes, and Alleghany counties. In 1773, part of Rowan was annexed to Surry; Wilkes County was formed in 1777 from Surry and Stokes County was formed in 1789 from Surry. In 1792, part of Wilkes County was annexed to Surry and in 1796, part of Stokes was annexed to Surry and in 1869, 1870, and 1875 parts of Surry were annexed to Alleghany County.

Surry County, North Carolina Deed, 1770-1797. (2 Volumes). By: W.O. Absher, Pub. 1981, Reprinted 2018.

Vol. #1, 1770-1778: 128 pages, Index, soft cover, ISBN #0-89308-172-8.

NC 8 $25.00

Vol. #2, 1779-1797: 128 pages, Index, ISBN #0-89308-172-8

NC 20 $20.00

Deed books A and B have been out of print for some time and now are being combined with Book C in a brand-new volume. Surry County was formed from Rowan in 1770 and is one of those very important counties in which so much migration came via Virginia, as well as New Jersey and Pennsylvania.

Surry County, North Carolina, History of. By: J.G. Hollingsworth, Orig. Pub. 1935, reprinted 2001, 288 pages, Hard Cover, New Index, ISBN #0-89308-748-3.

NC 58 $35.00

Surry county was formed from Rowan County in 1771. At the time of its creation, it was surrounded by Iredell, Rowan, Stokes, Wilkes counties, N.C. and to the North by Henry County, VA. The time frame of this book concentrates on the Colonial & Revolutionary era, with such topics as frontier life, Indians, trade & transportation, labor, farming, politics, education, newspapers and religion - all important in the development of the county. These types of HISTORY books can be very helpful in your research. They can help one develop ideas or pathways to those missing ancestors by showing the customs and traditions of local residents. This is very important in trying to figure out what significate factors were prevalent in the county, such as floods, droughts, matters of economic prosperity, matters of governmental intrusion or influence, or one of any number of things that might cause a person to stay or move on. The author has also included numerous lists: muster rolls of soldiers who served in the War of 1812, the detached Militia organization of 1814, petitioners in Surry County of 1840 Revolutionary or Military services, Pensions issued to Surry in 1833 for services in the War of 1812, Mexican War veterans, numerous Civil War Companies including commissioned & noncommissioned officers and privates, & Veterans of the Spanish-American War and WWI.

Deed Abstracts *of* Tryon, Lincoln *and* Rutherford Counties, North Carolina 1769-1786, *and* Tryon County Wills *and* Estates. By: Brent Holcomb, Pub. 1977, reprinted 2015, 244 pages, Index, ISBN #0-89308-047-0.

NC 4 $27.50

Tryon County was formed from Mecklenburg County in 1769. At one time Tryon County included all or part of the N.C. counties of Burke, Cleveland, Gaston, Henderson, Lincoln, Polk, Rutherford, McDowell, and the S.C. counties of York, Chester, Union, Cherokee, Spartanburg, Greenville, Laurens, and Newberry. These deeds, wills, and estates should provide many missing links for the researcher working on the Carolina frontier. Deeds are GREAT source for genealogical research due to the many and varied family members that are mentioned. Not only will the reader find the deed transaction itself, but often times such things as: marriages, relinquishment of dower, divisions of family farms among heirs, remarriages of widows are just a few of the matters you can anticipate finding within records of deeds.

Tryon *and* Lincoln Counties, North Carolina, Marriage Bonds of. By: Curtis Bynum, Orig. Pub. 1929, Reprinted 1994, 184 pages, Hard Cover, Index, ISBN #0-89308-316-X.

NC 10 $27.50

Lincoln County was formed in 1779 from Tryon County which had been formed in 1769 from Mecklenburg County. At the formation of Lincoln, another portion of Tryon became Rutherford County, and in 1782 a part of Burke County was added to Lincoln. The marriage bonds of Tryon and Lincoln cover the period from 1769-1869, and the more than 6,000 bonds herein abstracted are on file in the courthouse in Lincolnton, N.C.

Watauga County, North Carolina, History of. (With Sketches of Prominent Families.) By: John Preston Arthur, Pub. 1915, reprinted 1986, 433 pages, New Index, hard cover, ISBN #0-893608-001-2.

NC 1 $40.00

Even though this Watauga County was not created until 1849, this book covers well back into the period of the Old Watauga Settlement of Sevier. John Seiver along with many early pioneer settlers, moved into the area. First leasing and later purchasing these lands from the Cherokee Indian Nation back in the 1770's. This book consists of: the first settlement, Indian raids, churches, Revolutionary & Civil War activities, geological data, legislative & other officers, population & agriculture statistics, place names, schools, but also intertwines his book with numerous names of early settlers, biographical sketches, and anecdotes about county residents. The author even includes a chapter about Daniel Boones who was believed to have spent many a year hunting along the Watauga River. Of special interest to the genealogists are the biographical sketches of the following families: Adams, Baird, Banner, Bingham, Blackburn, Blair, Brown, Bryan, Bryant, Cable, Coffey, Cottrell, Councill, Critcher, Davis, Dugger, Eggers, Elrod, Farthing, Franklin, Gragg, Greene, Greer, Grider, Grubb, Hagaman, Hardin, Harman, Hartley, Hayes, Hodges, Holtzclaw, Horton, Ingram, Isaacs, Lenoir, Lewis, Linney, Lovill, McBride, McGhee, Mast, Miller, Moretz, Morphew, Norris, Penley, Perkins, Presnell, Reese, Rivers, Sands, Shearer, Sherrill, Shull, Smith, Story, Swift, Tatum, Tester, Thomas, Todd, Trivett, Tugman, Van Dyke, Vannoy, Ward, Watson, Welch, Wilson, Winebarger, Winkler, Woodring, and Yountz.

Wilkes County, North Carolina Court Minutes, 1778-1789. (Vols. #1 & 4). By: Mrs. W.O. Absher, Pub. 1989, reprinted 2013, soft cover, Index, ISBN #0-89308-646-0

Vol. #1, 1778-1789: 152 pages, soft cover, Index, ISBN # 0-89308-674-6..

NC 39 $18.50

Vol. #2, 1789-1797: 132 pages, Index, ISBN #89308-647-9.

NC 40 $18.50

In the minutes, one will find local office holders being appointed and/or qualified, including clerks of courts, registers of deeds, sheriffs, coroners, etc. The court controlled the levying and expenditure of local taxes, matters dealing with public buildings, roads, bridges, etc. were handled by this court and it also selected and summoned juries. Among the other responsibilities of the court found in its minutes were licenses granted to operators of taverns, as well as deeds and bills of sale being acknowledged by the grantors. the court oversaw a wide range of matters involving estates, including probate of wills, settlements of estates, and appraisements as well as matters dealing with bastardy, and many other valuable bits of information.

Wilkes County, North Carolina Deeds, 1778-1815. (2 Volumes). By: Mrs. W.O. Absher, Pub. 1989 & 1990, reprinted 200.

Vol. #1, 1778-1803: 152 pages, soft cover, Index, ISBN # 0-89308-674-6..

NC 28 $20.00

Vol. #2, 1795-1815: 220 pages, soft cover, Index, ISBN #0-89308-676-2

NC 29 $20.00

This book containing both deeds and original land grants in Wilkes County contains the names of approximately 8,000 individuals found therein. This book covers the deed books A-H. It contains both deeds and original land grants for the years 1795-1815. The index mentions approximately 11,000 persons.

Wilkes County, North Carolina Land Entry Book, 1778-1781. By: W.O, Absher, Pub. 1989, Reprinted 2018, 130 pages, Index, ISBN #0-89308-645-2.

NC 38 $20.00

The best contemporary documentary evidence for an accurate location of these settlers when the county was created is the original Land Entry Book. It has better details than that to be found in the subsequent land grants. It was customary for the settler to describe the location of his plantation on some stream or head waters of some stream, or on some mountain. Each entry is dated. There were numerous transfers of entries before the issuance of a grant. Some are referred to in the entry, but generally the entry taker would mark through the name of the original entree and insert the name of the one to whom it was transferred. Not only was the first named entered, frequently marked out, but many times erased, and the next name written in its place. Many of the entries had as many as four names marked out and written in with no way of knowing whose name was the last one written. North Carolina started its Land Entry Book when the county was organized in March 1778. This old Entry Book Abstracts will be of help to many whose ancestors either passed through or remained in Wilkes County.

Some Pioneers *from* Wilkes County, North Carolina. By: Mrs. W.O. Absher, Pub. 1989, Reprinted 2007, 315 pages, Index, ISBN #0-89308-644-4.

NC 37 $35.00

The information contained in this book is an attempt to research the extant records of Wilkes County and some of Surry, Rowan and other counties and to present a compilation of these records about the early pioneers who lived on the waters of the streams that flowed into the Yadkin River and along the line drawn between Surry and Wilkes counties in 1778.

Wilkes County, North Carolina Wills, 1778-1811. By: Mrs. W.O. Absher, Pub. 1990, reprinted 2020, 118 pages, Index, ISBN #0-89308-675-4.

NC 30 $18.50

This book contains not only wills of individuals, but also guardians and administrator's bonds, bastardy, apprentice, trustees, sheriffs and treasurers' bonds, and inventories of estates. The names of more than 6,000 persons are found in these legal records of this important county.

Miscellaneous Records

The Colonial Clergy *of* Virginia, North Carolina *and* South Carolina, 1607-1776. By: Frederick Lewis Weis, Pub. 1955, Reprinted 2021, 108 pages, soft cover, ISBN #978-1-63914-031-2.

VA 193 $17.50

This book is alphabetical list of approximately 950 colonial clergymen from 1607-1776 who settled in Virginia, North Carolina and South Carolina. These annotations furnish such useful genealogical data as date & place of birth, date & place of death, names of parents, college of matriculation, date of ordination, denomination, names of parishes, dates in which tenure was held, and a variety of other similar data.

The History *of* Taxation *in* North Carolina *during the* Colonial Period, 1663-1776. By: Coralie Parker, Pub. 1928, reprinted 2022, 190 pages, Index, soft cover, ISBN #978-1-63914-085-5.

NC 82 $22.50

This book is a comprehensive history of taxation within the state of North Carolina covering the policies of England all the way thru Independence in 1776. The reader will find topics on: English Trade & Navigation; English customs and Revenue systems; Direct & Local Taxes in England; QUIT-RENTS, its history, its administration, its fiscal Importance and its significance; CUSTOMS DUTIES, Types and Purposes of Customs Levied in the State, Export Tax on Tobacco and Hides, Import Duties on Liquors and Rice, Tonnage Duties; POLL TAX, its advent, description and basis of it; LAND and MISCELLANEOUS TAXES, the Land Tax, Tax on Lawsuits, License Taxes, Lotteries; and LOCAL TAXES, authority and Influence of the Local System, and the Parrish Levies.

Index *to* North Carolina Bankrupts, Acts of 1800, 1841, *and* 1867. By: William Doub Bennett, Pub. 1994, reprinted 2022, 86 pages, soft cover, ISBN #978-1-36914-069-5.

NC 121 $15.00

This is an alphabetical listing of all men who filed for bankrupt under the first three federal bankruptcy acts for which records survive at the National Archives-Southeastern Region. An introduction explains the provisions of the various bankruptcy acts and describes the holdings from North Carolina at the National Archives-Southeastern Region.

Known Military Dead *during* The American Revolutionary War, 1775-1783. By: Clarence Stewart Peterson, Pub. 1959, reprinted 2021, 198 pages, Index, soft cover, ISBN #978-1-63914-028-2.

USA 6 $22.50

This book is an alphabetically list of approximately 10,000 "Known" military dead during the American Revolution. Information to be found within: names with rank, date of death, and state of birth or service or place where buried.

The LOYALISTS *in* NORTH CAROLINA *during the* Revolution. By: Robert O. DeMond, Pub. 1940, Reprinted 2019, 294 pages, Index, ISBN #0-89308-426-3.

NC 49 $30.00

North Carolina may have had a greater number of Loyalists in proportion to its population than any other Colony. This book covers motivation and buildup of the impending revolt. The author covers the military activities of the Loyalists, along with the various sufferings of these persons, including Laws against these supporters of the Crown and their loss of personal property through confiscation. There is even a chapter on the compensation and pensions allowed by the Crown and then the exodus of these Loyalists. This book identifies large numbers of little know Loyalists. The genealogists will delight in: the lists of soldiers and citizens who supported the King of England throughout the Revolution, lists of Loyalists who suffered land confiscation, lists of Loyalists who made application to England for compensation for loss of said property or office and lists of North Carolina Loyalists who received pensions from England.

Muster Rolls *of the* Soldiers *of the* War *of* 1812, North Carolina. By: Adjutant General & Maurice S. Toler, Pub. 1851, reprinted 2022, 196 pages, Index, soft cover, ISBN #978-1-63914-086-2.

NC 87 $25.00

This book is a complete muster roll of the State's 12,000 soldiers who were detached from the NC Militia. These lists contain the names of both officers and men and are presented in two separate sections: one covering the detachments of 1812, the other the detachments of 1814.

North *and* South Carolina Marriage Records, 1683-1865. By: William Montgomery Clemens, Orig. 1927, reprinted 2017, 306 pages, ISBN #089308-843-9.

NC 26 $27.50

These marriages covering both of the Carolina's mentions approximately 7,500 unions. They are listed / arranged alphabetically by surname. Information included: date and place of marriage and maiden name of bride.

Roster *of* Soldiers *from* NORTH CAROLINA *in the* American Revolution. By: NC Daughters of the American Revolution, Pub. 1932, Reprinted 2017, 722 pages, soft cover, Index, ISBN #0-89308-921-4.

NC 86 $52.50

This book contains the names of approximately 36,000 soldiers. Service records include as rank, company, date of enlistment or commission, period of service, combat experience, and whether captured, wounded, or killed. This is a complete roster of soldiers named in both published and unpublished sources.

Slavery *and* Servitude *in the* Colony *of* North Carolina. By: John Spencer Bassett, Phd., Pub. 1896, reprinted 2023, 86 pages, soft cover, ISBN #978-1-63914-129-6.

NC 123 $17.50

North Carolina Wills 1663-1760, Abstracts *of*. By: J. Bryan Grimes, Pub. 1910, Reprinted 2017, 500 pgs, New Index, ISBN #0-89308-575-8.

NC 31 $47.50

Compiled from original and recorded Wills in the Office of Secretary of State. Arranged alphabetically by the name of the testator, this work covers 1663-1760. The abstracts give the name of the testator, his residence, and the names of wife, children, legatees, witness, and probate officer. The index has approximately 20,000 names, and an appendix gives the reference to where each will is located.

OHIO

The Official Roster *of the* Soldiers *of the* American Revolution Buried *in the* State *of* Ohio. By: Frank D. Henderson, Pub. 1929, reprinted 2022, 463 pages, soft cover, ISBN #978-1-63914-046-6.

OH 1 $45.00

This book is an authentic and complete list of Revolutionary soldiers that were buried in the state of Ohio. The large numbers of Revolutionary soldiers buried here can be directly associated to the proximity of this Northwestern Territory to the Colonies themselves. When the land grants were issued, the New Englanders moved into regions around Lake Erie, the large numbers of Pennsylvanians crossed over into central Ohio and the Virginians and the Carolinians settled lands in the southern part of Ohio. Information that can be gleamed from within: Name, rank, service location and record, Names of family members, pension date, date of death, county buried in, residence prior to revolution, occupation and other tidbits of genealogical information.

The Official Roster *of the* Soldiers *of the* American Revolution *who* Lived *in the* State *of* Ohio. By: D.A.R. of Ohio, Pub. 1938, reprinted 2022, 436 pages, ISBN #978-1-63914-047-3.

OH 2 $45.00

This book contains the data of some 1,500 applications for pensions for those persons who had moved to Ohio following their service in 1775-1783. These persons were from all 13 colonies. Veterans are listed in alphabetical order. Types of data that the reader can discover: Name, rank, location of enlisting and service, county in Ohio of residence, Date and location of birth, name of spouse, name of children and their spouses, name of parents, Name of his siblings, date and location of death, information on land deeds, information of family's movements and general data, and many, many more useful items of genealogical interest. Also contained in this volume is addenda to the first volume (Official Roster of the Soldiers of the American Revolution Buried in the State of Ohio) furnishing new facts which clarify previous statements, giving newly found clues; or correcting errors reported by those who hold authentic records.

Columbiana County, Ohio *with* Illustrations *and* Biographical Sketches *of some of its* Prominent Men *and* Pioneers, History of. By: D.W. Ensign & Co., Pub. 1879, reprinted 2023, 450 pages, Index, ISBN #0-89308-353-4.

OH 3 $45.00

Columbiana County was created in 1803 from Jefferson County. It was settled early on by Quakers and Scotch-Irish from Pennsylvania but was later settled primary by Germans. The county itself sits in the eastern side of the state bordering Pennsylvania with the Ohio River on its southern boundary. The first chapters of this book are devoted to the general history of the County and are introduced by such an account of French and Spanish discoveries as was deemed of value in connection with that history. Other general chapters treat Indian Occupation, Land Titles, Geology, Organizations, Education, Politics, County's Military history, and a roster of the early Militia and soldiers who served in the Civil War. The author has also given histories of the various townships along with biographies of their residents. Some surnames of these biographies: Armstrong, Arter, Aten, Bell, Carr, Cook, Davis, Dickinson, Dobson, Dysart, Entriken, Farmer, Heacock, Hill, Hime, Holloway, Johnson, Johnston, Keeler, Kerr, Long, Martin, McClellan, Murray, Oyster, Pike, Robinson, Stanton, Strawn, Thompson, Walter, and Whinnery. The New Index that was created for this reprint mentions approximately 21,000 persons.

Stark County, Ohio, History *of*. By: William Henry Perrin, Pub. 1881, reprinted 2023, 1,100 pages, New Index, soft cover, ISBN #978-1-63914-121-0.

OH 4 $75.00

Stark County was carved out of Columbiana County in 1807. The majority of these early settlers were of German descent from Pennsylvania along with other settlers coming from Virginia, New York, and New England. The author has devoted approximately 300 pages to biographical sketches of these early settlers.

PENNSYLVANIA

Adams County, Pennsylvania, History of. By: Warner, Beers & Company 1886, reprinted 2022, 756 pages, New Index, soft cover, ISBN #978-1-63914-084-8.

PA 36 $65.00

Adams County was created in 1800 from York County which in turn was carved out of Lancaster County. It lies in the south-central portion of the state along the Maryland State line. First settlers started arriving in the area around 1730. The majority of these immigrants were Scotch-Irish along with a smaller population of English and Germans. This book is broken down into three parts. The first is a history of the state of Pennsylvania from 1624-1886. The second is a history of the county with such topics as: the German, Scotch-Irish and Jesuit immigration; early settlers, French Huguenots, roads, customs, politics, religion, War of 1812, Civil War, education, newspapers, citizens of Gettysburg, 1717-1829; Battle of Gettysburg, various townships listing early land owners and value of land, Lists of first claims of land at Manor Maske giving dates and acreage, list of early marriages 1774-1808, Roster of officers during the Revolutionary War. The third is a biographical sketch section of approximately 387 persons with a New Index that was produced for this reprint which mentions approximately 23,000 persons.

Armstrong County, Pennsylvania, History *of.* By: Robert W. Smith, Pub. 1883, reprinted 2023, 826 pages, New Index, soft cover, ISBN #978-1-63914-101-2.

PA 39 $75.00

Index has approximately 14,500 entries...

Beaver County, Pennsylvania, History of. By: A. Warner and Company 1888, 1035 pages, New Index, soft cover, ISBN#978-1-63914-081-7.

PA 33 $75.00

Beaver county was created in 1800, from parts of Allegheny and Washington counties. It lies in the extreme western portion of the state along the Ohio State line. Settlers started arriving around 1785 and were almost exclusively Scotch-Irish Presbyterians. This book is broken down into two sections. The first is a history of the county with such topics as: first settlers / pioneers, Indians, formation of townships, the French and the English Claims of the Ohio Valley, Medicine, Education, Religion, Newspapers, Civil War, Legal system, Roster of troops in the War of 1812 and the Mexican War. The second is a biographical sketch section of approximately 1,010 persons with a New Index that was produced for this reprint which mentions approximately 26,000 persons.

Bedford, Somerset, *and* Fulton Counties, Pennsylvania, History of. By: Waterman, Watkins and Company, Pub. 1884, reprinted 2020, 924 pages, New Index, ISBN #0-89308-734-3.

PA 25 $65.00

Bedford County was created in 1771 from Cumberland County and is the parent county to: Huntington, Somerset, Blair, Cambria and Fulton. Somserset County as created in 1795 and Fulton was created in 1850. It sits in the southern portion of the state boarding Maryland. This area is where the French and Indian War occurred. It was a vital area for development of the country. Upon the defeat of the French and Treaties with the native Indians, westward expansion was allow : to progress. This book is not too different fron. other county history books of this era. With such topics as trade & transportation, labor, farming, towns rows, Boundary Lines, politics, Military Service, the Whiskey Insurrection, French Occupation, Land and religion - all important in the development of the county - are carefully discussed. This type of county history book can help one develop ideas or paths to those missing ancestors by showing the customs and traditions of the local residents. A particular useful feature of this book is the extensive biographical information included. This volume contains more than 276 biographical sketches, included in which are some 10,000 additional family members. The New Index for this edition has approximately 32,000 entries.

Berks County, Pennsylvania *in the* Revolution *from* 1774 to 1783, History *of.* By: Morton Montgomery, Orig. Pub. 1894, reprinted 2021, 300 pages, Index, ISBN #978-1-63914-015-2.

PA 26 $22.50

Berks County was created in 1752 from: Chester, Lancaster, and Philadelphia Counties. It sits in the southeastern portion of the state. Early immigrants who came to this area were from England, Germany and the Netherlands. This book is arranged in two parts. Part 1: covers the history of Berks County and her residents during the Revolution. With such things as, the county's Associators, the various militia companies and their campaigns including their militia rolls, prisoners of war, matters of supply, proclamations, and estimates of men in service. Part 2: includes approximately 50 biographical sketches of persons with a focus on the individual's participation in the war and, giving names of spouses and children.

BUCKS County, Pennsylvania, 1684-1700, Records *of the* Courts of Quarter Sessions *and* Commonn Pleas *of.* By: The Colonial Society of Pennsylvania, Pub. 1943, Reprinted 2019, 454 pages, Index, ISBN #0-89308-907-9.

PA 12 $40.00

The court was held 4 times a year and heard such cases of assault, batteries, trespass, all breaches of the peace. They held authority of administration in intestate estates and orphans, granted license to build water grist mills, to taverns and ordinaries, and to build and maintain public ferries. The court also appointed Constables and Overseers of Roads, and named the men who lived within the bounds to keep them in repair., as well as imposing taxes for roads, courthouses and goals, appointed all county officers, civil and military, all lists of Jurors and probates of Wills. These records are extremely valuable for the researcher, especially if an ancestor died intestate (without a will), and in some instances a person may be listed in these court records and nowhere else in the county records

Bucks County, Pennsylvania, History of. By: J.H. Battle, Pub. 1887, reprinted 2020, 1086 pages, New Index, Hard Cover, ISBN #0-89308-912-5.

PA 23 $78.50

Bucks County was created in 1682 and was one of the first three counties created within the state. It is the parent county to Northampton and Lehigh counties. It sits in the Delaware Valley just north of Philadelphia in the Southeastern portion of the state boarding New Jersey. This book is broken up into two main sections. The first deals with the history of the county with such things as:early settlements on the Delaware, Dutch occupation, Indian hostilities and land claims, pioneer life, Dutch & English immigration, the Militia, the court system, slavery within the county, along with the discussion of the development & history of the various towns or boroughs found thought the county. The second section of this book is devoted to 1028 biographical sketches of these early settlers broken down via townships or boroughs and followed up with a new Full Names Index with approximately 27,000 entries.

(Bucks County) Old RICHLAND Families. By: Ellwood Roberts, 1898, reprinted 2021, 300 pages, Index, ISBN #978-1-63914-023-7.

PA 27 $30.00

Richland township is located in Bucks County, Pennsylvania. It is located less than 40 miles from Philadelphia. This area was settled by English & Welsh Quakers and also Germans seeking refuge for religious reasons. Information that will be gleamed from this book: Naming and creation of the township, the Friends' Meeting, Records of Richland Meeting, Original Documents, a section entitled Notes which has various data of these settlers and then the remaining half of the book is devoted to biographical sketches of the following surnames: Roberts, Lancaster, Lester, Johnson, Foulke, Strawn, Moore, Jamison, Penrose, Ball, Morris, Greens, Shaws, Edwardes, Heacocks, Thomsons, Hallowells and Spencers.

Early Friends Families *of* UPPER BUCKS COUNTY, PENNSYLVANIA. By: Clarence V. Roberts, Pub. 1925, Reprinted 2019, 742 pages, Index, ISBN #0-89308-736-X.

PA 10 $58.50

Bucks County was created in 1682 and was one of the first three counties created within the state. It is the parent county to Northampton and Lehigh counties. It sits in the Delaware Valley just north of Philadelphia in the Southeastern portion of the state boarding New Jersey. This book is a collection of genealogical and historical information about the first settlers who located in the upper part of Bucks County. Each of the 44 families for which a chapter is devoted to came from Wales or England. Families for which the reader will find genealogies: Adamson, Ashton, Ball, Blackledge, Burson, Cadwallader, Carr, Chapman, Clothier, Custard, Dennis, Edwards, Foulke, Green, Griffith, Hallowell, Heacock, Hicks, Iden, Jamison, Johnson, Kinsey, Lancaster, Lester, Levick, Lewis, Lott, McCarty, Miller, Morgan, Morris, Nixon, Penrose, Phillips, Rawlings, Roberts, Shaw, Strawn, Thomas, Thomson, Walton and Zorns.

Chester County, 1681-1697, Record *of the* Courts *of.* By: The Colonial Society of Pennsylvania, Pub. 1910, Reprinted 2018, 430 pages, Index, ISBN #0-89308-907-9.

PA 3 $45.00

Chester County was one the first three counties in Pennsylvania and was created in 1682. It sits in the southeastern corner of the state boarding Maryland. This book is a copulation of multiple types of courts such as: Court of Common Pleas and Court of Quarter Sessions and Orphans' Court. In these minutes of pleas & quarters sessions you will find appointments of county officials, appointed administrators, marked public roads, granting of licenses to "ordinaries", taxes being levied, civil actions of a wide variety, persons being tried for offenses against the peace & dignity of the State, list of juries, guardian accounts of orphans, Wills, and countless numbers of Deed Acknowledgements.

Chester County, Pennsylvania, Genealogical & Biographical Sketches, History of. By: J. Smith Futhey & Gilbert Cope, Orig. Pub. 1881, 1196 pages, Index, ISBN #0-89308-978-8.

PA 24 $85.00

Chester County was one the first three counties in Pennsylvania and was created in 1682. It sits in the southeastern corner of the state boarding Maryland. This book is not too different from other county history books of this era. With such topics as trade & transportation, labor, farming, towns & burrows, Boundary Lines, politics, Proprietary Interests & Land Titles, and religion - all important in the development of the county - are carefully discussed. This type of county history book can help one develop ideas or paths to those missing ancestors by showing the customs and traditions of the local residents. A particular useful feature of this book is the extensive biographical information included. This volume contains more than 350 biographical sketches, included in which are some 10,000 additional family members. The New Index for this edition has approximately 32,000 entries.

Cumberland Valley, Pennsylvania, 1776-1876, Men *of* Mark *of.* BY: Alfred Nevin, Pub. 1876, 502 pages, Index, soft cover, ISBN #978-1-63914-040-4.

PA 29 $45.00

The Cumberland Valley sits in the south-central portion of the state bordering Washington County, Maryland. It covers the Pennsylvania counties of Cumberland and Franklin along with the Washington County Maryland. This book begins with a historical sketch of the region discussing: immigrants, religion, churches, cities, Indians, education, early settlements, and etc.. The bulk of this work (almost 600 pages) is devoted to biographical sketches or mini genealogies of some 125 individuals of the region. Surnames of the persons within: Agnew (3), Allen, Allison, Armstrong (3), Audenreid, Boggs, Brownson, Buchanan (2), Cathcart, Craighead (2), Crain, Crawford (4), Chambers (2), Creigh, Culbertson (2), Davidson (2), Denny (2), Duffield, Duncan, Dunlop, Elliott (3), Findlay, Findley, Fisher, Foster, Fullerton, Gibson, Graham, Grier, Gustine, Hamilton, Harbaugh, Herron, Johnston, Junkin (3), Kaufman, Kennedy (3), King, Knox, Krebs, laird, Lane, Linn, McCarrell, McClelland, McClure, McConaughy, McCoskry, McCulloh, McCullough, McElroy, McGill, McGinley, McKibbin, McKinley, McKnight, McLanahan, McPherson, Moodey, Moore, Bevin (2), Nisbet, Penrose (3), Pomeroy (2), Rankin (2), Rauch, Reed, Richards, Ritner, Sanderson, Schneck, Scott, Senseny, Stewart, Sharp, Smith, Snodgrass, Snowden (2), Speer, Speel, Stevens, Thompson, Thomson (3), Watts (3), Weir, Wilkins, Williams, Wilson, Williamson, Wing, Whitehill, Woods (3), and Young.

Cumberland County, Pennsylvania, History of. By: Warner, Beers & Company 1886, reprinted 2022, 816 pages, New Index, soft cover, ISBN #978-1-63914-083-1.

PA 35 $65.00

Cumberland County was created in 1750 from Lancaster County. It lies in the south-central portion of the state along the Maryland State line. First settlers started arriving in the area around 1730. The majority of these immigrants were Scotch-Irish along with a smaller population of English and Germans. This book is broken down into three parts. The first is a history of the state of Pennsylvania from 1624-1886. The second is a history of the county with such topics as: Pioneers / early settlers, Indians, Revolutionary War, War of 1812, Civil War, Slavery, religion, education, court system, formation of townships, Medicine, Newspapers, early landowners, Lists of Taxes paid 1736-1749, lists of settlers of North Valley, Lists of Taxables in the county 1762. The third is a biographical sketch section of approximately 564 persons with a New Index that was produced for this reprint which mentions approximately 20,500 persons.

Dauphin, Cumberland, Franklin, Bedford, Adams, *and* Perry Counties, Pennsylvania, History of. By: I. Daniel Rupp, Pub. 1846, reprinted 2021, 720 pages, New Index, ISBN #978-1-63914-016-9.

PA 35 $65.00

From the noted author of his time, I.D. Rupp, comes the reprint of his important work covering south central Pennsylvania. These counties were officially created around the 1780's but settlers started arriving in the area around the 1730's. Early immigrants were of German and Scotch-Irish descents with some Amish being sprinkled in. There is much genealogical information to be found interspersed throughout this book. A new Index has been completed for this reprint with approximately 12,000 entries.

Franklin County, Pennsylvania, American Revolutionary Soldiers *of.* By: Virginia Shannon Fendrick, Pub. 1944, reprinted 2019, 294 pages, Index, soft cover, ISBN #0-89308-752-1

PA 6 $30.00

Franklin County was created in 1784 from Cumberland County which in turn was carved out of York County and prior to that Lancaster County. It lies within the Cumberland Valley in the south-central portion of the state bordering Maryland. The 1639 soldiers listed within this book are in alphabetical order. Such information that the reader can discover under each soldiers' mini biographies: service records; names of wife, children and parents; date of birth; date of death; location of burial place; date of Will along with names of beneficiaries and inventory of estate; his residence; land holdings and etc...... The author has also listed another 196 soldiers who were buried in 26 different cemeteries throughout Franklin County with similar mini biographies being listed of them.

Jefferson County, Pennsylvania 1755-1844, A Pioneer History of. By: W.J. McKnight, Pub. 1898, Reprinted 2019, 670 pages, Index, ISBN #0-89308-925-7.

PA 21 $52.50

Jefferson County was created in 1805 from Lycoming County. The county is located in the west-central portion of the state. This is an extremely rare book and should be a part of the library of anyone who is doing research on the state of Pennsylvania.

Lancaster County, Pennsylvania, 1729-1850, An Index *to* Will Books *and* Intestate Records *of.* By: Eleanor Jane Fulton & Barbara Kendig Mylin, Pub. 1936, Reprinted 2018, 158 pages, Index, soft cover, ISBN #0-89308-314-3.

PA 2 $20.00

Lancaster County was created in 1729 and was formed from Chester County. This book has the names of nearly 15,000 Lancaster County residents who left wills or died intestate, between the years of 1729-1850. Arranged in two alphabets, the researcher will discover the full name of the deceased, the year of occurrence, the book volume and page wherein the records are to be found. There is also a brief history of the early inhabitants of the area.

Northampton County, Pennsylvania, The Scotch-Irish *of.* By: The Northampton County Historical & Genealogical Society, Orig. Pub. 1926, Reprinted 2020, 644 pages, ISBN #0-89308-911-7.

PA 11 $52.50

Northampton County was created in 1752 from Bucks County. It is situated in the eastern most region of the state along the Delaware river, just across the border from Warren and Sussex Counties New Jersey. It is the parent county in whole or part to: Cabon, Lehigh, Monroe, Pike, Schuylkill and Wayne counties. This book is filled with data that might help that researcher with family connections in eastern Pennsylvania. The narratives of the Scotch-Irish Settlements in Northampton County, biographical sketches of prominent persons, lists of genealogy, of taxables, of Revolutionary soldiers and of burials together with other valuable records, have been collected from the unpublished manuscripts as well as the published writings of Dr. John C. Clyde and incorporated in this volume. Surnames that the reader will discover within the biographical sketch section among many, many others are: Allen, Allison, Andress, Appleman, Armstrong, Arnold, Baldwin, Barber, Barrick, Barnes, Barr, Barrett, Bartholomew, Baugh, Berry, Bisel, Bitner, Blackmar, Blair, Bond, Boyd, Brown, Buckalew, Buckman, Clyde, Culbertson, Craigs, Gregg, Hays, Horner, Kerr, King, Lattimer, McKeen, McNair, Ralston, Rosbrugh, Walker, Wilson and Wolf.

(Northampton County) Some *of the* First Settlers *of* "The Forks *of the* Delaware" *and their* Descendants. By: The Rev. Henry Martyn Kieffer, Pub. 1902, reprinted 2022, 512 pages, Index, soft cover, ISBN #0-89308-452-3.

PA 14 $48.50

This book which was transcribed by the author from German to English of the record books of the First Reformed Church of Easton are contemporaneous in their origin with the beginnings of the settlement of the city of Easton. The city of Easton lies with Northampton County. This book contains information on thousands of descendants from Easton and Northampton County. These records are in chronological order starting around 1760 and continuing on to the 1850's and are divided into three main categories: (1) baptisms: giving parents' names, infant's name, date of birth, and names of godparents; (2) deaths and burials: giving names and dates and sometimes place of residence; and (3) marriages: giving names of brides and grooms and dates. The Index has over 13,000 entries of these individuals within this book.

A Genealogical Index of Northampton County, Pennsylvania, 1752-1802. By: John Eyerman, Pub. 1899, reprinted 2023, 86 pages, ISBN #978-1-63914-094-7

PA 38 $17.50

Northampton County was created in 1752 from Bucks County. It is situated in the eastern most region of the state along the Delaware river, just across the border from Warren and Sussex Counties New Jersey. It is the parent county in whole or part to: Cabon, Lehigh, Monroe, Pike, Schuylkill and Wayne counties. This book should have been titled, Will Abstracts of Northampton County, PA., 1752-1802. The entire book is devoted to abstracts of Wills from the county for 1752-1802.

Northumberland County, Pennsylvania.

Wills *and* Administrations *of.* By: Charles A. Fisher, Pub. 1950, reprinted 2023, 81 pages, Index, soft cover, ISBN #978-1-63914-106-7.

PA 40 $17.50

When Northumberland was created in 1772, it was the largest county in the state of Pennsylvania. 27 counties have been formed, wholly or in part from it. The Wills and Administrations given in the book are abstracts of the records of the four following counties: Northumberland, Mifflin, Indiana and Union. Data to be found within: Northumberland County 1772-1813, Mifflin County 1789-1793, Union County 1813-1818 and Indiana County 1818-1849.

Warren County, Pennsylvania *with* Illustrations *and* Biographical Sketches *of some of its* Prominent Men *and* Pioneers, History of. By: J.S. Schenck, Pub. 1887, reprinted 2023, 997 pages, Index, ISBN #978-1-63914-093-0.

PA 37 $75.00

Warren County was created in 1800 from Allegheny and Lycoming counties. It sits in the Northwestern corner of the state boarding New York. This history begins with chapters devoted to the Province of Pennsylvania, Penn in Pennsylvania, its French Dominion, its English Dominion, Native Indians, early settlements, organization of the county, considerable amounts of data on the Civil War, along with the usual topics of such histories as: buildings, townships, agriculture, newspapers, county officials, navigation via rail, road or water ways, the Bench and Bar, and histories of the various townships. The genealogists will be delighted with the biographical section. The New Index that was created for this reprint mentions approximately 18,000 entries.

Warren County, Pennsylvania, Revolutionary Soldiers of. By: Lucy M. Davis Cowan, Pub. 1926, reprinted 2023, 98 pages, Index, soft cover, ISBN #978-1-63914-109-8.

PA 41 $18.50

Warren County was created in 1800 from Allegheny and Lycoming counties. It sits in the Northwestern corner of the state boarding New York. This book is compilation of Revolutionary Soldiers who were buried in Warren County. Each entry is a mini biography of the soldier giving much data on the proven military service records, along with personal family data and connections. The author has also provided data on soldiers whose military service records who have not been proved. There is a section on tombstone inscriptions of Revolutionary Soldiers and their wives who were buried in Warren County, along with locations of their graves. The final chapter concludes with Warren County Pensioners.

Westmoreland County, Pennsylvania, History *of.* By: George Dallas Alberts, Pub. 1882, reprinted 2022, 1010 pages, NEW INDEX, soft cover, ISBN #978-1-63914-080-0.

PA 32 $75.00

Westmoreland County was created in 1773 from Lancaster, Northumberland and Bedford Counties. It lies in the southwestern corner of the state and was the parent county to: Allegheny, Armstrong, parts of Bedford, Fayette, Greene, Indiana, and Washington. These early settlers were of Scotch-Irish, German, Franch Huguenots and English American descent. This book is broken down into two sections. The first is a history of the state by looking at its colony status followed by the county with such topics as: first settlers / pioneers, Indians, formation of county and townships, French occupation, Expeditions to the western portion of the State, Roads and transportation, the Whiskey Insurrection, Medicine, Education, Religion, Newspapers, Slavery, Dunmore's War, Revolutionary War, Civil War, War of 1812, Legal system. In the appendix section, the author has included: a list of negro and mulatto slaves, roster of various Revolutionary soldiers, Roster of various Civil War soldiers, Muster Rolls of the War of 1812. The second is a history of the townships with hundreds and hundreds of biographical sketches interspersed. All this is followed up with a New Index that was produced for this reprint which mentions approximately 23,000 persons.

Miscellaneous Record

A Collection *of* Upwards *of* 30,000 Names *of* German, Swiss, Dutch, French *and other* Immigrants *in* Pennsylvania *from* 1727 *to* 1776. *(Indexed Edition)* By: I. D. Rupp and M.V. Kroger, Pub. 1876 and 1935, 826 pages with Index, soft cover, ISBN #978-1-63914-100-5.

PA 4 $62.50

This book is considered one of the most useful tools for identifying persons who came to North America between 1727 and 1776. It contains 319 ships passenger list with more than 30,000 names. Its main emphasis is on the early Palatine immigration. The lists are arranged in chronological order according to date of arrival, listing the names of the ships on which the passengers arrived and the places from which they emigrated. In addition, the appendices list over a thousand early settlers who landed at some port other than Philadelphia, but who afterwards came to Pennsylvania from New York, North Carolina, and Georgia. Included are "Names of the First Palatines in North Carolina, 1709 and 1710," and "Names of Salzburgers Settled in Georgia, 1734-1741." To make this book even more useful, we have included Kroger's 232-page full name index of which the original is lacking. Without this index, this book can be difficult to use.

The Colonial Clergy *of the* Middle Colonies, 1628-1776. By: Frederick Lewis Weis, Pub. 1957, Reprinted 2021, 188 pages, soft cover, ISBN #978-1-63914-024-4.

PA 30 $22.50

This book is alphabetical list of approximately 1,250 colonial clergymen from 1628-1776 who settled in New York, New Jersey, and Pennsylvania. These annotations furnish such useful genealogical data as date & place of birth, date & place of death, names of parents, college of matriculation, date of ordination, denomination, names of parishes, dates in which tenure was held, and a variety of other similar data.

Early Pennsylvania Births, 1675-1875. By: Charles A. Fisher, Pub. 1947, Reprinted 2018, 108 pages, Index, soft cover, ISBN #0-89308-394-1.

PA 1 $15.00

This book is arranged alphabetically in each of its various sections by the surname. The reader will find the following information: name of the child, date of the birth or baptism, names of the parents, and names of sponsors (often relatives). There are approximately 10,000 persons are mentioned in the text.

Early Pennsylvania Land Records, 1686-1732. By: William Henry Egle, Orig. Pub. 1893, Reprinted 2019, 789 pages, Index, ISBN #0-89308-367-4.

PA 9 $58.50

The early days of the new Colonies in America were dictated by the King Charles II and his granting of land within them. William Penn played a huge role in the development of Pennsylvania shortly after receiving his grant in 1680. He offered portions of his new lands up for sell to be purchased out right or a person could purchase the "Rights" to lands that the final parcel has not yet been determined. When purchased out right, the buyer would be delivered a description of the land in terms of metes and bounds. When someone purchased the "Rights" to lands, he would receive a warrant for his money. He would then provide this to the Surveyor General when he arrived in Pennsylvania and choose his parcel land. Many times, these warrants or "Rights" to lands would be purchased as investments and alter put back up for sell as the original purchaser had no intentions on coming to the new world. This book is invaluable for the researcher of early Pennsylvania genealogy. This book is based on the minutes of the Board of Property beginning in the year 1687 and ending in 1732. It not only gives the history of the property in detail but also provides a great deal of genealogical information about the family who purchased these lands.

Immigration *of the* IRISH QUAKERS *into* Pennsylvania, 1682-1750. By: Albert Cook Myers, Pub. 1902, Reprinted 2019, 558 pages, Index, ISBN #0-89308-901-X.

PA 15 $45.00

This book is a wonderful history of the Quakers in Ireland along with their immigration into Pennsylvania. The genealogist will find the appendix of great interest. It represents approximately one-third of the book and includes biographical sketches and abstracts of certificates of removal received at various monthly meetings, together providing such information as dates of birth, marriage and death, places of residence in Ireland, names of family members, dates of immigration, and places of residence in Pennsylvania.

Names *of* Persons *who took the* Oath *of* Allegiance *to the* State *of* Pennsylvania between the years 1777 and 1789. By: Thompson Westcott, Pub. 1865, reprinted 2021, 190 pages, Index, soft cover, ISBN #978-1-63914-035-0.

PA 28 $22.50

This book is a list of approximately 2,000 persons who signed the Revolutionary oath of allegiance in Philadelphia giving the name of signer, the date of signing, and sometimes giving the occupation and residence of the signer. In many instances, the signer was previously from one of the other Thirteen Colonies, and this as well as his European origins are mentioned.

Names *of* Foreigners *who took the* Oath *of* Allegiance *of the* Province *and* State *of* Pennsylvania, 1727-1775. By: William Henry Egle, Pub. 1890, reprinted 2021, 788 pages, Index, soft cover, ISBN #978-1-63914-034-3.

PA 31 $58.50

In 1727, the British controlled Provincial Council passed a law requiring all male "foreign" immigrants age 16 and older to swear an oath of allegiance to the Crown. This book is is an extensive list of "non-British born" foreigners - mostly Germans, who immigrated into the State of Pennsylvania between the years 1727 and 1775 and again during the years 1786-1808. It is a collection of ships' passenger lists, with Captains' lists of passengers running up to the year of 1808. Along with the full name of the immigrant, including the names of all males over the age of sixteen, information is given including name of ship, date of arrival, port of origin, and in some instances, ages, names of wives, and names of children. The 118-page Index contains the names of approximately 35,000 persons.

Ohio Valley Genealogies. By: Charles A. Hanna, Pub. 1900, Reprinted 2022, 172 pages, soft cover, ISBN #978-1-63914-079-4.

PA 34 $20.00

This book contains in alphabetical order approximately 350 genealogies of the first families who settled in western Pennsylvania between the Blue Ridge Mountains and the Alleghenies, along with genealogies of those first families who migrated west into the Northwest Territory now known as Ohio. These 350 plus families are listed in alphabetical order. Data to found with in this book: records of the first immigrant settler, including place and date of birth and death, place of residence, name of wife and date of marriage, names of children and their dates and places of birth, and names of grandchildren and great-grandchildren.

Pennsylvania German Pioneers, A Publication *of the* Original Lists *of* Arrivals *in the* Port *of* Philadelphia *from* 1727 *to* 1808. (2 Volumes). By: Ralph Beaver Strassburger and William J. Hinke, Orig. Pub. 1934, reprinted 2019.

Vol. #1: 828 pages, soft cover, ISBN #0-89308-611-8.

PA 18 $62.50

Vol. #2: 734 pages, Index, soft cover, ISBN #0-89308-612-6.

PA 19 $58.50

This 2-volume set of books is a consolidation of 506 original lists of persons who arrived in Pennsylvania through the port of Philadelphia from 1727-1808. Information to be found within: immigrants name, ages, occupation, birthplace, names of ships, dates of arrival, and places of origin. All information was compiled from the state archives. This volume I covers the period 1727-1775 and contains 324 ship passenger lists, including captains' lists, signers of the oath of allegiance, and signers of the oath of abjuration. The index for this volume is to be found in volume 2 of this set of books and mentions approximately 50,000 persons.

PENNSYLVANIA GENEALOGIES: Chiefly Scotch-Irish *and* German. By: William Henry Egle, Orig. Pub. 1886, 806 pages, Index, ISBN #0-89308-866-8.

PA 16 $58.50

This book is a set of genealogies based on 66 families mainly from early Lancaster County, which was one of the original 4 counties of Pennsylvania. The reader will discover that these genealogies will take these families from the mid 1600's up to the late 1880's. The Index for this book has approximately 3,000 entries. Surnames for the families found within: Ainsworth, Allen, Alricks, Anderson, Andrews, Awl, Ayres, Barnett, Beatty, Boas, Bomberger, Boyd, Bucher, Byers, Cowden, Craig, Crain, Curtin, Denny, Dixon, Eagley, Egle, Elder, Espy, Ferguson, Fleming, Forster, Fulton, Galbraith, Gray, Gregg, Greenawalt, Gross, Hamilton, Hays, Hoge, Keller, Kendig, Kunkel, Linn, Lobingier, Lyon, Maclay, McCormick, McNair, Muller, Murray, Neville, Orth, Parker, Roan, Robinson, Rutherford, Simonton, Stewart, Swan, Thomas, Wallace, Weir, Wiestling, Wiggins, Wilson, and Wyeth.

Pennsylvania Marriage Licenses Previous *to* 1790. By: John B. Linn & William H. Egle, Orig. Pub. 1890, Reprinted 2019, 286 pages, Index, ISBN #0-89308-056-X.

PA 17 $30.00

These marriage licenses were issued from the Office of the Provincial Secretary of Pennsylvania under the authority of the England, those listed in this work date back from 1742. Some earlier registers of licenses and some kept at a later date are missing, yet this work still features a base list of 6,500 marriages of which all of them are based on public records as opposed to church records.

PENNSYLVANIA-GERMANS *in the* Revolutionary War, 1775-1783. By: Henry M. Muhlenberg Richards, Pub. 1908, Reprinted 2019, 542 pages, Index, ISBN #0-89308-864-1.

PA 7 $48.50

This work succeeds in consolidating the records of the vast majority of Pennsylvania-Germans who took part in the Revolutionary War and is probably as close as we are likely to get to a definitive history and roster. Quite apart from the invaluable rosters and service records, the book explores the history of the various units, their organization, personnel, and campaigns. Inevitably, the bulk of the work focuses on the Pennsylvania-Germans in the Continental Army, the Pennsylvania Line, the German Regiment, and the Flying Camp, though there is considerable data on the Pennsylvania-Germans in Maryland and Virginia regiments. Of almost equal importance are the chapters on the Emergency Men, patriots and non-combatants, each with biographical sketches of eminent men.

Quaker Arrivals *at* Philadelphia, 1685-1750. By: Albert Cook Myers, Pub. 1902, reprinted 2022, 140 pages, Index, soft cover, ISBN #978-1-63914-062-6.

PA 20 $20.00

This work is very important to the genealogists who is interested in tracing early immigrants to Penn's Colony. This book is a chronological list of Quaker immigrants who registered with the Philadelphia Monthly Meeting of Friends, upon their arrival in Philadelphia. This meeting house is the largest of all Quaker meeting in the province. The information is based on the certificates of removal from the Meetings of Friends of which they were members in other countries and other colonies. A large proportion of the Quakers who immigrated into the Province of Pennsylvania took up residence in Philadelphia. Of the nineteen monthly meetings established in Pennsylvania prior to 1750, the Philadelphia Monthly Meeting easily ranks first in the number of certificates received. As a rule, the certificates give the following information: name, date of certificate, former place of residence, former meeting, date of receipt, and other details of quaint and useful interest.

Welsh Settlement *of* Pennsylvania. By: Charles H. Browning, Pub. 1912, reprinted 2022, 632 pages, Index, ISBN #0-89308-464-6.

PA 8 $48.50

The early Welsh immigrants to Pennsylvania were mostly Quakers who had borne the brunt of religious persecution in their English homeland. Given the opportunity to secure relief from their religious oppression, they were among the first to accept William Penn's offer to settle in his new colony of Pennsylvania. The Welsh Tract as it was known as, was approximately 40,000 acres located on the west side of the Schuylkill, north and west of Philadelphia. Its lies in present-day counties of Montgomery, Chester, and Delaware. These Quaker settlers began arriving around 1682 and by 1715 there were more than 23,000 of them. This book follows hundreds upon hundreds of Welsh Quaker pioneers moving into Pennsylvania thru the records of the various land companies who re-settled William Penn's famous land grant along the Schuylkill River. This book utilizes lists of settlers, land patents, plat maps, and biographical sketches to provide more information on the process of settlement in Merion and the adjacent townships of Haverford and Radnor. The genealogist will be delighted with the index which has over 5,000 entries of these individuals.

SOUTH CAROLINA

1790 Census *of* South Carolina, Heads of Families at the First Census of the U.S. taken in the year 1790. Orig. Pub. 1908, Reprinted 1990, 154 pages, Hard Cover, Index, ISBN #0-89308-459-X.

SC 39 $32.50

The index lists the names of more than 27,000 household heads.

1850 South Carolina Mortality Schedule. By: Brent Holcomb, Pub. 1980, reprinted 2014, 56 pages, Index, ISBN #0-89308-194-9.

SC 11 $10.00

At the same time the seventh census of the United States of America was taken in 1850, the enumerator also recorded all the deaths in his district for the previous year. This mortality schedule listed the name of the deceased; age; sex; color; whether free or a slave; married or single; place of birth; month of death; cause of death and number of days ill.

Abbeville County, South Carolina Federal Census *for* 1810-1840. By: Larry Pursley, Pub. 2005, 288 pages, soft cover, Index, ISBN #0-89308-232-5.

SC 49 $32.50

Abbeville County was a very important area of migration of early settlers / pioneers heading West. Since many of the land records being lost or burned for this area of SC, makes this pre-Civil War time frame very important in placing a person within the county during this HIGHLY Trafficked time of migration.

Early Anderson County, South Carolina Newspapers, Marriage & Obituaries, 1841-1882. By: Tom C. Wilkinson, Pub. 1978, reprinted 1994, 268 pages, Index, ISBN #0-89308-103-5.

SC 38 $30.00

The three newspapers included in this book are: The Highland Sentinel published at Calhoun, Anderson District, S.C.; The Anderson Gazette published at Anderson, S.C., with last record dated 1848; and The Anderson Intelligencer, beginning with 1860 down to 1878 and a few scattered issues.

Camden, South Carolina 1816-1865, Marriage & Death Notices *from the*. By Brent Holcomb, Pub. 1978, reprinted, 2005, 166 pages, Index, ISBN #0-89308-110-8.

SC 34 $25.00

Notices included in this book are from Camden, Kershaw District, Fairfield and also Chester, York, Darlington, Newberry, Marlboro, Orangeburg, and

Charleston District, and the border counties of North Carolina, viz Anson, Richmond and Union. Notices of persons who removed to the states of Alabama, Georgia, Louisiana, Mississippi and Florida are found. Obituaries from persons who served in the Revolutionary, War of 1812, Mexican and Confederate Wars are contained in this volume.

Camden District, South Carolina Wills & Administrations, 1781-1787. By: Brent Holcomb, Pub, 1978, reprinted 2004, 120 pages, Hard Cover, Index, ISBN #0-89308-050-0.

SC 6 $17.50

These are abstracts of Wills and all Estate Papers for the period 1770-1796. These include the later counties of York, Chester, Fairfield, Richland, Lancaster, Kershaw, Sumter, Clarendon, Claremont, Salem and Lee. Heretofore, these records have not been microfilmed and hence have only been available to the genealogists at the Court House in their original packages.

Charleston *in* 1883. By: Arthur Mazyck and Gene Wadell, Orig. Pub. 1883, Reprinted 1984, 176 pages, 8 1/2" x 11" soft cover, Index, ISBN #0-89308-428-X.

SC 73 $20.00

This book contains more than 70 important photographs showing nearly all of the city's most significant buildings a few years before they were damaged by the earthquake of 1886. This uniquely comprehensive record of the city's architecture. This edition contains extensive additions by Gene Waddell. Mr. Waddell has prepared architectural notes on more than 100 buildings that are illustrated and has written an introductory article on what life was like in Charleston in 1883. All new and original material is thoroughly indexed.

Charleston: The Place *and the* People. By: Mrs. St. Julien Ravenel, Pub. 1906, reprinted 2021, 564 pages, Index, soft cover, ISBN #0-89308031-4.

SC 44 $38.50

This intriguing book, first published in 1906, is a thorough and historical story of the beginning of one of America's most famous cities. Mrs. St. Julien Ravenel not only tells the history of earliest days and the move from Old Towne to Charleston, as its known today, but brings life to the personalities of many of the lord proprietors and even the bold captain, Robert Sanford, who landed in Port Royal and "took sezin by turffe and twiggs" in the name of the King and realm of England. Some of the topics covered in the book are the history of the ill-fated Scotch colony, naturalization of the Huguenots; church acts; the conquest of pirates; the controversy between the King and the Lords; establishment of the State Government; the seige and fall following the Prevost's raid; capture, deliverance and restoration during Revolutionary times; the visits of Washington and La Fayette and structure of society. The final chapters deal with the War of 1812; the social topics during the Mexican War and Confederate Charleston. Truly, the book is the story of Charleston and its people.

Charles Town, South Carolina, 1720-1758, Register *of* St. Phillip's Parish. (Volume #1). By: A.S. Salley, Pub. 1904, reprinted 2022, 360 pages, Index, ISBN #978-1-63914-056-5.

SC 121 $35.00

St. Philip's was one of the ten original parishes created by the Church Act of 1706. Considering that the state of South Carolina did not officially record vital records until 1911 makes any resource that mentions these items of extreme importance to the genealogists. In 1751 the parish covering Charleston was divided into two parishes. This register is filled with births, christenings, marriages, and burials of all persons from Charleston from 1720-1758. The index mentions approximately 9,500 entries.

Charles Town, South Carolina, 1754-1810, Register *of* St. Phillip's Parish. (Volume #2). By: A.S. Salley, Pub. 1927, Reprinted 2022, 508 pages, Index, ISBN #978-1-63914-057-2.

SC 122 $35.00

St. Philip's was one of the ten original parishes created by the Church Act of 1706. Considering that the state of South Carolina did not officially record vital records until 1911 makes any resource that mentions these items of extreme importance to the genealogists. In 1751 the parish covering Charleston was divided into two parishes. This register is filled with births, christenings, marriages, and burials from the newly divided parish that covered all persons including negros, mollatoes and Indian Slaves north of Broad Street from 1754-1810. The reader will also discover the author has including extra genealogical data from mini biographies to general family information within the footnotes on various persons. The index mentions approximately 13,000 entries.

Charleston Orphan House, 1790-1860, History *and* Records *of the*. By: Susan L. King, Pub. 1984, Reprinted 2019, 198 pages, soft cover, Index, ISBN #0-89308-292-9.

SC 67 $25.00

The Charleston Orphan House was the first municipal orphanage in the United States, having been formed by an ordinance ratified in 1790 "for the establishment of an Orphan House in the City of Charleston for the purpose of supporting and educating poor orphan children and those of poor, distressed and disabled parents who are unable to support the maintenance of them". Many of the orphans were children of revolutionary soldiers. The records of the orphan house were not only an extremely important genealogical source, but they are also a major source for the social history of Charleston. This book contains the records of approximately 1,800 children, orphans, etc. and provides access for the first time to the enormous amount of information in the original documents.

Index *to* Wills *of* Charleston County, South Carolina, 1671-1868. By: Charleston Free Library, Pub. 1950, reprinted 2021, 328 pages, soft cover, ISBN #978-1-63914-029-9.

SC 1 $35.00

Until 1782, South Carolina had only one probate court in the entire state and it was located in Charleston. So, until 1782, if you wanted to record your Will, you had to travel to Charleston to have it recorded. The Wills in this book are entered in alphabetical order with approximately 10,000 names of testators with the identifying page number and volume of the original record.

The Story *of the* Citadel. By: Col. O.J. Bond, Orig. Pub. 1936, Reprinted 2021, 280 pages, Soft Cover, Index, ISBN #0-89308-682-7.

SC 89 $32.50

This is the story, told by it former President, of a remarkable institution; one of the last reaming state -assisted military colleges in America. Beginning with the account of an aborted slave insurrection in June 1822, the author tells in detail of the city of Charleston, and of a later decision by the State Legislature to use the facility, as well as an arsenal in Columbia, to educate a corps of cadets and to train them for the defense of the state. Just before Commencement in 1861, the cadet corps, stationed on Morris Island, fired the first shots of the Civil War at the "Star of the West", a supply ship sent to relieve Ft. Sumter. A member of the first class to graduate after the war (1886), the author was immediately appointed an assistant professor and was thereafter a member of the faculty for 45 years. His personal involvement in every aspect of Citadel life during that time allowed him to include personal reminiscences that are both fascinating and poignant. He was appointed Superintendent (President) in 1908.

(Cheraw) St. David's Parish, South Carolina Minutes *of the* Vestry, 1768-1832, *and* Parish Register, 1819-1924. By: Brent Holcomb, Pub. 1979, Reprinted 2017, 172 pages, Index, ISBN #0-89308-144-2.

SC 9 $22.50

St. David's was the last colonial parish to be formed in 1768. This parish was co-terminus with Cheraw District and included the later counties of Chesterfield, Marlboro and Darlington. The Vestry Minutes are extremely important as they contain lists of voters, care of widows, orphans, and the members of the church.

(Cheraw, SC) Rambles *in the* Pee Dee Basin. By: Harvey Toliver Cook, Pub. 1926, Reprinted 2018, 494 pages, Index, soft cover, ISBN #0-89308-447-6.

SC 93 $45.00

This is an excellent companion to Gregg's History of the Old Cheraws. In a charming written narrative, Professor Cook takes the reader on a fascinating journey back into time. Beginning with the settlement of the land baronies near Georgetown, the "tour" extends down to South Carolina's adoption of the Federal Constitution. Stops along the way include the coming of the Scotch Presbyterian, the establishment of the first schools, the Revolutionary activities of General Francis Marion of Swamp Fox fame, and much more.

Old Cheraws, History *of the*. (With:) Addenda Comprising Additional Facts Concerning the Eight PEE DEE Counties and Sketches of the Persons for Whom They are Named. By: John J. Dargan, Orig. Pub. 1867, Reprinted 2004, 704 pages, New Index, Hard Cover, ISBN #0-89308-448-4.

SC 91 $52.50

History of the Old Cheraw District of South Carolina and of the settlement of the territory now part of the eight Pee Dee counties of Chesterfield, Darlington, Florence, Georgetown, Horry, Marion, Marlboro, and Williamsburg from their first settlement in the 1730's down to about 1810, with lists of early land grantees and genealogical NOTICES OF EARLY FAMILIES AND SKETCHS of individuals. Some of the families dealt with in this volume are: Allison, Auld, Bacot, Baxter, Bedgegood, Bedingfield, Benton, Bethea, Blakeney, Brockington, Buckholdt, Carlisle, Carter, Chapman, Coker, Coxe, Craig, Crawford, Crosland, Dabbs, Daniel, Dargen, Dewitt, DuBose, Edwards, Ellerbe, Evans, Falconer, Gibson, Gillispie, Godbald, Godfrey, Gregg, Grice, Harllee, Harrington, Hart, Hewstiss, Hicks, Hodge, Hunter, Irby, James, Lide, Luke, Kershaw, Kolb, McCall, McIntosh, McIver, Mikell, Murphy, (Murfee), Parker, Pawley, Pearson, Pegues, Pledger, Pouncy, Powe, Pugh, Quick, Rogers, Saunders, Smith, Sparks, Spencer, Steward, Strother, Sweeney, Terrell, Thomas, Wilds, Williams, Williamson, Wilson, Witherspoon, Youngblood, and Zimmerman.

Chester County, South Carolina Minutes *of the* County Court, 1785-1799. By: Brent Holcomb, Pub. 1979, reprinted 1920, 433 pages, map, Soft Cover, Index, ISBN #0-89308-148-5.

SC 22 $40.00

This volume contains a map of the original land

grants on Rocky Creek in that county. Also, includes lists of deeds and probates recorded, tavern licenses, bastardy bonds cases (naming usually both parents), jury lists and several previously unknown marriage bonds. Many settlers from Virginia and Pennsylvania are found here as well as many Revolutionary War veterans.

Columbia, South Carolina Newspapers 1792-1839, Marriage *and* Death Notices *from*. By: B. Holcomb, Pub. 1982, reprinted 2014, soft cover, Index, ISBN #0-89308- 270-8.

SC 52 $20.00

Edgefield County, South Carolina, History *of*. By: John A. Chapman, Pub. 1897, Reprinted 2009, 521 pages, Index, Hard Cover, ISBN #0-89308-004-7.

SC 4 $48.50

This history begins with the colonial settlement and goes through 1897. Edgefield County was formed in 1785 and from it were formed Saluda County and a portion of Greenwood County. Contains Edgefield's participation in the Revolutionary War, War of 1812, the Confederate War and family sketches including among others: Abney, Adams, Anderson, Bacon, Bates, Bean, Berry, Bland, Blocker, Bowles, Brazier, Brooks, Burkhalter, Burt, Butler, Caldwell, Carroll, Carson, Chappell, Coleman, Crouder, Culbreath, Denny, Dorn, Dozier, Dunlap, Dunovant, Edwards, Elzey, Gantt, Garrett, Gary, Geiger, Glascock, Goodwyn, Gray, Gregg, Griffin, Grimke, Haddon, Haltiwanger, Hammond, Hazel, Jennings, Jeter, Johnson, Jones, Kennedy, Lake, Landrum, McCarty, McDuffie, Martin, Meriwether, Mims, Mobley, Moore, Morange, Nicholson, Norris, Nunn, Outz, Pattison, Perry, Pickens, Pope, Quattlebaum, Ramsey, Riley, Ryan, Scott, Scury, Shaw, Sheppard, Simkins, Smyley, Stallworth, Stewart, Summers, Tillman, Tomkins, Towles, Travis, Trotter, Walker, Wardlaw, Waters, Watson, Watts, Werts, and Yarbrough.

Edgefield County, South Carolina Minutes *of the* County Court, 1785-1795. By: Brent Holcomb, Pub. 1979, reprinted 2018, 204 pages, soft cover, Index, ISBN #0-89308-158-2.

SC 23 $25.00

These court minutes are the earliest extant records from this crucial South Carolina County. Many persons left Edgefield and migrated across the Savannah River into Georgia and other states west. In these records are listings of more than 175 early deeds which cannot now be located! This makes these probably the MOST VALUABLE court minutes in all of South Carolina. Also, Edgefield was one of the largest counties in South Carolina at the time, comprising all or part of the present counties of Edgefield, Saluda, Aiken, Greenwood, and McCormick.

Edgefield County, South Carolina Abstracts *of* Deed Book 1-12, 1786-1796. By: Ge Lee Corley Hendrix, Pub. 1985, reprinted 2001, 304 pages, Hard Cover, Index, ISBN #0-89308-545-6.

SC 79 $32.50

These records are unique because the frontiersman, who settled in this geographical location (next to Indians lands), seldom had the opportunity to record his legal records until the end of the American Revolution when county courthouses were established. Therefore, many of the early deeds contain chains of titles from the original colonial landowner to the present owner at the time of the recording. They also contain many types of instructions, such as conveyances of land, marriage contracts, wills, sheriff's sales, deeds of gifts, plats or surveys (a facsimile of same is included in these abstracts), bills of sale, mortgages, affidavits, powers of attorney, slave sales and others. The deeds often reveal additional information, such as geographical locations, residence, adjoining neighbors, occupation, and heirships as widows, sons, daughters and their husbands, brothers, sisters, and uncles and sometimes the death date of the former property owner. An appendix section of South Carolina Colonial and State Land and Probate Laws is included to aid the student of genealogy and history.

Edgefield County, S.C. Records, 1746-1858. By: Janie Revill, Pub. 1984, reprinted 2016, 246 pages, Index, ISBN #0-89308-531-6.

SC 74 $30.00

These abstracts are a panorama of available records such as jury lists, wills estate records, deeds, plats, tombstone, etc... of a particular surname in Edgefield County. These records cover a period to and after the Revolutionary War, often reaching into other counties and states for additional information citing her source. Her records are known for her fairness and accuracy. Since the records were typed in alphabetical format, only those names within the body of the abstract (and different from name flanked with left margin) were indexed. Female names were often indexed under both maiden names and married names. For the first time her renowned card abstracts of Edgefield County, SC heretofore housed in the Washington Memorial Library, Macon, GA. are published with a full-name index of all persons within the 246 pages.

Edgefield County, South Carolina Wills, 1787-1836. By: James & Vivan Wooley, Pub. 1991, reprinted 2007, 238 pages, Hard Cover, Index, ISBN #0-89308-663-0.

SC 92 $35.00

This book contains the first 4 Will Books of the county which have now been rebound and combined as follows: original Books A & B have been bound into what is now called Will Book A, and original Books C & D have now been bound into what is now called Will Book C. This book will be another valuable asset for people who have had family in what was originally Old 96 District, S.C. as it contains the names of approximately 18,500 individuals including slaves.

Fairfield County, South Carolina Court Minutes, 1785-1789. By: Brent Holcomb, Pub. 1981, Reprinted 2018, 198 pages, Index, soft cover, ISBN #0-89308-212-0.

SC 41 $25.00

Fairfield was one of the counties formed from the Camden District in 1785. It is surrounded by the counties of: Chester, Kershaw, Newberry, and Union. Part of this county was taken in 1791 to form Kershaw County. These minutes contain lists of deed recorded, wills, and estates probated, road juries, petit and grand juries, tavern licenses issued and small court cases.

Georgetown South Carolina Newspapers 1791-1861, Marriage, Death *and* Estate Notices *from*. By: Brent Holcomb, Pub. 1978, reprinted 2014, 236 pages, soft cover, Index, ISBN #0-89308-150-7.

SC 35 $25.00

The reader is cautioned to note that all legal records for Georgetown County were destroyed by fire in 1865. These notices cover the counties of Georgetown District, viz. Georgetown, Horry, Marion, and Williamsburg. Also, notices are to be found from neighboring counties of Charleston, Darlington and Sumter.

Greenville County, South Carolina, History *of*. By: James Richardson, Pub. 1930, Reprinted 2015, 342 pages, New Index, ISBN #0-89308-504-9.

SC 95 $35.00

The narrative history of Greenville County is an excellent companion volume to Landrum's History of Spartanburg County, SC and Chapman's History of Edgefield County, SC, both neighboring counties of Greenville with much overlapping on both history and families. This history not only completes the history of this midsection of Upper South Carolina but in addition provides the reader in many instances with detailed histories of over 167 of the early prominent families. These family sketches will help the "new comer" to the area to better understand the sometime complexities of family relationships brought about by the many intermarriages of these pioneer families. The book is profusely illustrated with photographs of many of the biographies. The NEW INDEX that was produced for this reprint contains the names of approximately 3,000 individuals.

Hilton Head Island, A Sea Island Chronicle. By: Virginia C. Holmgren, Orig. Pub. 1957, reprinted 1985, 176 pages, Hard Cover, Index.

SC 80 $30.00

This is the surprising history of Hilton Head Island, dating back to the days of Spanish, French, and English discovery, settlement and struggle for possession.

Historic Goose Creek, South Carolina, 1670-1980. By: Michael J. Heitzler, Pub. 1983, reprinted 2021, 314 pages, Index, soft cover, ISBN #0-89308-274-0.

SC 66 $35.00

Goose Creek lies with the county of Berkeley. This engrossing book, although extensively researched and well documented, is not an ordinary date-battle-times-places history. On the contrary, it brings the Goose Creek story to life through accounts of rebellious dissenters, witches and ghosts, pestilence, wild Indians and uprisings. The author weaves together the exploits of thrilling heroes and the everyday problems of the common people who fought and loved and won and lost in a community that lived and died and lived again.

Lancaster County, South Carolina Deeds, 1787-1872. By: Brent Holcomb, Pub. 1981, 240 pages, soft cover, Index, ISBN #0-89308-213-9.

SC 10 $35.00

Since the Lancaster County probate records were destroyed in 1865, this is the only basic record left for this valuable county. A few wills were recorded in these deed books, as well as a number of deeds for the BURNED-OUT Chesterfield County. Kershaw County was formed from part of Lancaster in 1791. Deeds are one of favorite research tools of the genealogists due to the wide variety of family connections found within them. Not only will the reader find the deed transaction itself, but often times such things as: marriages, relinquishments of dower, divisions of family farms among heirs, remarriages of widows are just a few of the matters you can anticipate finding within records of deeds.

Laurens County, South Carolina Deed Abstracts 1785-1793. (4 Volmues) By: Larry Vehorn, Pub. 2004.

Vol. #1, 1785-1793: 248 pages, Hard Cover, Index, ISBN #0-89308-728-9.

SC 114 $32.50

Vol. #2, 1793-1800: 300 pages, Hard Cover, Index, ISBN #0-89308-815-3.
SC 115 $35.00

Vol. #5, 1820-1845: 520 pages, Soft Cover, Index, ISBN #0-89308-805-1.
SC 127 *(Available 2024)*

Vol. #6, 1845-1872: 436 pages, Soft Cover, Index, ISBN #0-89308-851-X.
SC 128 *(Available 2024)*

These abstracts of Deeds begin with the creation of the county court system in South Carolina, 1785. Laurens county was created out of the Old Ninety-Six District of S.C., which at one time comprised the entire Upstate. Laurens county was one of the major paths of migration into South Carolina as well as from S.C. to Georgia, Alabama and points West. Deeds are a wonderful source for genealogical research due to the many family members being mentioned within. Even though these deeds begin with the creation of the court system, there are deeds within this book that go back to as early as 1769. This book is even of more importance to the researcher since S.C. did not officially record Vital Records until the year 1911.

Laurens County, South Carolina Newspapers 1845-1895, Marriage & Death Notices *from the.* By: Steven Rayford, Pub. 2007, 270 pages, soft cover, Index, ISBN #0-89308-842-0.
SC 125 $35.00

Laurens county is a very special upstate county within South Carolina. It is located just south of Spartanburg & Greenville Counties and was once part of the Old 96 & Abbeville Districts. These notices come from 2 separate newspapers: the Laurensville Herald and the Laurens Advertiser. Newspaper abstracts are very special to SC research due to the state not officially keeping vital records until 1911.

Laurens County, South Carolina Wills, 1784-1840. By: Colleen Elliott, Pub. 1988, reprinted 2014, 356 pages, soft cover, Index, ISBN #0-89308-606-1.
SC 85 $38.50

Laurens County was one of the major paths of migration into South Carolina as well as from S.C. to Georgia, Alabama and points west. This book contains the names of more than 34,000 persons mentioned in these records, which include wills, proven dates of wills, estate inventories, appraisals and sales, purchasers at these sales, gifts of slaves to individuals not in estate settlements, guardianship decrees, contesting of wills, executorship's revoked and their replacements, remarried widows naming new spouse, heirs vs. executors cases, in-depth instructions for "unfortunate children", names of persons from other counties, and states in some cases, and clues to where the family Bible went. This is a veritable gold mine for the genealogist because in many cases this may be the only place where a person is found mentioned in the Laurens County records.

Marion County, South Carolina, A History *of.* By: John C. Sellers, Pub. 1902, reprinted 2023, 720 pages, New Index, Soft Cover, ISBN #0-89308-699-1.
SC 95 $50.00

Located in the heart of the Pee Dee Basin, Marion County is surrounded by Darlington, Dillion, Florence, Georgetown, Horry, Marlborough and Williamsburg counties. It was carved out of Georgetown District in 1785. It was originally called Liberty County until the act of 1798 when its name changed to Marion. This book should be a companion book of Gregg's History of the Old Cheraws for persons doing research in the Pee Dee Area. This should be the book to help you locate those elusive ancestors who were living in this area of South Carolina. The major portion of this book (429 pages) is devoted to family histories and genealogies that go back as many as five generation. There are also other chapter that will intrigue the genealogist. These chapters represent 84 pages of the book and are devoted to lists of: clerks of courts, sheriffs, Representatives in the Legislature, Senators, ordinaries and probate judges, proprietary Governors, lawyers, and Rosters of Marion County soldiers who served in the Civil War. These Rosters of 21 different Companies not only list the soldiers name and rank, but many times when they listed, what battles they were in, and if and how they were wounded or killed during service.

Marlborough County, South Carolina Minutes *of the* County Court, 1785-1799, and Minutes *of the* Court *of* Ordinary, 1791-1821. By: Brent Holcomb, Pub. 1982, Reprinted 2018, 152 pages, Index, soft cover, ISBN #0-89308-298-8.
SC 56 $20.00

Marlboro county was created in 1785 and is located in the historic area known as the Pee Dee region. This is the first book of legal records to be published from this county. These records contain lists of deeds, wills, and administrations recorded tavern licenses, bastardy cases, road commissioners, etc... It is analogous to the Virginia Order Books which most genealogists are familiar with.

Newberry County, South Carolina Minutes *of the* County Court, 1785-1798. By: Brent Holcomb, Pub. 1977, 356 pages, Hard Cover, Index, ISBN #0-89308-051-9.
SC 54 $40.00

This is the first book of legal records to be published from this county. These records contain lists of deeds, wills, and administrations recorded tavern licenses, bastardy cases, road commissioners, etc... It is analogous to the Virginia Order Books which most genealogists are familiar with. Many German emigrants settled in the lower part of this county. The county was a major migration point of early S.C. settlers into FL., GA., and AL.

Newberry, South Carolina, Annals of. (2 parts in 1). By: John B. O'Neall & John A. Chapman, Pub. 1892, Reprinted 2018, 859 pages, NEW INDEX, ISBN #0-89308-634-7.
SC 71 $65.00

The first part is a detailed history of the town and the district from its first settlement to the early 1800's. During this time, O'Neall recounts many interesting facts and stories about the people and places of Newberry. The second part starts off with a section on some accounts of the most prominent families who migrated from this district to Ohio, and then goes into a biography of the O'Neall family. Chapman then sets off to fill in the omissions and also to carry on where O'Neall left off, Namely the 1862 session from the Union. The rolls of all companies associated with Newberry during the War between the States and the War with Mexico are listed. Most importantly are the genealogies or biographical sketches of some 90 pioneer families/persons of the area including among others: Abrams, Aull, Barre, Bauskett, Baxter, Bedenbaugh, Berly, Blackburn, Blease, Boland, Bond, Boozer, Bowers, Brown, Caldwell, Carwile, Chapman, Counts, Cromer, Crosson, Davis, Dominick, Dugan, Fair, Feagle, Folk, Frean, Gallagher, Garlington, Gary, Glenn, Goggans, Graham, Gregg, Greneeker, Harmon, Harrington, Hawkins, Hentz, Herbert, Herndon, Higgins, Houseal, Hunt, Hunter, Hurd, Kibler, Kinard, Lester, Lipscomb, Maffett, Martin, McCalla, McMorries, Montgomery, Monts, Moore, Mosley, Nance, Packer, Page, Pratt, Ramage, Reid, Renwick, Richey, Riser, Rutherford, Schumpert, Shealys, Simkins, Spence, Suber, Todd, Turner, Wadlington, Welch, Werts, Wheeler, Williams, Wise, and Young. The NEW INDEX that was produced for this reprint contains the names of approximately 9,000 names.

Ninety-Six District, South Carolina Journal *of the* Court *of* Ordinary, Inventory Book Will Book, 1781-1786. By: Brent Holcomb, Pub. 1978, reprinted 2013, 78 pages, soft cover, Index, ISBN #0-89308-109-4.
SC 14 $16.00

This book contains an exact transcript of the Journal of the Court of Ordinary, which contains several marriage licenses, and estates are mentioned of which original papers are extant. At least one will and some inventories which cannot elsewhere be found are contained here. This volume greatly supplements the well-known book by Pauline Young on Old 96 and Abbeville Dist. Wills & Bonds.

Ninety-Six District & Abbeville County, South Carolina Equity Records. By: Pauline Young, Pub. 1957, reprinted 2013, 110 pages, Index, ISBN #0-89308-530-8.
SC 76 $15.00

Equity records are a wonderful source of genealogical information. in the course of settling disputed or complicated inheritances, names of children, stepchildren, half siblings, maiden names, deceased spouses, first, second, third spouses, and extended family relations may all be part of testimony. Other official records and family Bibles cannot compare with the revelation of troubles and relationships found in Equity Court holdings. In many suits, dozens of pieces of evidence have been compressed into a few paragraphs of names, dates, situations and decrees. these equity records cover the time frame 1782-1860.

Ninety-Six & Abbeville District, South Carolina, 10,600 Marriages *from.* By: Larry Pursley, Pub. 2013, 176 pages, soft cover, ISBN #0-89308-198-1.
SC 48 $32.50

This volume is a BRAND-NEW-NEVER-BEFORE-PUBLISHED book. These 10,600 marriages have been consolidated by the author from over 160 unique sources into one volume arranged alphabetically by groom with a bride's name index. These marriages cover the years 1734-1898. Considering South Carolina did not keep official Vital Records until 1911, Mr. Pursley's sources for producing such a work were: family Bibles, genealogies, newspapers, church records, personal papers of clergymen, probate records, tombstones, journals and other sources that are not readily available to the average researcher.

(Old) Ninety-Six and Abbeville District, South Carolina Wills *and* Bonds, Abstracts *of.* (Volume #1). By: Pauline Young, Orig. Pub. 1950, reprinted 2018, 677 pages, Hard Cover, New Index, ISBN #0-89308-036-5.
SC 16 $52.50

This is probably the MOST important book on the Up-Country of South Carolina. It contains more than 3,500 abstracts of wills, bonds and administrations between 1774 and 1860 and more than 30,000 names of persons mentioned in these records. Old Ninety-Six and Abbeville District are the present-day counties of Abbeville, Anderson, Cherokee, Edgefield, Greenwood, Greenville, Laurens, Newberry, Pickens, Oconee, Saluda, Spartanburg, and Union. Old Ninety-Six District bordered Georgia on its western boundary and was the ancestral home of many early Georgia settlers.

(Old) Ninety-Six & Abbeville District, S.C. Wills & Bonds - Volume #2. By: Larry Pursley, Pub. 2016, 220 pages, Index, ISBN #0-89308-348-8.

SC 51 $27.50

Abbeville County was a very important area of migration of early settlers / pioneers heading West. Probate records are a wonderful set of records when they are available because they mention such things as: proving wills, administrations & divisions of estates, estate sales, guardians appointed and mentions of marriages. These probate records cover the years 1840's - 1870's. This book should be considered a companion book to Pauline Young's book "Old 96 & Abbeville Dist. SC Wills & Bonds".

Orangeburg County, S.C., History *of.* From *its* First Settlement *to the* Revolutionary War, 1704-1782. By: Alexander S. Salley, Pub. 1898, reprinted 2001, 600 pages, Hard Cover, Index, ISBN #0-89308-627-4.

SC 97 $48.50

This book is a "MUST" for those who are trying to research in this burned county. Sections of this book are devoted to its early settlers and pioneers of the Colonial and Revolutionary periods. Also, included are Giessendanner records (probably the most complete set of church records kept in this time period). These records consist of 125 pages of transcripts of marriages, births, and deaths for the years of 1737-1761.

(Orangeburg County) The Church Records *of* Saint Matthews Lutheran Church, Orangeburg, County S.C. and "The Red Church". Beginning in 1799, Giving Births, Christenings, Confirmations, Marriages, *and* Burials, 1767-1838. By: Anne M. Haigler, Pub. 1985, Reprinted 2017, 138 pages, soft cover, Index, ISBN #0-89308-563-4.

SC 78 $20.00

This book contains church records from two of St. Matthews churches in Orangeburg, S.C., area; St. Matthews Lutheran Church in Orangeburg, and the other, St. Matthews Episcopal Church at Fort Mootem S.C., also known as "The Red Church". The St. Matthews Episcopal Parish traces its beginning to a few English and French Huguenot families and many German Swiss who were living in Amelia Township, in what was then Berkeley County. The chapel was built in 1757, and the Parish was established in 1765 extending from Nelson's Ferry (above Eutawville) to Beaver Creek and from the Santee and Cooper Rivers to the Edisto River. The church was moved in 1800, 1815-1819 and again in 1852 when is was erected on its present site near Fort Motte. These records from St. Matthews Lutheran Church are going to be of utmost importance for genealogist working in Orangeburg and Lexington counties since both are burned counties and so many of the people are found in these church registers for descendants living later in Lexington County.

Pendleton District South Carolina, Settlement *of the.* By: Frederick Van Clayton, Pub. 1988, Reprinted 2016, 112 pages, Index, ISBN #0-89308-639-8.

SC 87 $28.50

The author prepared this book as part of the requirement for the completion of a Master's degree, but it remains the most useful reference available on the early settlement of the Pendleton District. After finding 95% of all land grants available to him in the Pendleton District up to 1800 and locating the majority of them on maps, most of these are presented here for the researcher. The author does an excellent job of ascertaining the origin of the settlements of Pendleton District, with there being two main sources of immigration into the district, namely removal of within the State from south to north and other influxes of moving there from Pennsylvania, Maryland, Virginia, North Carolina and Georgia. The author also takes people living at various points of South Carolina as found in the 1790 census and shows which of these moved later into Pendleton District, as well as breaking down the names and county of family's residence of those coming into Pendleton District from North Carolina, Virginia, Missouri, Pennsylvania and including some Georgia loyalists. Also contained is a list of boundary land holders who served in the Revolutionary War from South Carolina and received land on the Keowee and Tugaloo Rivers between 1777 and 1800. This book is an excellent source of information on the early settlers of Pendleton District, not only giving the names of these settlers but the number of acres and date received and also telling many of the names of persons who owned adjacent land. This book contains the names of more than 1,320 early settlers of Pendleton District between 1777 and 1800.

Pendleton Messenger, 1807-1851, Marriage *and* Death Notices *from.* By: Brent Holcomb, Pub. 1977, reprinted 2014, 124 pages, soft cover, Index, ISBN #0-89308-049-7.

SC 32 $20.00

These notices of marriage and deaths are taken from the first newspaper in Upper South Carolina. they cover the entire state of S.C. as well as from counties in Georgia and North Carolina. They contain a wealth of genealogical information in that they often give the parents of the bride, as well as former place of residence of those whose obituaries appear herein. Pendleton District was a major point of migration from S.C. into Georgia and other states.

Pendleton District & Anderson County, South Carolina Wills, Estates, *and* Legal Records, 1793-1857. By: Virginia Alexander, Colleen Elliott and Betty Willie, Pub. 1980, Reprinted 2013, 512 pages, Index, ISBN #0-89308-143-4.

SC 17 $45.00

Pendleton Dist. from which Anderson, Pickens, Oconee, and other counties were created was one of the major routes of migration through S.C. in the late 1700's and the 1800's. Until the publication of this book, nothing of major significance has been available on this area and people seeking to do research in the Anderson Courthouse have found that the original records are available only at the State Archives. This volume consists of: Pendleton Probate Judge Estate Records, 1793-1799 and Guardian Book 1801-1819, Book C; Will Books A, 1800-1835 and Book B, 1835-1857; Probate, Inventories, Apportionments, Sales, 1839-1851; and Tax Returns 1835-1861.

(Old) Pendleton District *and* Genealogy *of* Leading Families, History of. By: R.W. Simpson, Pub. 1913, reprinted 1996, 264 pages, Hard Cover, New Index, ISBN #0-89308-101-9.

SC 18 $35.00

At the close of the Revolutionary War, all the territory embraced in the present counties of ANDERSON, GREENVILLE, PICKENS, and OCONEE belonged to the Cherokee Indians. By an Act of March 1783, this territory was attached temporarily to the adjoining counties of Abbeville, Laurens, and Spartanburg. Pendleton County, as afterwards established, was attached to Abbeville County and for the time being was in the judicial district of Ninety-Six. In 1789 this former Indian land was divided with part being laid off into a county called Pendleton and the other Greenville County. The major portion of this book is devoted to detailed genealogies of many of the families/individuals of this district such as: Adams, Adger, Anderson, Bee, Bellotte, Benson, Blassingame, Bowen, Broyles, Burns, Burt, Calhoun, Cornish, Craig, Davant, Davis, Dickinson, Dickson, Dupree, Earle, Gaillard, Gibbs, Hall, Hamilton, Hanckel, Harrison, Hastie, Hayne, Hubbard, Hunter, Jenkins, Latta, Ligon, Lorton, Martin, Mavrick, Mays, McBryde, McElhenny, Miller, Newton, North, Owen, Pickens, Pike, Pinckney, Poe, Potter, Randell, Reese, Robinson, Ross, Scott, Seaborn, Shanklin, Shaw, Simpson, Sitton, Sloan, Smith, Steel, Stevens, Stirling, Symmes, Taliaferro, Taylor, Thompson, Trescott, Warley, Watkins, Whitefield, and Whitner. Many of these families and individuals were from Pennsylvania, Maryland, Virginia, and North Carolina, as did many of the wealthy residents of the low-country of South Carolina.

Families *of* OLD Pendleton District, South Carolina, (4 Volumes). By: Linda Cheek, Pub. 2006.

Vol. #1: 634 pages, Soft Cover, Index, ISBN #0-89308-819-6

SC 116 $60.00

Vol. #2: 648 pages, Soft Cover, Index, ISVBN #0-89308-820-X.

SC 117 $60.00

Vol. #3: 668 pages, Hard Cover, Index, ISBN #0-89308-821-8.

SC 118 $60.00

Vol. #4: 629 pages, Hard Cover, Index, ISBN #0-89308-822-6.

SC 119 $60.00

Southern Historical Press is proud to announce to you a Brand-New SERIES of books from the author/genealogist that brought you the 3 vol. set of Pickens County, S.C. Deeds Abstracts. This NEW series is one of the MOST impressive research undertakings on the Up-State of South Carolina since Pauline Young was alive. This series of books covers the ENTIRE Old Pendleton District, S.C. which covers Abbeville, Anderson, Cherokee, Edgefield, Greenwood, Greenville, Laurens, Newberry, Pickens, Oconee, Saluda, Spartanburg and Union Counties. With many clues and details to family members who have moved on to other upstate counties or out of the state entirely.

Pickens County, South Carolina Deeds, 1828-1838. (2 Volumes). By: Linda Cheek, Pub. 1999, Hard Cover, Index, ISBN #0-89308-774-2.

Vol. #1, Deed Books A-1, 1828-1831: approx. 205, Hard Cover, Index, ISBN #0-89308-774-2.

SC 77 $30.00

Vol. #3, Deed Book C-1, 1834-1838: 205 pages, Hard Cover, Index, ISVBN #0-89308-713-0.

SC 107 $30.00

Here is a new valuable research tool on Upper South Carolina. Located in the Northwestern part of the state, Pickens County was carved out of the Infamous

"Pendleton District" in the year 1828. It is surrounded by the present-day counties of Anderson, Greenville, Oconee Counties, S.C. and on the North by Transylvania County, N.C. Even though this book contains the abstracts from a very specific time frame, there will be references to many persons from earlier times or dates. In an effort to make this book even more helpful for the researcher, the author has even included numerous land plats for this county during this time frame.

Pickens County, South Carolina, It Happened *in*. By: Pearl Smith McFall, Pub. 1959, Reprinted 2020, 224 pages, Index, ISBN #0-89308-613-4.

SC 120 $25.00

This book is a history of the county with the usual topics being covered, such as: creation of the county, Indians, first towns, wars, labor, and etc.... But it is more so an accumulation of facts and traditional stories the author has collected over a 25-year time frame. This type of county history book can help one develop ideas or paths to those missing ancestors by showing the customs and traditions of the local residents.

(Pickens District, S.C.) The Keowee Courier. By: Colleen M. Elliott, Pub. 1979, reprinted 2018, 214 pages, soft cover, Index, ISBN #0-89308-152-3.

SC 31 $25.00

This book of newspaper abstracts not only covers the Pickens District but also Pendleton District. Located in the Northwestern part of the state, Pickens District was carved out of Pendleton District in the year 1828. These abstracts from this newspaper concentrate on the MARRIAGE & DEATH NOTICES covering the time frame of 1849-1851, 1857-1861 & 1865-1868.

Pickens Sentinel, 1870-1915, Newspaper Abstracts *from the*. By: Judy Ballard, Pub. 2003, 390 pages, 8 1/2" x 11" soft cover, Index, ISBN #0-89308-788-2.

SC 31 $25.00

Newspapers are a great source for genealogical research. Even more so for the state of South Carolina since it did not officially record Vital Records until the year 1911. So, when a researcher is looking for a relative through a birth, a death or a marriage, newspaper abstracts are one of the few sources that the genealogist will have at their disposal. This book consists of abstracts on all the marriages, births and deaths that were contained within this newspaper. This newspaper not only covered the county of Pickens but also surrounding counties. If you have relatives lost in the Northwestern portion of the State, this book could have that missing link.

Prince Frederick Winyaw 1713-1777, The Register Book *for the* Parish. By: NSCD of America, Pub. 1916, Reprinted 2018, 264 pages, Index, soft cover, ISBN #0-89308-299-6.

SC 47 $30.00

The entries for this parish register included here show baptisms for more than 800 persons, approximately 200 marriages and a number of deaths. The vestry minutes included such items as care for the poor, voter lists, apprenticeship, etc., for persons in the parish whether members of the church or not. This book is a MUST for persons with ancestry in the Pee Dee Area of South Carolina and boarders the counties of North Carolina such as: Anson and Bladen. The boundary lines for this parish started in the South along the Pee Dee River in Georgetown County and extended North to the North Carolina State line.

Quakers *in* South Carolina, Wateree *and* Bush River, Cane Creek, Piney Grove *and* Charleston Meetings. Edited by: The Rev. S. Emmett Lucas, Jr., Orig. Pub. 1905, 1892, 1936, Reprinted in Consolidation format 2018, 150 pages, soft cover, Index, ISBN #0-89308-450-6.

SC 90 $20.00

The material appearing in this volume has been taken from three major sources viz. "Historic Camden, S.C." by Kirklan & Kennedy, "The Annals of Newberry" by O'Neall and "Encyclopedia of America Genealogy, Vol. #1, N.C." by Hinshaw. The material appearing in the first two titles consists of considerable early records pertaining to many of the pioneer Quaker families that settled in S.C., many of whom intermarried with other pioneer families and were assimilated into other religious denominations, while still others left and moved to Tennessee, Ohio, Indiana, and other states. Many South Carolina families, prominent and otherwise will be surprised to find that they have Quaker roots. Because of the valuable information found in Camden and Newberry books, we have also reprinted the minutes from Hinshaw's N.C. volume listing marriages, deaths, births, etc. for not only Bush River but also Cane Creek, Piney Grove and Charleston Monthly meetings in S.C. but also that of the Wrightboro, Georgia Meeting. This consolidated title will provide a veritable storehouse of information not found elsewhere in one volume.

Richland County, South Carolina, A History *of*. By: Edwin L. Green, Orig. Pub. 1932, reprinted 1996, 395 pages, Hard Cover, Index, ISBN #0-89308-698-3.

SC 98 $40.00

Located in the Camden District, Richland County is surrounded by Calhoun, Clarendon, Fairfield, Kershaw, Lexington, Orangeburg, and Sumter counties. Due to the 1800 Federal Census being lost for Richland County, the researcher will find this book to be of great use. Two chapters are devoted to will abstracts from the probate offices of Charleston, Camden, Winnsboro, and Richland County. One chapter entitled early landowners is quite useful for the genealogist as the plat books have often been followed in locating owners, as the plats often contain interesting information in the notations made on them. The figures in parenthesis indicate the holding and the date, followed by location and neighbors. These plat books cover the time frame 1732-1776. One chapter in particular is devoted to the Revolutionary period: it lists soldiers, their service records, and also lists bounty land grants for the county of Richland. There are two other chapters devoted strictly to the early settler / pioneers of this region of which genealogies or biographical sketches are given in great detail on such families/individuals as: Adams, Bates, Benson, Blanding, Bookter, Brown, Bynum, Center, Chappell, Clarkson, Clifton, Compty, Denley, Dinkins, Douglas, Dubard, Dunlap, Edmunds, Egan, English, Entzminger, Goodwyn, Green, Guignard, Hampton, Hay, Hirons, Hopkins, House, Howell, Hunt, Killingsworth, Kinsler, Lithgow, Lunsford, Lykes, Marshall, Myers, Partridge, Patterson, Pearson, Purvis, Rainford, Reese, Rives, Scott, Smith, Smyth, Spigner, Stark, Taylor, Tucker, Turnipseed, Wade, Waring, Weston, and the vast mentioning of other pioneer settlers....

Spartanburg County, South Carolina, History *of*. By: John B. O. Landrum, Pub. 1900, reprinted 2023, 544 pages, Index, Soft Cover, ISBN #9787-1-63914-104-3.

SC 27 $48.50

A native of the Piedmont section of South Carolina, Dr. J.B.O. Landrum wrote the History of Spartanburg County as a continuation of his Colonial and Revolutionary History of Upper South Carolina. This reprint reproduces the original 1900 edition and covers the period from the organization of the county in 1785 to the Civil War. Over 100 family sketches and more than 125 portraits make this volume of primary interest to the genealogist, and thousands of names of early Spartans are reported. The first census of Spartanburg County taken in 1790, estimates the population at 8,800, and the heads of families residing in the area at the time are listed. Included also are the names of all the Spartanburg men who served in the Civil War, with the names of battle for those killed or wounded. Although it also contains descriptions of the textile industry, churches, schools, and politics, this work is mainly an aid to family history and contains much valuable genealogical material. Surnames of persons or families included in the biographical sketches that the author included in this book, are: Allen, Amos, Anderson, Archer, Ballenger, Barry, Benson, Berwick, Bishop, Blake, Blassingame, Bomar, Bowden, Brockman, Brown, Burke, Burnett, Caldwell, Calvert, Camp, Cannon, Carlisle, Carpenter, Chapman, Choice, Clarke, Cleveland, Cofield, Compton, Crocker, Dean, Douglass, Drummond, Duncan, Earle, Edwards, Elford, Evins, Ezell, Farley, Farrow, Fielder, Fleming, Foster, Griffith, Hampton, Harris, Henneman, High, James, Jordan, Judd, Kennedy, Kilgore, Lake, Lanford, Landrum, Lee, Legg, Lipscomb, Martin, Mason, McCullough, McDowell, McMillen, Monk, Montgomery, Moore, Nesbitt, Nicholls, Odel, Pendleton, Petty, Poole, Reid, Richardson, Rowland, Rudisail, Russell, Sloan, Smith, Snoddy, Switzer, Thomas, Thompson, Trimmier, Tucker, Turner, Vernon, Walker, Westmoreland, Wilkins, Wilmot, Wilson, Wingo, Winsmith, Wofford, Wood, Woodruff, and Zimmerman.

Spartanburg County, South Carolina Minutes *of the* County Court, 1785-1799. By: Brent Holcomb, Pub. 1979, 325 pages, Soft Cover, Index, ISBN #0-89308-175-2.

SC 26 $35.00

This volume contains abstracts of the county court minutes for an important up-country county. Spartanburg County included a large portion of present Cherokee County, S.C. and was bordered by Greenville, Laurens, and Union Counties, S.C. and Rutherford County, North Carolina. The border changes between Spartanburg, Greenville, and Union counties make it an important tool for researching those counties as well. These minutes contain lists of deed recorded, wills, and estates probated, road juries, petit and grand juries, tavern licenses issued and small court cases.

Spartanburg County / District, South Carolina, Deed Abstracts, Book A-T, 1785-1827. By: Albert Bruce Pruitt pub. 1989, 872 pages, Hard Cover, Index, ISBN #0-89308-553-7.

Vol. #1, Deed Books A-T, 1752-1852: 872 pages, Hard Cover, Index, ISBN #0-89308-553-7.

SC 86 *(Out-of-Print)*

Vol. #2, Deed Book U-W, 1827-1829: 545 pages, Index, hard cover, ISBN #0-89308-742-4.

SC 102 $50.00

Vol. #3, Deed Book X-Z, 1839-1848: 529 pages, Index, hard cover, ISBN #0-89308-743-2.

SC 103 $50.00

Vol. #4, Deed Book AA-BB, 1848-1852: 240 pages, Index, soft cover, ISBN #0-

89308-717-3

SC 104 $30.00

Vol. #5, Deed Books CC-FF, 1852-1860: 536 pages, Index, hard cover, ISBN #0-89308-780-7.

SC 112 $50.00

Spartanburg County is surrounded by the present-day counties of Cherokee, Greenville, Laurens, and Union Counties, S.C. and to the North by Cleveland, Polk and Rutherford Counties, N.C. Deeds are GREAT source for genealogical research due to the many and varied family members that are mentioned. Not only will the reader find the deed transaction itself, but often times such things as: marriages, relinquishment of dower, divisions of family farms among heirs, remarriages of widows are just a few of the matters you can anticipate finding within records of deeds.

(Spartanburg County) Genealogical Abstracts *from the* Carolina Spartan, 1866-1872. By: Larry W. Vehorn, Pub. 1999, 210 pages, Hard Cover, Index, ISBN #0-89308-716-5.

SC 105 $30.00

In this volume, the researcher will find all items of genealogical interest appearing in this newspaper. The vast majority of the abstracts concern events in Spartanburg and Greenville Counties, S.C. Besides marriages and deaths, other items of genealogical interest are included, such as: probates, administrations, sheriff's sales, church committees, county commissioners lists, unclaimed letters, and etc... Lists of defendants in court cases often name South Carolinians who moved out of state. The intent was to abstract any item which showed a relationship or put an individual in a place and time.

Spartanburg County, South Carolina Newspapers, 1872-1879, Genealogical Abstracts *from.* By: Larry Vehorn, Pub. 2004, 335 pages, soft cover, Index, 0-89308789-0.

SC 110 $35.00

This volume picks up where the above book "Genealogical Abstracts from the Carolina Spartan, 1766-1872" leaves off. The author used two newspapers to complete this work and they are: The Carolina Spartan and the Spartanburg Herald. Besides marriages and deaths, other items of genealogical interest are included, such as: probates, administrations, sheriff's sales, church committees, county commissioners' lists, unclaimed letters, and etc.... Lists of defendants in court cases often name South Carolinians who moved out of state. The vast majority of this volume concerns events in Spartanburg County but also neighboring counties such as: Greenville, Union & Laurens.

(Spartanburg County) New Prospect Baptist Church Minutes, 1820-1855 *and* Cemetery Survey. By: Larry Vehorn, Pub. 1999, 134 pages, soft cover, Index, ISBN #0-89308-719-X.

SC 106 $20.00

This book is transcription of the minutes of the Baptist Church at New Prospect from the founding in 1820 until 1855. The earliest minutes for this church were lost in a fire. Sometime after 1858, an ancestor of the author copied the minutes, and that copy is the basis for this work. Many families who lived in Upper Spartanburg County are well represented in the minutes. Church minutes are often the only record for families who lived briefly in an area. Also is a survey of the over 1,000 tombstone inscriptions in the church cemetery.

St. Helena's Parish, South Carolina, 1726-1812, The Vestry Book *of.* By: Alexander S. Salley, Jr., Orig. Pub. 1919, reprinted 2020, 296 pages, soft cover, Index, 0-89308-295-3.

SC 57 $28.50

St. Helena's parish was established in 1712 by the General Assembly of South Carolina. It was bounded on the east by St. Helena's sound and the Combahee River on the north by a line from the head of the Combahee River to the Savannah River and on the south to the ocean. Early parish vestry minutes are extremely important as often times they contain lists of voters, car of widows, orphans and he poor, and apprenticeships for all persons of the parish, which include not only members of the church. These records are very important since they are the only existing records for Beaufort District after 1785.

St. Mark's Parish, Santee Circuit, *and* Williamsburg Township, South Carolina 1731-1885, Chronicles *of.* By: James M. Burgess, Pub. 1888, Reprinted 1991, 108 pages, soft cover, ISBN #0-89308-458-1.

SC 94 $12.50

A capsule historical overview of the evolution of churches in S.C., their founders, ministers, prominent laymen and women. The author uniquely interweaves the ecclesiastical background in brief sketches of his wife's ancestral churches for the benefit of their children, Biographical sketches and detailed St. Mark's Parish church activities update the history since circa 1681 when the first Episcopal church was built in Charleston, the creation of St. Mark's Parish by Act of Assembly, 21 May 1757, & through the Revolutionary War.

Sumter County, South Carolina, History *of.* By: Anne King Gregorie, Pub. 1954, Reprint 2018, 574 pages, Index, ISBN #0-89308-857-9.

SC 96 $48.50

Sumter County sits on the banks of the Wateree River in central SC. It was created in 1800 from Craven County and in turn was created in 1682. Early records show that these early land grants east of the Wateree River were all located in the now extinct Craven County. Sumter county itself sits within the largest of all SC parishes, St. Mark's Parish. This volume should be considered a companion to all books on this region.

Union County, South Carolina Minutes *of the* County Court, 1785-1799. By: Brent Holcomb, Pub. 1979, Reprinted 2014, 523 pages, soft cover, Index, ISBN #0-89308-159-0.

SC 25 $45.00

Union was one of the counties formed from Ninety-Six District in 1785. This volume contains lists of deeds and probate records, minor court cases, bastardy cases, jury lists, etc. The jury lists of Union are very interesting in that Quakers are distinguished by "affirming" instead of "swearing". Revolutionary War veterans are found here as well as early settlers from Virginia, North Carolina, and Pennsylvania.

Williamsburg, South Carolina, History *of.* Something About the People of Williamsburg County, S.C., from its First Settlement by Europeans About 1705 until 1923. By: William Boddie, Pub. 1923, Reprinted 2021, 664 pages, Index, Soft Cover, ISBN #0-89308-754-8.

SC 82 $48.50

A pine tree on the north bank of the Black River, called the King's Tree by an early explorer, became the focal point of settlement in what is now Williamsburg County, and gave the name to the county seat. This interesting history begins with an account of the first settlement under the Lords Proprietors and gives the names of everyone who had settled there by 1737. It is particularly rich in genealogical material, which is contained in sketches of individuals, lists of county officers, lists of ministers and members of churches, early documents, names of settlers and officials, wills with names of family members involved, sketches of Revolutionary War officers and lists of land claims and owners in 1788. Genealogical information is also found in the census of 1790; taxpayers and amounts paid in 1811; muster rolls of the Civil War units, with officers, deaths of soldiers and excerpts from diaries; lists of teachers, officers of banks and lists of soldiers in the Spanish-American War and World War I. The general history of the county is discussed under the topics of economic and agricultural conditions, churches, government, social life, wars, religion, roads and ferries, nullification, transportation, slavery, and Secession, Reconstruction, post-Civil War history, education and growth and development of the county in the 20th Century.

Probate *and* Land Records

Probate Records *of* South Carolina, (3 Volumes. By: Brent Holcomb, Pub. 1977, Reprinted 2007). The three following volumes represent a guide to the intestate (and some testate) records of the Colonial and Revolutionary periods of South Carolina. They cover the entire state, province, or counties not functioning until 1785.

Vol. #1, An Index to Inventories, 1746-1785: 72 pages, Maps, Index, ISBN #0-89308-052-7.

SC 28 $15.00

This most valuable book contains over 5,000 entries. It is an Index to both Intestate and Testate Inventories, Divisions of Estates, Estate Sales, etc... for the entire state of S.C. until 1784.

Vol. #2, 1741-1755: 336 pages, Index, ISBN #0-89308-053-5

SC 29 $40.00

Journal of the Court of Ordinary 1771-1775, Abstracts of Letters of Administration for S.C. and Charleston Dist. 1775-1785, Abstracts of Letters of Administration with the Will Annexed Volume K , 1778-1821. This 2nd book of the series contains many heretofore unknown probate records from the Colonial and Revolutionary period. The Ordinary's Journal contains references to Testate and Intestate state records and some Marriage Licenses. The Letters of Administration are recently discovered intestate records. This volume covers the Wills and Administrations for the Entire State for this period.

Vol. #3, Journal of the Court of Ordinary, 1746-1771: 154 pages, soft cover, Index, ISBN #0-89308-149-3.

SC 30 $25.00

This book is similar in form to the Journal transcribed in Volume 2 of this series, showing: proving wills, administrations of estates, guardians appointed, and mention of marriage in the back of this volume. This volume covers all of South Carolina and is an invaluable tool for South Carolina research.

South Carolina Deed Abstracts 1719-1771. 4 Volumes. By: Clara B. Langley, Pub. 1984, reprinted 2001, 400 pages, Hard Cover, Index, ISBN #0-89308-317-8.

Vol. #1, 1719-1740: 392 pages, Hard Cover, Index, ISBN #0-89308-271-6.
SC 59 $40.00

Vol. #2, 1741-1755: 370 pages, Hard Cover, Index, ISBN #0-89308-272-4.
SC 60 $40.00

Vol. #3, 1755-1768: 386 pages, Hard Cover, Index, ISBN #0-89308-273-2.
SC 61 $40.00

Vol. #4, 1768-1771: 400 pages, Hard Cover, Index, ISBN #0-89308-317-8.
SC 62 $40.00

These four volumes contain the abstracts of the records of the Register of the Province of South Carolina from 1719-1772. These abstracts of conveyances and deeds, and occasionally miscellaneous records, cover all parts of the state, from the Proprietary period until just prior to the Revolution. The original copies remain in Charleston in the Office of the Register of Mesne Conveyance, where all deeds for the entire state were recorded until the state capital was moved to Columbia well after the Revolution. After 1785, the individual counties in South Carolina began recording their own deeds, but prior to this date, one must look for his or her ancestor's deed in these volumes being abstracted. These abstracts were prepared for the Works Progress Administration by Miss. Langley in the 1930's. They have been thoroughly indexed for grantors, grantees, adjacent property owners and all other individuals whose names appeared in such conveyances. Each volume contains a full-name index of individuals; a place name index of all places such as rivers, plantations, towns, countries; as well as an occupation index.

Miscellaneous Record

A Collection *of* Upper South Carolina Genealogical *and* Family Records. (3 Volumes). (From the Private Files of the Late Pauline Young.) By: James E. Wooley, Editor, Pub. 1980, reprinted 2018, 416 pages, soft cover, Index, ISBN #0-89308-157-4.

Vol. #1: 416 pages, soft cover, Index, ISBN #0-89308-157-4.
SC 19 $40.00

Vol. #2: 404 pages, soft cover, Index, ISBN #0-89308-210-4.
SC 20 $40.00

Vol. #3: 354 pages, Hard Cover, Index, ISBN #0-89308-243-0.
SC 21 $40.00

These records comprise the loose files of the late Pauline Young, one of South Carolina's most widely known genealogist on Upper South Carolina. Each family record is filed with names of persons mentioned, these records consists of estate settlements, bastardy bonds, deeds, wills, coroner's inquests, abstracts of letters pertaining to estates, guardianship, tavern licenses, etc... It is estimated each book contains more than 40,000 names of early settlers in Upper South Carolina from the mid 1700's down to the 1850's. These records are primarily from Upper South Carolina counties such as: Pendleton District, Abbeville, Edgefield, Greenville, and Pickens Counties.

The Colonial Clergy *of* Virginia, North Carolina *and* South Carolina, 1607-1776. By: Frederick Lewis Weis, Pub. 1955, Reprinted 2021, 108 pages, soft cover, ISBN #978-1-63914-031-2.
VA 193 $17.50

This book is alphabetical list of approximately 950 colonial clergymen from 1607-1776 who settled in Virginia, North Carolina and South Carolina. These annotations furnish such useful genealogical data as date & place of birth, date & place of death, names of parents, college of matriculation, date of ordination, denomination, names of parishes, dates in which tenure was held, and a variety of other similar data.

A Compilation *of the* Original Lists *of* Protestant Immigrants *to* South Carolina, 1763-1773. By: Janie Revill, Pub. 1939, reprinted 2021, 162 pages, Index, soft cover, ISBN # 978-1-63914-019-0.
SC 2 $20.00

This book is a great source for trying to locate an early ancestor's place of settlement within South Carolina. The 4,000 immigrants listed in this book were Protestant refugees from Europe who came to South Carolina in search of new lands and religious freedom. Arranged chronologically, and taken verbatim from the original Council Journals, 1763-1773, the information given in the certificates and petitions for lands under the Bounty Act includes the date and the location and acres of land granted. In some cases, the immigrants are listed with their age, country of origin, and name of the vessel on which they arrived.

(Courthouses and Jails) Robert Mill's. By: Gene Waddell & Rhodri W. Liscombe, Pub. 1982, 143 pages, 8 1/2" x 11", Hard Cover, Index, ISBN #0-89308-249-X.
SC 63 $30.00

The first section discusses five types of courthouses and two types of jails designed by Mill's, district buildings by William Jay (the architect of Savannah mansions), Mill's public and private buildings that are similar to his courthouses and jails, and buildings influenced by Mill's designs. An appendix discusses the courthouses and jails in each district between 1800 and 1865, and another appendix prints samples of contemporary architectural documents.

The Dictionary *of* South Carolina Biography, Vol. 1. By: Richard Cote and Patricia Williams, Pub. 1985, 404 pages, Hard Cover, Index, ISBN #0-89308-275-9.
SC 58 $38.50

This book is a major new multi-volume finding aid to tens of thousands of biographies, autobiographies and biographical sketches of South Carolinians found in hundreds of volumes of individual and collective biographies; local, state, church, and family histories and periodicals. Each volume is self-indexing for the subjects, and lists the name, birth and death years, primary residences, primary occupations and full source references for more than 10,000 sketches of 17th through 20th century South Carolinians. Separate indexes to occupations and places of residence are provided. The series, if continued, could possibly consist of five volumes.

A Genealogical Collection *of* South Carolina Wills *and* Records. (Volume # 1). By: Pauline Young, Pub. 1955, Reprinted 2019, 274 pages, Soft Cover, Index, ISBN #0-89308-037-3.
SC 24 $30.00

Volume 1 contains more than 460 legal records with some 3,000 names of early South Carolina settlers named in the Districts of Edgefield, Laurens, Pendleton, Pickens, Spartanburg, and York, and such records as: wills, deeds, estate administration, slave papers, petitions, inquest, and equity records.

A Genealogical Collection of South Carolina Wills *and* Records. (Volume # 2). By: Pauline Young, Pub. 1984, 328 pages, Hard Cover, Index, ISBN #0-89308-532-4.
SC 75 $35.00

The book covers a spectrum of abstracts of wills and estates of Abbeville, Pickens and Anderson counties; real estate's books and sales (division among heirs); citizenship papers of Pickens County; and other selected records of Pauline Young's genealogical collection.

The Huguenots *of* Colonial South Carolina. By: Arthur Henry Hirsch, Phd., Pub. 1928, reprinted 2022, 398 pages, Index, soft cover, ISBN 978-1-63914-061-9.
SC 8 $38.50

The first group of French Huguenot settlers arrived in South Carolina around 1669. This book provides a historical background to their emigration with extensive discussion of their religious and political affairs, along with their role in the development of the colony. The author also provides a detailed discussion of their settlements at Charleston, Santee, St. Thomas, St. Dennis, the Orange Quarter, St. John's Berkley, St. Stephen's, Purrysburg and Hillsboro. The genealogist will find the biographical sketches of many of these early settlers quite helpful with those relatives who found their way to the South Carolina low-country.

Known Military Dead *during* The American Revolutionary War, 1775-1783. By: Clarence Stewart Peterson, Pub. 1959, reprinted 2021, 198 pages, Index, soft cover, ISBN #978-1-63914-028-2.
USA 6 $22.50

This book is an alphabetically list of approximately 10,000 "Known" military dead during the American Revolution. Information to be found within: names with rank, date of death, and state of birth or service or place where buried.

Local *and* Family History *in* South Carolina: A Bibliography. By: Richard Cote, Pub. 1981, Reprinted 1991, 520 pages, soft cover, Index, ISBN #0-89308-200-7.
SC 42 $32.50

This is the first place a researcher interested in South Carolina should cheek. It lists an enormous number of sources of printed (and some manuscript) information which are useful for studying S.C. families, churches, and local history. Eighty-three libraries throughout the state have provided lists of their books and pamphlets on local, church, and family history. The result is a bibliography which contains nearly eight times the number of sources as Dr. J. Harold Easterby's standard Guide to the Study and Reading of South Carolina History. This bibliography contains more than 8,000 entries and goes far beyond any previous work. The family, church, as local historian who does not consult this book is likely to duplicate research already done and published, as well as overlook many publications that would aid him in his work. Cote drew heavily on the collections of South Carolina Historical Society, the South Carolinian Library at the Univ. of S.C., and on numerous county, college, university, historical society and research libraries for his material. Some 1,900 sources for the study of towns, counties, and institutions are provided; an equal number of published genealogies, and an equal number of sources for S.C. church history records, along with thousands of sources on other subjects relating to the state. Locations of Scarce items are cited.

Journal *of* The Rev. Godfrey Drehr, 1819-1851. By: Brent Holcomb, Pub. 1978, reprinted 2022, 104 pages, Index, soft cover, ISBN #0-89308-060-8.

SC 7 $17.50

This book has been transcribed verbatim from the original 180-page journal from the well-known Lutheran minister who preached in Lexington, Newberry, Orangeburg and Edgefield Districts. SC. It contains many baptisms, marriages, deaths, and burials, as well as the churches and other places where Drehr preached. Also listed are some occasional private communions administered to sick or elderly persons. This journal is a much-needed reference tool for persons with families in these counties.

Revolutionary Claims Filed *in* South Carolina, 1783-1786. By: Janie Revill, Pub. 1941, reprinted 2021, 387 pages, soft cover, ISBN #978-1-63914-017-6.

SC 13 $35.00

This is a copy of the original index book showing Revolutionary War claims filed in South Carolina between August 20, 1783 and August 31, 1786. The approximate 11,000 Claimants are listed in alphabetically order, with multiple references to the returns showing the page number of the entry book. Since the Index was kept by the Auditor General of South Carolina, this book constitutes an authoritative source for Revolutionary War claims. The author has also included a section on officers in the hospital and men of the Frigate South Carolina to whom certificates had been awarded.

Some Heroes *of the* American Revolution *in the* South Carolina Upper Country. By: Rev. J.D. Bailey, Orig. Pub. 1924, Reprinted 2018, 296 pages, soft cover, Index, ISBN #0-89308-002-0.

SC 3 $28.50

An excellent reader for all ages on the part that Upper South Carolina played in the War for Independence. Chapters on several leading figures in the Revolution are given with family information and origins and the battles in which they participated. Also, many lesser figures. Patriot and Loyalists are mentioned, and many interesting incidents of the Revolution not elsewhere mentioned are included. A must for people with Colonial and Revolutionary ancestry in Old Ninety-Six and Camden Districts of South Carolina.

The Scotch-Irish *and their* First Settlements *on the* Tyger River *and other* Neighboring Precincts *in* South Carolina. By: George Howe, Orig. Pub. 1861, Reprinted, 2020, 36 pages, New Index, soft cover, ISBN #0-89308-465-4.

SC 53 $12.50

Dr. Howe gives a brief recount of the people who moved from Scotland to Ireland and hence to Pennsylvania and South Carolina. The major families of Lancaster, Union and Spartanburg Districts of that migration are mentioned, as well as their activities in the Revolution. Some of the ministers and dates of establishments of the Presbyterian churches are given, which makes this an excellent general history. An Index has been added for easy reference. Some surnames in this Index are: Alexander, Allison, Anderson, Barry, Bay, Beaty, Brandon, Brown, Caldwell, Calhoun, Clowney, Collins, Creswell, Cunningham, Davies, Davis, Dickinson, Dillard, Dodd, Edwards, Ferguson, Fuller, Fulton, Gaston, Gilleland, Hamilton, Hammond, Hughs, Jamison, Jolly, Kennedy, Kershaw, Knox, Lewis, McAden, McCreary, McElhenny, McIlwaine, Martin, Miller, Norton, Orr, Otterson, Patton, Pearson, Peden, Ramsay, Richardson, Simpson, Snoddy, Storey, Summer, Tate, Templeton, Tennent, Thomas, Thompson, Vance, Waddel, Williams, Wilson, Wood, and Young.

Some South Carolina Genealogical Records. By: Janie Revill, Pub. 1985, reprinted 2006, 456 pages, Hard Cover, Index, ISBN #0-89308-539-1.

SC 70 $45.00

This is the second volume of records taken from the index cards of Miss Revill which are housed in the Washington Memorial Library in Macon, GA. These records contain such miscellaneous records as abstracts of equity records, deeds, wills, tombstone inscriptions, jury lists, etc. The counties covered in this volume are as follows: Abbeville, Anderson, Barnwell, Chester, Fairfield, Greenville, Laurens, Newberry, Richland, Spartanburg, Union, and York.

***Some* South Carolina County Records, Volume #1.** By: Silas Emmett Lucas, Jr., Pub. 1989, Reprinted 2018, 154 pages, Index, ISBN #0-89308-014-4.

SC 5 $20.00

This book contains abstracts of various county records from around the state: Spartanburg County Wills, Marlboro County Deeds, Cheraw District Equity Decrees, Lexington District Deed Book, Columbia Equity District Guardian & Trustee Bond Book, Fairfield County Wills.

***Some* South Carolina County Records, Volume #2.** By: Silas Emmett Lucas, Jr., Pub. 1989, Reprinted 2016, 634 pages, Index, Hard Cover, ISBN #0-89308-648-7.

SC 88 $60.00

This book contains records from Union County: Will Book A, 1792-1815, Deed Books A & B, 1785-1791, Miscellaneous Records Book 1 & 2, and Probate Office, 1785-1800; Pickens County: Real Estate Sales Book A & B, 1830-1855; Naturalizations, Estates Records, 1829-1840, and Miscellaneous Records; Laurens County: Deed Books A, B, & C, 1785-1791, Naturalizations, 1807-1827, Guardians Returns, 1807-1825, Plat Books A & B, 1807-1816; Sumter County: Deed Book A, 1801-1803; Marion County: Tax Lists, 1811-1814 and 1824; Fairfield County: Will Book 3 & 4, 1800-1803; Settlers from Old 96 District to Georgia and Alabama; Greenville County: Deed Books A, B, & C, 1786-1794; York County: Deed Book A, 1787-1796; Newberry County: Equity Records, 1818; and Chester County: Deed Books A, B, & C, 1786-1794.

South Carolina *in the* Spanish American War. By: General J.W. Floyd, Pub. 1901, Reprinted 2018, 268 pages, soft cover, ISBN #0-89308-781-5.

SC 45 $35.00

This is a historical roster and itinerary of South Carolina volunteer troops who served in the War between the United States and Spain 1898. Coupled with brief sketches of the movements from the beginning to the end of the conflict.

Marriage & Death Notices *from the* Southern Christian Advocate, 1837-1867. (2 Volumes). By: Brent Holcomb, Pub. 1979-80, Reprinted 2019.

Vol. #1, 1837-1860: 764 pages, Index, ISBN #0-89308-111-6

SC 36 $58.50

Vol. #2, 1861-1867: 276 pages, Index, ISBN #0-89308-154-X.

SC 37 $30.00

The Southern Christian Advocate was the publication of the Methodist Conference of both South and North Carolina, Georgia and Florida for the period 1837-1878. It also covered other states as well, such as: Tennessee, Mississippi, Alabama and occasionally containing notices from other states as well. Vol. #1 contains the names of approximately 70,000 individuals and Vol. #2 which covers the Civil War period, contains the names of approximately 30,000 individuals. The marriage notices will often times have "son of" "daughter of" etc.. This is very important source for information when doing Methodist ancestry. Considering that the State of South Carolina did not officially start keeping vital records until 1911, these notices take on an added importance. North Carolina requirement for marriage licenses (as opposed to bonds) did not come into effect until 1868. And some Georgia counties have lost their marriage records. Considering the time frame of these books makes these marriage notices important because many times couples will move away from where they were married and finding a marriage record can be very difficult to locate if the county and state of the marriage are not already known. The death notices within these books are mini biographies of the deceased persons, often times giving places of birth and former residences. During the Civil War years, many persons could not afford tombstones or erected only wooden markers which have not survived and hence these books become even more important to the researcher.

Southern Patriot, 1815-1848, Marriage & Death Notices *from the.* (2 Volumes). By: Teresa E. Wilson and Janice L. Grimes, Pub. 1982.

Vol. #1, 1815-1830: 262 pages, Soft Cover, Index, ISBN #0-89308-279-1.

SC 55 $30.00

Vol. #2, 1831-1848: 248 pages, Soft Cover, Index, ISBN #0-89308-280-5.

SC 64 $30.00

The Southern Patriot began publication in Charleston, S.C. in 1815 and was published into 1848. The marriage and death notices in both Volumes 1 & 2 are not limited to the Southern states but include many other states such as New York, Virginia, Pennsylvania, Ohio, Florida, Tennessee, Connecticut, Vermont, Massachusetts, Rhode Island, etc...

Upper South Carolina Newspapers 1843-1865, Marriage *and* Death Notices *from.* By: Brent Holcomb, Pub. 1977, reprinted 2014, 176 pages, soft cover, Index, ISBN #0-89308-043-8.

SC 33 $20.00

These marriage and death notices have been abstracted from The Laurensville Herald, Spartanburg Express, The Spartan, the Conservatist (Newberry), The Newberry Sentinel, The Rising Sun (Newberry) and The Lexington Flag, Temperance Standard and Lexington Telegraph. These are the only newspapers that could be located from the Districts of Spartanburg,

Laurens, Newberry, and Lexington, South Carolina, for the years prior to 1866. These notices contain the names of over 5,207 persons mentioned in these newspaper extracts.

Upper Country of South Carolina, Vol. #2, History *of the.* By: John H. Logan, Pub. 1910, reprinted 2014, 126 pages, soft cover, Index, ISBN #0-89308-195-7.

SC 12 $18.50

These records herein deal primarily with the Revolutionary War in the Upper Country of South Carolina and Dr. Logan lists among other things members of various Revolutionary Regiments, leaders and officers in the Revolution; detailed descriptions of skirmishes and battles, etc. Also he gives histories of a number of families in this Upper part of South Carolina, which having been written during the Revolution, carry families back to the 1700's. A new complete full-name index has been prepared for this edition.

TENNESSEE

Anderson County, Tennessee 1801-1831, Land Deed Genealogy of. By: Rev. Silas Emmett Lucas, Jr., Pub. 1999, 209 pages plus Index, Hard Cover, ISBN #0-89308-527-8.

TN 129 $30.00

This East Tennessee County was formed in 1801 from parts of Knox and Grainger counties. It lies partly in the valley of East Tennessee and partly on the Cumberland Plateau. This book contains abstracts of the deeds for this county running from 1801 and going through 1831 with some references going back into the late 1700's. Deeds are GREAT source for genealogical research due to the many and varied family members that are mentioned. Not only will the reader find the deed transaction itself, but often times such things as: marriages, relinquishment of dower, divisions of family farms among heirs, remarriages of widows are just a few of the matters you can anticipate finding within records of deeds.

Bedford County, Tennessee, The Historical & Genealogical Digest *of.* By: Helen & Tim Marsh, Pub. 2004, 425 pages, Index, 7"x10" Hard Cover, ISBN #0-89308-702-5.

TN 155 $65.00

Once in a while, someone comes up with a genealogical reference book that seems to fill in all those loose blanks. This NEW book by the Marsh's is just one of those books. It is a unique publication that contains an Early History and a Genealogical Reference section (approx. 250 pages) for the SERIOUS researcher. The material contained in this volume has never been available to the general public in a printed format. This book is a potpourri of UNPUBLISHED records including archival and court records; Deeds, Wills, Cemeteries and locator maps, Plats and maps drawn and researched by the authors both county and North Carolina; War of 1812 soldiers; 1812 & 1836 Tax lists; Biographical Sketches; lists of First Explorers of Middle Tennessee; Revolutionary soldiers and an actual directory of Bedford and Marshall counties settlers. It also contains much research on Shelbyville town lot owners and first settlers, along with many Marsh Collection Documents that are Not found elsewhere.

Bedford County, Tennessee Bible Records. (2 Volumes). By: Helen C. & Timothy R. Marsh, soft cover, Index.

Vol. #1: Pub. 1977, reprinted 2010, 221 pages, ISBN #.0-89308-470-0 **TN 99 $25.00**

Vol. #2: Pub. 1985, reprinted 2005, 192 pages, ISBN #0-89308-570-7. **TN 92 $22.50**

Bedford County was formed in 1807 out of Rutherford County. Bible records are another unique source of research material that can help one bridge that gap in the family line that may be lacking in other legal records.

Bedford County, Tennessee, Cemetery Records *of.* By: Helen & Timothy Marsh, Pub. 1986, reprinted 1998, 352 pages, map, soft cover, Index, ISBN #0-89308-569-3.

TN 91 $38.50

Bedford County was formed in 1807 out of Rutherford County. To the best of the authors knowledge, all known cemeteries are listed. This book contains over 400 cemeteries along with maps on their location.

Bedford County, Tennessee, Earliest County Court Records of. By: Helen & Timothy Marsh, Pub. 1986, reprinted 2013, 184 pages, soft cover, Index, ISBN #0-89308-568-5.

TN 90 $25.00

Bedford County was formed in 1807 out of Rutherford County. And in turn, the lower half of Bedford County was cut off to form Lincoln county in 1809. These are the oldest surviving Minutes of the County Court (1848-1860), all minutes prior to this date were destroyed in the Courthouse fire of 1863.

Bedford County, Tennessee Chancery Court Records, 1830-1865. By: Helen & Timothy Marsh, Pub. 1987, 336 pages, Hard Cover, Index, ISBN #0-89308-589-8.

TN 104 $37.50

This book is a valuable research and reference tool that often supplies that missing link of early Bedford County families, frequently naming fathers, mothers, children, grandchildren, brothers, sisters, aunts, and uncles. As these so-called friendly suits were heard in Chancery Court, estates were divided and settled in great detail, naming complete families, and often naming states where members of the families settled. Many lost or destroyed wills are reconstructed in great detail herein. Chancery Court records have provided many detailed breakthroughs in family research not found elsewhere. This is a MUST for serious Bedford County researchers.

Bedford County, Tennessee 1802-1869, Land Deed Genealogy *of.* (2 Volumes) By: Helen C. & Timothy R. Marsh, Index.

Vol. #1, 1802-1852: Pub. 1987, 484 pages, ISBN #0-89308-610-X **TN 105 $42.50**

Vol. #2, 1861-1869: Pub. 2003, 389 pages, ISBN #0-89308-785-8. **TN 149 $40.00**

These books include all deeds from 1802-1852, then skip the Burned years of 1852-1861 and then pick back up in 1861-1869. Information found in each volume: including family genealogical material, to giving names, dates, and places and early land grants contained in all deeds recorded in the Register's Office for the years given above.

(Bedford County, TN.) The "BURNED" Deed Index, 1852-1861. By: Helen & Tim Marsh, Pub. 1999, 438 pages, Hard Cover, ISBN #0-89308-526-X.

TN 98 $42.50

Here is a new research aid on Bedford County that until now has never been published or even available for the researcher looking for those lost relatives in this middle Tennessee county. This index is a true copy of a Registers notebook, kept by the Register of Deeds, immediately preceding the Civil War, in which an index of all transactions conducted in the office, were entered from 1852 to 1861 and served as an index to 9 books that were "LOST" in the courthouse fire of 1863. This "Burned Index" may prove to be both rewarding and at times a little frustrating. Rewarding, in the information it may disclose, however small, perhaps a piece of the puzzle. Frustrating, when one speculates about the important deeds that may have been forever lost.

(Bedford County) Caleb M. Thompson Funeral Records, 1920-40's. By: Helen Marsh, 2022, soft cover, 3 volumes.

Vol. #1, 1920's: 208 pages, ISBN #978-1-63914-074-9. **TN 192 $32.50**

Vol. #2, 1930's: 508 pages, ISBN #978-1-63914-075-6. **TN 193 $52.50**

Vol. #3, 1940's: 376 pages, ISBN #978-1-63914-076-3. **TN 194 $42.50**

These records are abstracted from the Caleb M. Thompson funeral home in Bedford County, which is located on Depot Street in Shelbyville, covering the period of 1920-40's. Given here is valuable family and genealogical information, such as date of births and deaths, parents, place of birth and place of death and interment, often time telling the type of garments the persons were buried in (suits, dress, slippers, underwear, etc..) whether a hearse was rented, or a car (or hack) rented for the preacher. Information as to whether the deceased was married or single, and the cause of death may be included. There are many people listed who were born in the early 1800's

Bedford County, TN., Hoover Funeral ***and*** **Burial Records.** By: Helen & Timothy Marsh, Pub. 1989, Reprinted 2018, 260 pages, Index, ISBN #0-89308-640-1.

TN 113 $28.50

These records are abstracted from two funeral homes in Bedford County, one which was once located in Bell Buckle, Tennessee, and the other in Shelbyville, covering a period from 1870's to the 1940's. Given here is valuable family and genealogical information, such as date of births and deaths, parents, place of birth and place of death and interment, often time telling the type of garments the persons were buried in (suits, dress, slippers, underwear, etc..) whether a hearse was rented, or a car (or hack) rented for the preacher. Information as to whether the deceased was married or single, and the cause of death may be included. There are many people listed who were born in the early 1800's.

Bedford County, TN., Revolutionary War Soldiers *of.* By: Helen & Timothy Marsh, Pub. 1989, reprinted 2018, 264 pages, Index, ISBN #0-89308-641-X.

TN 114 $28.50

This long awaited book gives information on some 136 men who served in the Revolutionary War and who later settled in Bedford County. It also gives similar information on a number of other men who served in the Revolutionary War and moved into Bedford County for a brief period before moving elsewhere. The main portion of this information is taken from the individual's Revolutionary War Pension Applications as well as from family sources, such as Bible records when such information was available to the authors. It contains one person's complete service record, depositions of other soldiers and neighbors regarding his service; battles, etc. he served in; when born, and death date, as well as, when available, where the soldier was buried. The authors also provide some information on the first generation of descendants of each soldier when such information is available.

Bedford County, Tennessee 1880-1898, Official Marriages *of.* (2 Volumes) By: Helen & Timothy Marsh, Pub. 1996, soft cover, Index.

Vol. #1, 1861-1880: 366 pages, ISBN #0-89308-482-4

TN 123 $40.00

Vol. #2, 1880-1898: 288 pages, ISBN #0-89308483-2

TN 124 $35.00

Due to the courthouse fire of 1863, the marriage books recorded before 1861 have been destroyed. These two volumes are the last is a series of books on Bedford County, TN. being compiled by the Marsh's.

Bedford County, Tennessee Wills & Vital Records *from* Newspapers. By: Helen & Timothy Marsh, Pub. 1984, Reprinted 2 into 1 volume 1996, 416 pages, Hard Cover, Index, ISBN #0-89308-573-1.

TN 95 $42.50

The wills, probate and settlement records of Bedford County suffered severe losses in the courthouse fire that occurred in the late fall of 1863. With the exception of about six wills that were registered and recorded in the early 1860's all wills were destroyed in the fire. All wills recorded after the Civil War are intact and abstracts of them, up to 1910, are reproduced in this publication. In addition, we have stepped back in time and included all probate records from the Marsh's private collection that they have gleaned from the Chancery Court Records, Deed Books, and the earliest County Court Minutes that survived the fire, spanning the years 1848 to 1860. The Chancery Court Records are of special interest and value as they were reconstructed as the product of the Chancery Court action. They often approach the originals in detail and substance. The second section of this book, entitled: "Vital Records from Newspapers" represents a valuable companion to the first section, placing in the hands of the researcher a broad and useful tool to be used in the research of Bedford County family history. Hundreds of Bedford County marriages, deaths, and events of local interest were abstracted from all available area newspapers and included in this section.

Blount County, TN. Marriages, 1795-1865. By: Will E Parham, Pub. 1982, Reprinted 2015, 270 pages, Index, ISBN #0-89308-240-6.

TN 52 $28.50

Blount County was formed in 1795 out of a part of original Greene County. This volume, arranged in alphabetical order by groom's name, contains approximately 5,000 marriage bonds and licenses.

Cannon County, Tennessee 1840-1880, Chancery Court Records *of.* By: Thomas E. Partlow, Pub. 2001, 184 pages, soft cover, Index, ISBN #0-89308-760-2.

TN 145 $25.00

Chancery court records are extremely important to researchers due to the many early settlers who died without leaving a will. These records provide many detailed breakthroughs in family research not found elsewhere. This book is a valuable research and reference tool that often supplies that missing link of the family, frequently naming fathers, mothers, children, grandchildren, brother, sisters, aunts and uncles.

Cannon County, Tennessee 1836-1857, Land Deed Genealogy *of.* By: Thomas E. Partlow, Pub. 2001, 274 pages, soft cover, Index, ISBN #0-89308-714-9.

TN 134 $30.00

Cannon County was carved-out of Coffee, Rutherford, Warren, and Wilson counties in 1836. This book is an abstract of the deeds for this middle Tennessee County. Deeds are one of the favorite research tools of the genealogists due to the wide variety of family connections found within them. Not only will the reader find the deed transaction itself, but often things such as: marriages, relinquishments of dower, divisions of family farms among the heirs, remarriages of widows are just a few of the matters you can anticipate finding within records of deeds.

Carter County, Tennessee Minutes *of the* County Court, 1862-1869. By: W.P.A., Pub. 1938, Reprinted 2015, 271 pages, Index, ISBN #0-89308-826-9.

TN 160 $28.50

Carter county was formed in 1796 by the General Assembly of North Carolina. It was created out of the eastern part of Washington County, an early county originally formed in 1777. The Watauga Settlement was located in present Carter County. At the time of the creation, its eastern boundary was the North Carolina line, its northwestern boundary was Sullivan Co., TN; its northern boundary was Washington Co., VA. In these minutes of pleas & quarters sessions you will find appointments of county officials, appointed administrators, marked public roads, granting of licenses to "ordinaries", taxes being levied, civil actions of a wide variety and persons being tried for offenses against the peace & dignity of the State.

Carter County, Tennessee, 17601861, Early History *of.* By: Frank Merritt, Pub. 1950, reprinted 2016, 214 pages, soft cover, Index, ISBN #0-89308-904-4.

TN 180 $20.00

Carter county was formed in 1796 by the General Assembly of North Carolina. It was created out of the eastern part of Washington County, an early county originally formed in 1777. The Watauga Settlement was located in present Carter County. At the time of its creation, its eastern boundary was the North Carolina line, its northwestern boundary was Sullivan Co., TN; its northern boundary was Washington Co., VA.

Carter County, Tennessee Marriages 1796-1870. By: Golden F. Burgner, Pub. 1987, reprinted 2018, 152 pages, soft cover, Index, ISBN #0-89308-601-0.

TN 100 $20.00

Carter county was formed in 1796 by the General Assembly of North Carolina. It was created out of the eastern part of Washington County, an early county originally formed in 1777. The Watauga Settlement was located in present Carter County. At the time of the creation, its eastern boundary was the North Carolina line, its northwestern boundary was Sullivan Co., TN; its northern boundary was Washington Co., VA. This book contains more than 3,000 marriages. The brides, grooms, officiates or bondsmen total approx. 12,000 names for this early and important eastern Tennessee county, which was a major migration center.

Claiborne County FOLKS. By: John Robertson, Pub. 1981, Reprinted 2019, 134 pages, soft cover, ISBN #0-89308-741-6.

TN 199 $18.50

Claiborne County was created out of Hawkins and Grainger counties in 1803. It sits in Eastern Tennessee just West of the interest to the Cumberland Gap, which was the gateway to the fertile lands of the Midwest. This book is consortium of various Biographical Sketches: Alexander, Beeler, Bolinger, Breeding, Burchfield, Cawood, Chumley (2), Cobb, Crutchfield, Ellis, Evans, Faulkner/Fortner, Ferguson, Gibson, Hurst/Harper/Henderson/Huddleston/Pearson/Thompson/Burch, Keck, Killion, Mayes, Maddox/Maddux, Mason, Monk, Moyers, Owens, Pearman, Pillion, Price, Robertson, Rogers, Russell, Singleton. The author has also listed over 1650 deaths with dates of various people taken from the Diary of John Robertson and from obituaries.

(Cocke County) Over *the* Misty Blue Hills. The Story *of* Cocke County, Tennessee. By: Ruth Webb O'Dell, Pub. 1951, Reprinted 2012, 485 pages, Hard Cover, New Index, ISBN #0-89308-276-7.

TN 53 $50.00

Cocke county was formed in 1797 and BURNED in 1878 making this book a MUST for those working in Cocke county and East Tennessee. This book contains vast amounts of historical and genealogical source material from early school superintendents, churches, postmasters, register of Deeds, sheriffs, tax assessors, Indian names, Indian Marriages, lists of soldiers in the Confederacy, Federal soldiers in the Civil War, World War I & II, militia 1808-1810, and much more. Detailed genealogies and biographical sketches are given on the following families: Allen, Ball, Boydston, Burnett, Christian, Clark, Dawson, Denton, Driskill, Faubion, Fine, Gillett, Gilland, Gorman, Gouchenour, Hopkins, Huff, Inman, Jobe, Jones, Lee, Lemings, Lillard, McKay, McNabb, Mims, Morell, O'Dell, O'Neil, Parrott, Palmer, Peck, Roadman, Sandusky, Smith, Stanberry, Stokely, Susong, Whitson, Wood, and many others.

Coffee County, Tennessee 1836-1850, Land Deed Genealogy *of.* (2 Volumes) By: Helen & Tim Marsh, Pub. 2006, soft cover, Index.

Vol. #1, 1836-1842: 304 pages, ISBN #0-89308745-9.

TN 143 $30.00

Vol. #2, 1843-1850: 262 pages, ISBN #0-89308-746-7.

TN 144 $30.00

Here they are! The LAST two books by the Marsh's. These two volumes are a set of only a few known abstracted legal records on Coffee County in a printed/book format. Coffee County was created in 1836 from Bedford, Franklin and Warren Counties. This area of middle Tennessee was a great source of migration into and from other parts of the Union. Deeds are one of favorite research tools of the genealogists due to the wide variety of family connections found within them. Not only will the reader find the deed transaction itself, but often times such things as: marriages, relinquishments of dower, divisions of family farms among heirs, remarriages of widows are just a few of the matters you can anticipate finding within records of deeds.

Coffee County, Tennessee Wills 1833-

1860. By: WPA, pub. 1938, reprinted 2014, 120 pages, soft cover, Index, ISBN 30-89308-548-0.

TN 166 $17.50

Coffee County was created in 1836 from Bedford, Franklin and Warren Counties. This area of middle Tennessee was a great source of migration into and from other parts of the Union. This book contains not only wills of individuals, but also guardians and administrators bonds; bastardy, apprentice, trustees, sheriffs and treasurers' bonds, and inventories of estates. The names of approximately 1,500 persons are found in these legal records of this important county.

Davidson County, Tennessee, History *of.* By: W.W. Clayton, Pub. 1880, Reprinted 2019, 832 pages, New Index, ISBN #0-89308-891-9.

TN 156 $65.00

This Middle Tennessee County was formed in 1837 out of parts of Cannon, Jackson, Warren, and Wilson counties. If you are researching Middle Tennessee, don't let this wonderful book slip by you. Davidson County was the cradle of Middle Tennessee Civilization that began in 1784 with the first settlers along the Cumberland, when that country was still North Carolina. It is a Genesis of the first pioneers that settled up and down the Cumberland River, west of the Cumberland mountains. A record of those valiant men who tamed the vast wilderness that was later to become most of Middle TN. and encompassed all or parts of the present TN. counties of: Bedford, Cannon, Cheatham, Clay, Coffee, Davidson, DeKalb, Fentress, Jackson, Macon, Marshall, Maury, Overton, Pickett, Robertson, Smith, Sumner, Trousdale, Warren, White, Williamson and Wilson, an area that was to father the western movement.

This book is filled from cover to cover with biographical sketches of these early settlers/pioneers who came to this new frontier. These biographical sketches are in GREAT detail, giving wonderful loads of information, like: the names of parents, grandparents, spouses, children, former residences (such as: NC, VA, NJ, England), births, deaths, education, travels, occupation, military service, land holdings and many, many other useful pieces of that genealogical puzzle that you have been looking for.

Davidson County, Tennessee 1783-1803, Land Deed Genealogy *of.* (3 Volumes) By: Helen & Timothy Marsh, Pub. 1992, Hard Cover, Index.

Vol. #1, 1783-1792: 290 pages, ISBN #0-89308-461-1.
TN 38 $35.00

Vol. #2, 1792-1797: 300 pages, ISBN #0-89308-462-X..
TN 49 $35.00

Vol. #3, 1797-1803: 258 pages, ISBN #0-89308-463-8.
TN 54 $35.00

These volumes are taken from legal records of this parent county of middle Tennessee. Davidson County was formed from Indian land in 1783, and it encompassed a major portion of middle Tennessee that originally included: Bedford, Cheatham, Marshall, Maury, Rutherford, part of Robertson, Sumner, and Williamson Counties. These three volumes together contain the names of approximately 45,000 of the earliest settlers of this area. Each is filled with original North Carolina Military Grants issued to soldiers who served in the North Carolina Continental Line. This vast Military Reservation encompassed a 55-mile strip that covered all of the Northern half of middle Tennessee. These are companion volumes to the 2 volumes of Davidson Co., TN. Wills, 1784-1832. The index for this volume mentions over 14,000 persons. Deeds are GREAT source for genealogical research due to the many and varied family members that are mentioned. Not only will the reader find the deed transaction itself, but often times such things as: marriages, relinquishment of dower, divisions of family farms among heirs, remarriages of widows are just a few of the matters you can anticipate finding within records of deeds.

Davidson County, Tennessee Marriage 1789-1837. By: Silas Emmett Lucas, Jr., Pub. 1979, Reprinted 1995, 166 pages, Hard Cover, Index, ISBN #0-89308-187-6.

TN 21 $30.00

These marriages for Davidson County come from "Record Book #1" and are extremely important to the genealogist since Davidson County was the earliest county to be formed west of the Watauga settlement and west of the Cumberland mountains. This volume contains 5,310 marriages.

Davidson County, Tennessee Wills *and* Inventories, 1784-1832. (2 Volumes) By: Helen & Timothy Marsh., Pub. 1989, Hard Cover, Index.

Vol. #1, 1784-1817: 272 pages, ISBN #0-89308-664-9.
TN 117 $37.50

Vol. #2, 1817-1832: 272 pages, ISBN #-893089-665-7.
TN 118 $37.50

These abstracts of the Official Wills and Inventories of Old Davidson County, Tenn., the cradle of Middle Tennessee Civilization that began in 1784 with the first settlers along the Cumberland, when that country was still N.C. It is a Genesis of the first pioneers that settled up and down the Cumberland River, west of the Cumberland mountains. A record of those valiant men who tamed the vast wilderness that was later to become most of Middle TN. and encompassed all or parts of the present TN. counties of: Bedford, Cannon, Cheatham, Clay, Coffee, Davidson, Dekalb, Fentress, Jackson, Macon, Marshall, Maury, Overton, Pickett, Robertson, Smith, Sumner, Trousdale, Warren, White, Williamson, and Wilson, an area that was to father the western movement.

DeKalb County, Tennessee, History *of.* By: Will T. Hale, Pub. 1915, Reprinted 2019, 266 pages, soft cover, ISBN #0-89308-935-4.

TN 191 $25.00

This Middle Tennessee County was formed in 1837 out of parts of Cannon, Jackson, Warren, and Wilson counties. This land was first settled in 1797 by settlers from Maryland. This book is not too different from other county history books of this era. With such topics as trade and transportation, labor, farming, politics, and race relations - all important in the development of the county - are discussed. This type of county history book can help one develop ideas or paths to those missing ancestors by showing the customs and traditions of the local residents.

DeKalb County, Tennessee 1844-1892, Chancery Court Records *of.* By: Thomas E. Partlow, Pub. 2001, 158 pages, soft cover, Index, ISBN #0-89308-761-0.

TN 146 $20.00

Chancery Court Records are extremely important to researchers because they contain estate settlements of many early settlers who died without leaving a Will (intestate). In addition to estate settlements, these records also include such things as divorces, and after 1865, some Civil War information. These records provide many detailed breakthroughs in family research not found elsewhere. This book is a valuable research and reference tool that often supplies that missing link of the family, frequently naming fathers, mothers, children, grandchildren, brothers, sisters, aunts, and uncles.

DeKalb County, Tennessee 1838-1900, Land Deed Genealogy *of.* (3 Volumes) By: Thomas E. Partlow, Soft Cover, Index.

Vol. #1, 1838-1868: Pub. 1999, 349 pages, ISBN #0-89308-722-X..
TN 130 $35.00

Vol. #2, 1868-1885: Pub. 2006, 227 pages, ISBN #0-89308-832-3.
TN 135 $28.50

Vol. #3, 1885-1900: Pub. 2016, 276 pages, ISBN #0-89308-786-6.
TN 171 $30.00

DeKalb county was formed in 1837 out of parts of Cannon, Jackson, Warren, and Wilson counties. These 3 volumes of deed abstracts for this important Middle Tennessee County. Deeds are one of favorite research tools of the genealogists due to the wide variety of family connections found within them. Not only will the reader find the deed transaction itself, but often times such things as: marriages, relinquishments of dower, divisions of family farms among heirs, remarriages of widows are just a few of the matters you can anticipate finding within records of deeds.

Dickson County, Tennessee Handbook. By: Jill K. Garrett, Pub. 1984, Reprinted 2017, 456 pages, soft cover, Index, ISBN #0-89308-604-6.

TN 76 $45.00

Dickson County was created in 1803 from Montgomery and Robertson counties. This land was first settled in 1793 when the State of North Carolina started issuing grants to persons with Revolutionary service. This book is a collection of records: Marriages 1805-1849; Wills 1804-1856; Estate Settlements 1823-1841; Vital Statistics or death, cause of death, whether married or single, and where the person was born; Deeds 1804-1816; Military records including Confederate soldiers; Circuit Court miscellany which included estate sales and settlements, divorce petitions, guardianships, bastardy charges, etc.; Dickson County Gazette, which is a listing of tons, villages, post offices, as well as churches and their locations here known; and a chronology which lists only some events or highlights in the history of Dickson County.

Dickson County, Tennessee, History *of.* By: Robert Ewing Corlew, Pub. 1956, Reprinted 2019, 244 pages, Index, soft cover, ISBN #0-89308-028-4.

TN 196 $25.00

Dickson County was created in 1803 from Montgomery and Robertson counties. This land was first settled in 1793 when the State of North Carolina started issuing grants to persons with Revolutionary service. This book is not too different from other county history books of this era. With such topics as trade and transportation, labor, farming, politics, and race relations - all important in the development of the county - are discussed. This type of county history book can help one develop ideas or paths to those missing ancestors by showing the customs and traditions of the local residents.

Dyer County Tennessee, Cemetery Inscription of. By: Mrs. Quintard Glass, Pub. 1977, Reprinted 2018, 238 pages, Index, soft cover, ISBN #0-

89308-085-3.

TN 1 $25.00

Dyer County was created in 1823 from Indians lands in the extreme western portion of the state. It is surrounded by Gibson, Haywood, Obion, and Tipton counties, TN and the Mississippi River on its western boundary.

Franklin County, Tennessee 1832-1837, Court Minutes *of.* By: WPA, Pub. 1938, reprinted 2014, 285 pages, soft cover, Index, ISBN #0-89308-549-9.

TN 167 $30.00

Franklin County is located in middle Tennessee and was created in 1807 from Warren and Bedford Counties. It was a major county of migration and is surrounded by the counties of: Bedford, Coffee, Lincoln, Marion, Warren, and the Alabama State line on the South. In these abstracts, one will find local office holders being appointed, the levying and expenditure of local taxes, selecting & summoning of juries, licenses being granted to operators of taverns, as well as deeds & bills of sale being acknowledge by the grantor. The Court also oversaw a wide range of matters involving estates, including probate of will, settlements of estates, and appraisement, as well as matters dealing with bastardy, and many other valuable bits of information.

Franklin County, Tennessee Wills *and* Deeds, 1800-1876. By: Thomas Partlow, Pub. 1991, 244 pages, Hard Cover, Index, ISBN #0-89308-684-3.

TN 119 $32.50

Franklin County is located in middle Tennessee and was created in 1807 from Warren and Bedford Counties. It was a major county of migration and is surrounded by the counties of: Bedford, Coffee, Lincoln, Marion, Warren, and the Alabama State line on the South. These abstracts begin with the first recorded records of the county. The Wills & Inventories cover the time frame of 1808-1876. Next, the Land Grants begin in 1801 and continue on through 1822. Following this are the Deeds of the county, starting with Book "B", 1808 and continuing on through Book "O" 1840.

Gibson County, Tennessee - Illustrated. By: W.P. Greene, Pub. 1901, Reprinted 2019, 152 pages, Index, ISBN #0-89308-882-X

TN 163 $18.50

Gibson County was created in 1823 out of Indian lands that were ceded from the Chickasaw Nation. It sits in the western portion of the state. This book is filled with just over 100 small biographies' /biographical sketches of these early citizens of the county.

Giles County, Tennessee County Court Minutes, 1822-1825. By: W.P.A., Pub. 1934, Reprinted 2018, 446 pages, Index, soft cover, ISBN #0-89308-590-1.

TN 185 $40.00

Giles County was created in 1809 out of Maury County, TN. It is surrounded by the counties of: Bedford, Lawrence, Lincoln, Maury, Marshall and the state of Alabama on its southern border. In these abstracts, one will find local office holders being appointed, the levying and expenditure of local taxes, selecting & summoning of juries, licenses being granted to operators of taverns, as well as deeds & bills of sale being acknowledge by the grantor. The Court also oversaw a wide range of matters involving estates, including probate of will, settlements of estates, and appraisement, as well as matters dealing with bastardy, and many other valuable bits of information.

Giles County, Tennessee, Settlement *and* Early History *of.* By: James McCallum, Pub. 1876, reprinted 2019, 134 pages, soft cover, Index, ISBN #0-89308-326-7.

TN 27 $17.50

Giles County was created in 1809 out of Maury County, TN. It is surrounded by the counties of: Bedford, Lawrence, Lincoln, Maury, Marshall and the state of Alabama on its southern border. This book is not too different from other county history books of this era. With such topics as First Settlers, trade and transportation, labor, Indians, farming, and politics - all important in the development of the county - are carefully discussed. This type of county history book can help one develop ideas or paths to those missing ancestors by showing the customs and traditions of the local residents.

Grainger County, Tennessee Court *of* Pleas & Quarter Sessions Record Book, #3, 1812-1816. By: Ella Lee Sheffield, Pub. 1983, 240 pages, soft cover, Index, ISBN #0-89308-281-3.

TN 59 $21.50

In these abstracts, one will find local office holders being appointed, the levying and expenditure of local taxes, selecting & summoning of juries, licenses being granted to operators of taverns, as well as deeds & bills of sale being acknowledge by the grantor. The Court also oversaw a wide range of matters involving estates, including probate of will, settlements of estates, and appraisement, as well as matters dealing with bastardy, and many other valuable bits of information.

Grainger County, Tennessee, Letters *of* Administrations, 1842-1854. By: Ella Lee Sheffield, Pub. 1983, 96 pages, soft cover, Index, ISBN #0-89308-296-1.

TN 50 $16.50

Grainger County, TN. Inventories *of* Estates *and* Wills, 1833-1852. By: Mary E. Reeves, Pub. 1989, reprinted 2016, 180 pages, Index, ISBN #0-89308-284-8.

TN 63 $22.50

Grainger County was created in 1796 from Hawkins & Knox Counties, TN. Wills are wonderful source for the researcher due to many and variety of family members being mentioned. Many times, marriages of various family members can be discovered within a will.

Greene County, TN., North Carolina Land Grants Recorded *in.* By: Golden F. Burgner, Pub. 1981, Reprinted 2017, 178 pages, soft cover, Index, ISBN #0-89308-2204-X.

TN 34 $22.50

This book contains approximately 2,000 land grants recorded in Greene County, TN. Some of these grants were made by the US Government to pay off debts to officers and soldiers who served in the Revolutionary War. Some of the grants were lands owned by Lord Granville, while other grants were issued by the state of North Carolina and Tennessee to encourage settlement in the new state of Tennessee.

Greene County, Tennessee Chancery Court Minutes, 1825-1831. By: Golden F. Burgner, Pub. 1987, 371 pages, Hard Cover, Index, ISBN #0-89308-602-9.

TN 102 $38.50

This book contains more than 22,000 names of persons between 1825 and 1876 and is a veritable gold mine of genealogical information for persons interested in Greene County and surrounding East Tennessee counties.

Greene County, Tennessee Minutes *of the* Court *of* Common Pleas, 1783-1807. (2 Volumes) By: Golden F. Burgner, Pub. 1981, Index.

Vol. #1, 1783-1795: Pub. 1981, 331 pages, ISBN #0-89308-278-3.

TN 29 $30.00

Vol. #2, 1797-1807: 331 pages, Index, ISBN #0-89308-201-5.

TN 30 $35.00

Greene County was originally Tennessee County, having been formed in 1783. Prior to its formation, it was part of North Carolina. It is the parent county to: Blount, Cocke, Jefferson, & Sevier. As will be seen, it is a veritable gold mine of genealogical information for persons interested in Greene County and surrounding East Tennessee counties. These records cover the time frame of 1783-1795. In the coroners, etc. The court controlled the levying and expenditure of local taxes, matters dealing with public buildings, roads, bridges, etc. were handled by this court and it also selected and summoned juries. Among the other responsibilities of the court found in its minutes were licenses granted to operaters of taverns, as well as deeds and bills of sale being acknowledged by the grantors. the court oversaw a wide range of matters involving estates, including probate of wills, settlements of estates, and appraisements as well as matters dealing with bastardy, and many other valuable bits of information.

Greene County, Tennessee Guardians & Orphans Court Records, 1783-1870; *and* 1830 Tax List. By: Sandra Kelton Houston, Pub. 1983, 144 pages, soft cover, Index, ISBN #0-89308-286-4.

TN 65 $25.00

This book names orphans who were placed in homes by the Court of Common Pleas, giving their Natural and adopted names, and in most cases the natural parents. The Tax List gives names of landowners, location, number of acres, black polls, white polls, public stores, and stud horses. This is a very entertaining book and gives much information on the persons listed.

Greene County, Tennessee Marriages 1783-1868. By: Golden F. Burgner, Pub. 1981, reprinted 2012, 390 pages, soft cover, Index, ISBN #0-89308-202-3.

TN 32 $35.00

Greene County was originally Tennessee County, having been formed in 1783. Prior to its formation, it was part of North Carolina. As will be seen from the marriage records, it is county rich with original legal records. This book contains approximately 16,000 marriage records for this 85-year period of time. This reprint has 77 missing marriages that the author was not aware of during its initial printing.

Greene County, TN. Power *of* Attorney Books, 1806-1904. By: Jan Maddux & Carolyn Gregg, Pub. 2018, 604 pages, soft cover, Index, ISBN #0-89308-775-0.

TN 203 $58.50

Greene County was originally Tennessee County, having been formed in 1783. Prior to its formation, it was part of North Carolina. It is the parent county to: Blount, Cocke, Jefferson, & Sevier. As will be seen, it is a veritable gold mine of genealogical information for persons interested in Greene County and surrounding East Tennessee counties.

These records are unique and sometimes the only piece or connection to a relative that has disappeared to the researcher. Some of these records will name children with their parents in a time when no other records exist to make these connections. These Power of Attorney Books are detailed records of people who have moved West and inherited from Greene County relatives as well as other business ventures from Greene County citizens. The greatest value of this book is the tracing women, their parents and other relatives and their locations when they moved from Greene County, TN. Another interesting feature of using this as a research aid, is the insight to a female relative because she had to be interview separately from her husband to ensure that she was aware of what she was signing and that she was not coerced into signing away their property.

Greene County, Tennessee Tax Digests, 1809-1817. By: Golden F. Burgner, Pub. 1986, reprinted 2019, 272 pages, soft cover, Index, ISBN #0-89308-277-5.

TN 36 $27.50

Greene County was originally Tennessee County, having been formed in 1783. Prior to its formation, it was part of North Carolina. It is the parent county to: Blount, Cocke, Jefferson, & Sevier. As will be seen, it is a veritable gold mine of genealogical information for persons interested in Greene County and surrounding East Tennessee counties. These tax digests contain the names of those persons paying taxes, and depending upon the person's circumstances, would contain quantity of land in each tract that was being listed, where said tract lay, information concerning title to said land, whether it was the deed, or entry, or improvement, or claim, etc. It also showed white polls for whom taxes were being paid, number of black polls, number of stud horses, number of retail stores, and a column for peddlers and hawkers, and on some occasions the number of towns lots owned by the person.

Greene County, Tennessee Wills 1783-1890. By: Golden F. Burgner, Pub. 1981, reprinted 2012, 150 pages, soft cover, Index, ISBN #0-89308-203-1.

TN 31 $20.00

This book contains some 1,138 wills. Approximately 20,000 names of persons are found mentioned in the body of these wills as heirs, witnesses, executors, etc...

Hardin County, Tennessee Records, 1820-1860. By: Thomas A Hays, Pub. 1985, Reprinted 2017, 272 pages, soft cover, Index, ISBN #0-89308-562-6.

TN 88 $32.50

Hardin county was formed in 1819. The entries found in this book cover the appointments of the administrators and guardians; indentured applications; reports of inquests juries; releasements, removals, and insolvencies from the tax lists; wills; inventory of administrator and guardian settlements', the requests of free blacks; survey of occupant claims; petition of widows' dowers; acknowledgement of bills of sale for slaves; certificates of deeds of conveyance; and pertinent records.

Hawkins County, Tennessee Circuit Court Minutes, 1810-1828. (2 Volumes) By: Silas Emmett Lucas & Ella Sheffield, soft cover, Index

Vol. #1, 1810-1821: 247 pages, ISBN #0-89308-346-1.

TN 116 $35.00

Vol. #2, 1822-1825 & 1827-1828: 176 pages, ISBN #0-89308-347-X.

TN 47 $21.50

Hawkins County was created in 1786 from Sullivan County, TN., which in turn was carved out of Washington County, TN which was in turn carved out of Wilkes and Burke counties, N.C. This area of Eastern Tennessee received a large influx of persons migrating West in search of new lands. Most of these early settlers were from North Carolina and Virginia, with a sprinkling from Pennsylvania. Hawkins county sits on the border with Virginia. More appropriately, directly under Washington County, Virginia which was considered the gate way to west through western Virginia. Circuit court records are another unique source for tracing those elusive family members. The type of records found within this book are: petitions for divorce, breach of peace, assault & battery, guardianship, horse stealing, indictments for murders, indictments for larceny, bigamy charges, oaths relating to service in Revolutionary War, deeds of gifts, possession of counterfeit money, and many, many other juicy tidbits of information concerning persons of Eastern TN. that are not found anywhere else.

Hickman County, Tennessee, The History *of.* By: Jerome & David Spence, Pub. 1900, Reprinted 2015, 532 pages, soft cover, Index, ISBN #0-89308-242-2.

TN 57 $38.50

This book is a narrative (family & otherwise) taken from the inhabitants living at the time of publication. The time period generally covers just prior to the Revolutionary War and continues up to about 1899. The people who settled came from Virginia, North Carolina and Georgia primarily, a few from Maryland with s smattering from overseas of New England. Land records are remarkable in that neighbors are listed and location of property with explanations as to location. Births & deaths plus places of burial are recorded; complete families are given, in many instances several generations. Many include place of birth of eldest. Marriages including place are included. A must for anyone with roots in North Carolina or Virginia who needs a missing link between the East and West. Some of the prominent names are Petty, Epperson, Sheegog, Robertson, Easley, Jones, Bates, Cotham. Many Creek Indians are named as well as slaves and freed slaves

Lincoln County, Tennessee, Early Unpublished Court Records. By: Helen & Timothy Marsh, Pub. 1993, 263 pages, soft cover, Index, ISBN #0-89308-492-1.

TN 70 $30.00

These records are a potpourri of early miscellaneous loose court records which have never been published nor microfilmed by the State of Tennessee. These records contain: Guardianship reports and settlements, first land deeds called "The Clerks List", which lists many of the early Grantees and Grantors not recorded in the regular deed index. Also included are early Tax lists before 1830 giving the names of taxable, acreage of deeded and Granted land plus location of same. These miscellaneous records cover the time period of 1809 to about 1840. For the person with lost ancestors in Lincoln County, these records may provide the answer to long sought after forbears.

Lincoln County, Tennessee 1828-1834, Land Deed Genealogy *of.* (3 Volumes) By: Helen & Timothy Marsh, Pub. 1996, Hard Cover, Index.

Vol. #1, 1809-1818: 255 pages, ISBN #0-89308-235-X.

TN 71 $35.00

Vol. #2, 1818-1828: 249 pages, ISBN #0-89308-236-8.

TN 72 $35.00

Vol. #3, 1828-1834: 238 pages, ISBN #0-89308-237-6.

TN 73 $35.00

These volumes are the latest a series of books of source material taken from the legal records of this Middle Tennessee County. Lincoln County was formed from Indian lands in 1809. From the year 1799, with the formation of Williamson County, Tennessee, the most western third of what was to become Lincoln County in 1809, was then a part of Williamson County, and so until 1807 the eastern two thirds of the area was a part of Rutherford County. And from Dec. 3, 1807, until Nov. 14, 1809, Lincoln was the southern half of Bedford County. Each volume is filled with family genealogical material, giving names, dates, places, and early land grants contained in all deeds recorded in the Register's Office. These are companion volumes to the other books on Lincoln County that the Marsh's have compiled. These are a definite must if you are researching family members in this part of Tennessee. Deeds are GREAT source for genealogical research due to the many and varied family members that are mentioned. Not only will the reader find the deed transaction itself, but often times such things as: marriages, relinquishment of dower, divisions of family farms among heirs, remarriages of widows are just a few of the matters you can anticipate finding within records of deeds.

Lincoln County, Tennessee Official Marriages, 1838-1880. By: Helen & Timothy Marsh, Pub. 1974, Reprinted 1920, 328 pages, soft cover, Index, ISBN #0-89308-571-5.

TN 93 $28.50

These records are compiled from the original licenses and bonds, family records and newspapers accounts.

Lincoln County, Tennessee 1810-1921, Wills *and* Inventories *of.* By: Helen & Tim Marsh, Pub. 1989, Reprinted 2004, 200 pages, soft cover, Index, ISBN #0-89308-654-1.

TN 115 $25.00

This book contains more than 1,600 Wills of persons who died in Lincoln County with names of Approx. 10,000 to 12,000 persons mentioned in these Wills.

Jefferson County, Tennessee 1792-1814, Land Deeds *of.* By: Boyd J. Holdaway, Pub. 1991, 306 pages, soft cover, Index, ISBN #0-89308-688-6.

TN 120 $35.00

Jefferson County was originally part of the Washington District. It was formed in 1792 from portions of Greene and Hawkins Counties. From it several other counties were formed: Cocke, Hamblen and Sevier. Jefferson County was settled soon after the Revolutionary War. Most of the early settlers came from North Carolina, Virginia and some from South Carolina. This is another of the MUCH-NEEDED books on Eastern Tennessee to fill in the gaps for families migrating into and through this area on their way westward.

(Jefferson County, TN.) Mount Horeb Church Minute Books, 1841-1923. By: Hazel Townsend, Pub. 2016, appr. 330 pages, Index, ISBN #0-89308-501-4.

TN 26 $35.00

Jefferson County was originally part of the Washington District. It was formed in 1792 from portions of Greene and Hawkins Counties. From it several other counties were formed: Cocke, Hamblen and Sevier. Jefferson County was settled soon after the Revolutionary War. Most of the early settlers came from North Carolina, Virginia and some from South Carolina. This is another of the MUCH-NEEDED books on Eastern Tennessee to fill in the gaps for families migrating into and through this area on their way westward.

Knox County, Tennessee Minutes *of the* County Court, 1792-1795. By: WPA, Pub. 1941, reprinted 2010, 296 pages, soft cover, Index, ISBN #0-89308-642-8.

TN 153 $35.00

These court minutes begin with the creation of the county in 1792. Knox County was created out of Greene & Hawkins and was one of the many Eastern Tennessee counties that saw a great influx of settlers migrating West. In these minutes of pleas & quarters sessions you will find appointments of county officials, appointed administrators, marked public roads, granting of licenses to "ordinaries", taxes being levied, civil actions of a wide variety and persons being tried for offenses against the peace & dignity of the State.

Knox County, TN. Marriage Records, 1792-1837. By: Work Projects Administration, Pub. 1934, Reprinted 2018, 453 pages, Index, ISBN #0-89308-694-0.

TN 187 $40.00

Knox County was created in 1792 from Greene and Hawkins counties, TN. This is another of the MUCH-NEEDED books on Eastern Tennessee to fill in the gaps for families migrating into and through this area on their way westward.

Lawrence County, Tennessee Marriages 1818-1870. By: S. E. Lucas, Jr, Pub. 1999, 114 pages, soft cover, Index, ISBN #0-89308-724-6.

TN 131 $20.00

This middle Tennessee County was formed in 1817 out of Hickman and Maury Counties. This book contains abstracts of the marriages starting at the creation of the county all the way though 1870. These marriages are listed alphabetically by groom and cross indexed with a bride's name index located in the rear of the book.

Lincoln - Moore Counties, Tennessee, Cemetery Records *of.* By: Helen & Timothy Marsh, Pub. 1981, reprinted 2013, 452 pages, maps, 8 1/2" x 11" soft cover, Index, ISBN #0-89308-234-1.

TN 97 $55.00

To the best of the author's knowledge, they have included all known cemeteries in these two counties; however, they realize they might have missed a few because many of the old family cemeteries have disappeared and many time during their searches they came across unmarked graves in unnamed cemeteries.

Lincoln County, Tennessee 1809-1826, First County Court Minutes *of.* (2 Volumes) By: Helen & Timothy Marsh, soft cover, Index.

Vol. #1, 1809-1819: Pub. 1989, 292 pages, ISBN #0-89308-643-6.

TN 116 $35.00

Vol. #2, 1820-1826: Pub. 1991, 270 pages, ISBN #0-89308-453-0

TN 84 $30.00

In these abstracts, one will find local office holders being appointed, the levying and expenditure of local taxes, selecting & summoning of jurors, licenses being granted to operators of taverns, as well as deeds & bills of sale being acknowledge by the grantor. The Court also oversaw a wide range of matters involving estates, including probate of will, settlements of estates, and appraisements, as well as matters dealing with bastardy, and many other valuable bits of information.

Lincoln County, Tennessee, Early Unpublished Court Records. By: Helen & Timothy Marsh, Pub. 1993, 263 pages, soft cover, Index, ISBN #0-89308-492-1.

TN 70 $30.00

These records are a potpourri of early miscellaneous loose court records which have never been published nor microfilmed by the State of Tennessee. These records contain: Guardianship reports and settlements, first land deeds called "The Clerks List", which lists many of the early Grantees and Grantors not recorded in the regular deed index. Also included are early Tax lists before 1830 giving the names of taxable, acreage of deeded and Granted land plus location of same. These miscellaneous records cover the time period of 1809 to about 1840. For the person with lost ancestors in Lincoln County, these records may provide the answer to long sought after forbears.

Lincoln County, Tennessee 1828-1834, Land Deed Genealogy *of.* (3 Volumes) By: Helen & Timothy Marsh, Pub. 1996, Hard Cover, Index.

Vol. #1, 1809-1818: 255 pages, ISBN #0-89308-235-X.

TN 71 $35.00

Vol. #2, 1818-1828: 249 pages, ISBN #0-89308-236-8.

TN 72 $35.00

Vol. #3, 1828-1834: 238 pages, ISBN #0-89308-237-6.

TN 73 $35.00

These volumes are the latest a series of books of source material taken from the legal records of this Middle Tennessee County. Lincoln County was formed from Indian lands in 1809. From the year 1799, with the formation of Williamson County, Tennessee, the most western third of what was to become Lincoln County in 1809, was then a part of Williamson County, and so until 1807 the eastern two thirds of the area was a part of Rutherford County. And from Dec. 3, 1807, until Nov. 14, 1809, Lincoln was the southern half of Bedford County. Each volume is filled with family genealogical material, giving names, dates, places, and early land grants contained in all deeds recorded in the Register's Office. These are companion volumes to the other books on Lincoln County that the Marsh's have compiled. These are a definite must if you are researching family members in this part of Tennessee. Deeds are GREAT source for genealogical research due to the many and varied family members that are mentioned. Not only will the reader find the deed transaction itself, but often times such things as: marriages, relinquishment of dower, divisions of family farms among heirs, remarriages of widows are just a few of the matters you can anticipate finding within records of deeds.

Lincoln County, Tennessee Official Marriages, 1838-1880. By: Helen & Timothy Marsh, Pub. 1974, Reprinted 1920, 328 pages, soft cover, Index, ISBN #0-89308-571-5.

TN 93 $28.50

These records are compiled from the original licenses and bonds, family records and newspapers accounts.

Lincoln County, Tennessee 1810-1921, Wills *and* Inventories *of.* By: Helen & Tim Marsh, Pub. 1989, Reprinted 2004, 200 pages, soft cover, Index, ISBN #0-89308-654-1.

TN 115 $25.00

This book contains more than 1,600 Wills of persons who died in Lincoln County with names of Approx. 10,000 to 12,000 persons mentioned in these Wills.

Marshall County, Tennessee, Cemetery Records of. By: Helen & Timothy Marsh, Pub. 1981, reprinted 2019, 338 pages, maps, 8 1/2" x 11" soft cover, Index, ISBN #0-89308-238-4.

TN 103 $38.50

This book contains records from all the cemeteries in Marshall County. It includes the revised first book by Whitesell. There are more than 400 cemeteries found here, including the Lone Oak Cemetery in Lewisburg.

Marshall County, Tennessee 1836-1845, Land Deed Genealogy *of.* (2 Volumes) By: Helen & Tim Marsh, Pub. 1998, soft cover, Index.

Vol. #1, 1836-1840: 265 pages, ISBN #0-89308704-1.

TN 125 $32.50

Vol. #2, 1840-1845: 284 pages, ISBN #0-89308-705-X.

TN 126 $32.50

Marshall County was formed in 1836 from parts of Lincoln, Bedford, and Maury Counties, to which was added a part of Giles in 1870. Deeds are GREAT source for genealogical research due to the many and varied family members that are mentioned. Not only will the reader find the deed transaction itself, but often times such things as: marriages, relinquishment of dower, divisions of family farms among heirs, remarriages of widows are just a few of the matters you can anticipate finding within records of deeds.

Maury County, Tennessee, Century Review *of.* By: D.P. Robbins, Pub. 1905, reprinted 1997, 426 pages, Hard Cover, Index, ISBN #0-89308-184-1.

TN 23 $45.00

This book is the definitive biographical history of the county. Approximately 250 pages are devoted to biographical sketches, with the information sometimes researching back 3 or 4 generations. These sketches are arranged by communities, towns, or creek settlements. All phases of the county's history are covered: religious, educational, professional, political and with many, many illustrations, all of which provide an invaluable reference tool for research in this county, with many references to adjoining counties and family lines. This reprint edition has a full-name index containing approximately 40,000 names.

Maury County, Tennessee Deeds 1807-1817. By: Virginia W. Alexander, Pub. 1965, reprinted 2012, 248 pages, soft cover, Index, ISBN #0-89308-185-X.

TN 2 $28.50

Maury County was created in 1807 from the vast Indian lands located in Middle Tennessee. It is surrounded by the counties of: Bedford, Giles, Hickman, Lawrence, Lincoln, Marshall, Rutherford, and Williamson. Deeds are one of favorite research tools of the genealogists due to the wide variety of family connections found within them. Not only will the reader find the deed transaction itself, but often times such things as: marriages, relinquishments of dower, divisions of family farms among heirs, remarriages of widows are just a few of the matters you can anticipate finding within records of deeds.

Maury County, Tennessee Marriages, 1807-1852. By: Virginia W Alexander, Pub. 1962, reprinted 2015, 182 pages, soft cover, Index, ISBN #0-89308-885-4. (2 volumes in one)

TN 158 $23.50

Maury county was created in 1807 from the vast Indian lands located in Middle Tennessee. It is surrounded by the counties of: Bedford, Giles, Hickman, Lawrence, Lincoln, Marshall, Rutherford and Williamson. Originally this book was printed in two volumes but has been combined into one volume for this printing. These two volumes have been out of print for over 40 years. So don't delay order yours today.

Maury County, Tennessee, War *of* 1812 Soldiers *of.* By: Jill K. Garrett, Orig. Pub. 1976, reprinted 2006, 237 pages, soft cover, Index, ISBN #0-89308-525-1.

TN 154 $23.50

Maury County was created in 1807 from the vast Indian lands located in Middle Tennessee. It is surrounded by the counties of: Bedford, Giles, Hickman, Lawrence, Lincoln, Marshall, Rutherford, and Williamson. This book is a listing of 1,335 soldiers and patriots from the county. Under each soldier's name is a small biographical sketch including such information as: birth, death, marriage, children, siblings, occupation, before enlistment, rank as soldier & company that he served in, along with many, many other tidbits of useful information.

Maury County, TN. Wills, 1807-1832. By: Jill K. Garrett & Marise P. Lightfoot, Pub. 1964, Reprinted 2018, 288 pages, index, ISBN # 0-89308-362-3.

TN 83 $30.00

Maury county was created in 1807 from the vast Indian lands located in Middle Tennessee. It is surrounded by the counties of: Bedford, Giles, Hickman, Lawrence, Lincoln, Marshall, Rutherford and Williamson. Wills are wonderful source for the researcher due to many and variety of family members being mentioned. Many times, marriages of various family members can be discovered within a will.

McMinn County, Tennessee Chancery Court Records, 1844-1894. By: Reba B. Boyer, Pub. 1980, reprinted 2012, 325 pages, soft cover, Index, ISBN #0-89308-345-3.

TN 81 $38.00

McMinn County was created in 1819 out of lands ceded by the Cherokee Indians in the southeastern corner of the state. It is located in Eastern Tennessee which was a pivotal point for migration into and through the State. At its inception as a county, it was surrounded by: Monroe, Rhea, & Roane counties, Indian lands and by Northern Georgia. Chancery court records have provided many a detailed breakthroughs in family research not found elsewhere. This book is valuable research and reference tool that often supplies that missing link of the family frequently naming fathers, mothers, children, grandchildren, brother, sisters, aunts and uncles, considering that these courts heard cases that covered land and inheritance.

McMinn County, Tennessee Deeds, 1820-1880. By: Reba Bayless Boyer, Pub. 1986, reprinted 2012, 245 pages, soft cover, Index, ISBN #0-89308-336-4.

TN 96 $32.50

This long-awaited book has been out-of-print shortly after its original printing back in 1986. McMinn County was created in 1819 out of lands ceded by the Cherokee Indians in the southeastern corner of the state. Deeds are GREAT source for genealogical research due to the many and varied family members that are mentioned. Not only will the reader find the deed transaction itself, but often times such things as: marriages, relinquishment of dower, divisions of family farms among heirs, remarriages of widows are just a few of the matters you can anticipate finding within records of deeds. The author has also included lists of Occupant Enterers 1824-1826, Marriage Notices from newspapers that are NOT included in her book on McMinn County, TN. Marriages, and Death Notices from newspapers.

McMinn County, Tennessee Marriages, 1820-1870. By: Reba B. Boyer, Pub. 1970, reprint 2013, 256 pages, soft cover, Index, ISBN #0-89308-330-5.

TN 82 $30.00

McMinn County was created in 1819 out of lands ceded by the Cherokee Indians in the southeastern corner of the state. It is located in Eastern Tennessee which was a pivotal point for migration into and through the State. At its inception as a county, it was surrounded by: Monroe, Rhea, & Roane counties, Indian lands and by Northern Georgia. These marriages are listed alphabetically by groom and cross indexed with a bride's name index located in the rear of the book.

McMinn County, Tennessee Wills *and* Estate Records, 1820-1870. By: Reba Bayliss Boyer, Pub. 1970, reprinted 2013, 202 pages, soft cover, Index, ISBN #0-89308-328-3.

TN 80 $25.00

This book contains: wills, estate records, circuit court records, chancery court records, newspaper notices, and etc......

Monroe County, Tennessee Records, 1820-1870. **(2 Volumes)** By: Reba Bayless Boyer, Pub. 1970, Reprinted 2017,

Vol. #1, 1820-1870: 236 pages, soft cover, Index, ISBN #0-89308-329-1.

TN 78 $27.50

Vol. #2, 1820-1870: 228 pages, Index, ISBN #0-89308-327-5

TN 79 $27.50

Monroe County was created in 1819 from Indian lands in the southeastern corner of the state. Volume #1 contains: marriages 1838-1870; marriage notices from newspapers; deeds 1820-1870. Volume #2 contains wills; estate records; county circuit and chancery court records; newspaper notices, etc... The index for each volume mentions approximately 10,000 persons.

Montgomery County, Tennessee County Court Minutes, 1808-1824. By: Work Projects Administration, Pub. 1934, reprinted 2018, soft cover,

Vol. #1, 1808-1810: 208 pages, Index, ISBN #0-89308-677-0.

TN 188 $22.50

Vol. #2, 1823-1824: 256 pages, Index, ISBN #0-89308-641-X.

TN 189 $25.00

Montgomery County was created in 1796 from Tennessee County which was created from the state of North Carolina shortly after the Revolutionary War. This is another of the MUCH-NEEDED books on Middle Tennessee to fill in the gaps for families migrating into and through this area on their way westward. Montgomery County was involved in the Walker Line dispute with the state of Kentucky which later they lost and portions of the county were granted to Kentucky. In these minutes of pleas & quarters sessions you will find appointments of county officials, appointed administrators, marked public roads, granting of licenses to "ordinaries", taxes being levied, civil actions of a wide variety and persons being tried for offenses against the peace & dignity of the State.

Obion County, TN. Court *of* Pleas *and* Quarter Sessions, 1834-1836. By: W.P.A., Orig. Pub. 1941, reprinted 2019, 152 pages, Index, soft cover, ISBN #0-89308-972-9.

TN 165 $20.00

Obion County was created in 1823 from the Western District. It sits in the north-western corner of the state boarding the Kentucky and Missouri. The court was held 4 times a year and heard such cases of assault, batteries, trespass, all breaches of the peace. They held authority of administration in intestate estates and orphans, granted license to build water grist mills, to taverns and ordinaries, and to build and maintain public ferries. The court also appointed Constables and Overseers of Roads and named the men who lived within the bounds to keep them in repair, as well as recommending three persons to the Governor, of whom one was made Sheriff, as well as imposing taxes for roads, courthouses and goals, appointed all county officers, civil and military, all lists of Jurors and probates of Wills. These records are extremely valuable for the researcher, especially if an ancestor died intestate (without a will), and in some instances a person may be listed in these court records and nowhere else in the county records.

OBION County, Tennessee, History *of.* By: E.H. Marshall, Pub. 1941, Reprinted 2019, 276 pages, soft cover, ISBN #0-89308-934-6.

TN 190 $25.00

Obion County was created in 1823 from ceded Indian lands in the northwestern corner of the state. This land was first settled in 1819 when the western portion of the state was being opened for settlement. This book is not too different from other county history books of this era. With such topics as trade and transportation, labor, farming, politics, and race relations - all important in the development of the county - are discussed. This type of county history book can help one develop ideas or paths to those missing ancestors by showing the customs and traditions of the local residents.

Putnam County, Tennessee Circuit Court Minutes, 1842-1856. By: Works Projects Administration, Pub. 1934, Reprinted 2018, 308 pages, Index, ISBN #0-89308-874-9.

TN 183 $30.00

Putnam County was created in 1842 from parts of: White, Overton, Jackson, Smith and DeKalb Counties. Circuit court records are another unique source for tracing those elusive family members. The type of records found within this book are: Petitions for divorce, breach of peace, assault & battery, guardianship, horse stealing, indictments for murders, indictments for larceny, bigamy charges, oaths relating to service in Revolutionary War, Deeds of gifts possession of counterfeit money, and many, many other interesting tidbits of information concerning persons of Putnam County that are not available elsewhere.

Putman County, Tennessee, History *of.* By: Walter S. McClain, Pub. 1925, Reprinted 2019, 156 pages, ISBN #0-89308-873-0.

TN 181 $20.00

Putnam County was created in 1842 from parts of: White, Overton, Jackson, Smith & DeKalb Counties. This book is similar to other county history books of the era, in that it discusses the counties development thru such things as social life, economy, geology/topagraphy of the county, and a section on biographical sketches of some of its early residents.

Rutherford County, Tennessee Chancery Records, 1845-1867. By: Thomas E. Partlow, Pub. 1999, 117 pages, soft cover, Index, ISBN #0-89308-723-8.

TN 132 $18.50

Chancery Court records have provided many detailed breakthroughs in family research not found elsewhere. This is a MUST for the serious Rutherford County researcher. This book is a valuable research and reference tool that often supplies that missing link of the family, frequently naming fathers, mothers, children, grandchildren, brothers, sisters, aunts, and uncles.

Rutherford County, Tennessee 1804-1824, Land Deed Genealogy *of.* (3 Volumes) By: Helen & Tim Marsh, Hard Cover, Index.

Vol. #1, 1804-1813: Pub. 2000, 276 pages, ISBN #0-89308-731-9.

TN 137 $35.00

Vol. #2, 1814-1819: Pub. 2000, 300 pages, ISBN #0-89308-732-7.

TN 138 $35.00

Vol. #3, 1820-1824: Pub. 2000, 328 pages, ISBN #0-89308-733-5.

TN 139 $35.00

Deeds are GREAT source for genealogical research due to the many and varied family members that are mentioned. Not only will the reader find the deed transaction itself, but often times such things as: marriages, relinquishment of dower, divisions of family farms among heirs, remarriages of widows are just a few of the matters you can anticipate finding within records of deeds.

Rutherford County Tennessee, History *of.* By: Carlton C. Sims, Pub. 1947, Reprinted 2018, 256 pages, Index, ISBN #0-89308-700-9.

TN 195 $27.50

This book is not too different from other county history books of this era. With such topics as trade and transportation, labor, farming, politics, and race relations - all important in the development of the county - are carefully discussed. This type of county history book can help one develop ideas or paths to those missing ancestors by showing the customs and traditions of the local residents. A particular useful feature of this book are the hundreds of mini biographies inter dispersed throughout the book.

Rutherford County, Tennessee 1804-1840, Wills *of.* (2 Volumes) By: Helen & Tim Marsh, Hard Cover, Index.

Vol. #1, 1804-1828: Pub. 1998, 246 pages, ISBN #0-89308-7036-8

TN 127 $35.00

Vol. #2, 1828-1840: Pub. 1998, 278 pages, ISBN #0-89308-707-6.

TN 128 $35.00

This middle Tennessee county was created in 1803 from Davidson, Williamson & Wilson Counties. It is surrounded by the present-day counties of: Bedford, Cannon, Coffee, Davidson, Marshall, Williamson, & Wilson counties.

Smith County, Tennessee 1824-1871, Chancery Court Records *of.* By: Thomas E. Partlow, Pub. 2001, 282 pages, Hard Cover, Index, ISBN #0-89308-749-1.

TN 147 $35.00

Chancery Court Records are extremely important to researchers because they contain estate settlements of many early settlers who died without leaving a Will (intestate). In addition to estate settlements, these records also include such things as divorces, and after 1865, some Civil War information. These records provide many detailed breakthroughs in family research not found elsewhere. This book is a valuable research and reference tool that often supplies that missing link of the family, frequently naming fathers, mothers, children, grandchildren, siblings, aunts, and uncles.

Smith County, Tennessee 1799-1804, Court Minutes *of.* By: WPA, Pub. 1938, reprinted 2014, 139 pages, soft cover, Index, ISBN #0-89308-332-1.

TN 168 $18.50

Smith County was formed in 1799 from part of Sumner County, and most of the early settlers were from N.C., and VA. via East Tennessee. In these abstracts, one will find local office holders being appointed, the levying and expenditure of local taxes, selecting & summoning of juries, licenses being granted to operators of taverns, as well as deeds & bills of sale being acknowledge by the grantor. The Court also oversaw a wide range of matters involving estates, including probate of will, settlements of estates, and appraisement, as well as matters dealing with bastardy, and many other valuable bits of information.

Smith County, Tennessee Deeds, 1800-1835. (5 Volumes) By: Thomas Partlow, soft cover, Index.

Vol. #1, 1800-1835: Pub. 1993, 402 pages, Index, ISBN #0-89308-489-1

TN 69 $38.50

Vol. #2, 1835-1852: Pub. 1997, 358 pages, Index, ISBN #0-89308-383-6.

TN 74 $38.50

Vol. #3, 1852-1860: Pub. 1999, 167 pages, Index, ISBN #0-89308-765-3

TN 150 $23.50

Vol. #4, 1860-1876: Pub. 1999, 283 pages, Index, ISBN #0-89308-766-1

TN 151 $35.00

Vol. #5, 1876-1884: Pub. 2005, 121 pages, Index, ISBN #-89308-767-X

TN 152 $17.50

Smith County was formed in 1799 from part of Sumner County, and most of the early settlers were from N.C., VA. via East Tennessee. The deeds of Smith County are probably the most complete records available for this time period and with the marriages available in printed format from 1838-1881 these Deed Abstracts make an excellent source to try and reconstruct marriages as implied in the Deeds of Smith County for this early time period. Smith County adjoined Sumner and Wilson counties at the time of its formation. Deeds are GREAT source for genealogical research due to the many and varied family members that are mentioned. Not only will the reader find the deed transaction itself, but often times such things as: marriages, relinquishment of dower, divisions of family farms among heirs, remarriages of widows are just a few of the matters you can anticipate finding within records of deeds.

Sumner County, Tennessee 1786-1833, First Land Grants *of.* By: Helen & Tim Marsh, Pub. 2001, 184 pages, soft cover, Index, ISBN #0-89308-744-0.

TN 141 $25.00

Sumner County was created in 1786 out of Davidson County. The first major influx of settlers arrived in 1779. It was only the 2nd county created by the State of N.C. in the Cumberland Country. From Sumner County's original boundary lines were created in whole or in part the counties of: Cannon, Clay, DeKalb, Jackson, Macon, Pickett, Putnam, Robertson, Rutherford, Smith, Trousdale, and Wilson. These northern counties were subject to the Walker Line, which was the disputed State line between KY. & TN.

Washington County, Tennessee Deeds 1775-1817. 2 volumes. By: Lorraine Rae, Pub. 1991 & 2010, Index.

Vol. #1, 1755-1800: 234 pages, Hard Cover, Index, ISBN #0-89308-689-4.

TN 121 $35.00

Vol. #2, 1797-1817: 200 pages, soft cover, ISBN #0-89308-488-3.

TN 122 $30.00

Deeds are GREAT source for genealogical research due to the many and varied family members that are mentioned. Not only will the reader find the deed transaction itself, but often times such things as: marriages, relinquishment of dower, divisions of family farms among heirs, remarriages of widows are just a few of the matters you can anticipate finding within records of deeds.

Washington County, Tennessee Marriages, 1780-1870. By: Golden Burgner, Pub. 1985, reprinted 2012, 224 pages, soft cover, Index, ISBN # 0-89308-564-2.

TN 89 $30.00

Washington county was formed in 1777 from part of Wilkes & Burke counties, North Carolina, and included all of the present state of Tennessee. It is the oldest county in the state and from it all of the other counties in Tennessee were carved out. Most of these early settlers were from North Carolina & Virginia.

Washington County, Tennessee Settlements *of* Estates, 1790-1841. By: Emmett Lucas, Jr & Ella Sheffield, Pub. 1999, 200 pages, Index, Hard Cover, ISBN #0-89308-528-6.

TN 133 $32.50

This East Tennessee County was created in 1777 from Wilkes and Burke counties, North Carolina. From it, all the other counties in Tennessee have been carved.

Washington County, Tennessee, Superior Court Minutes, 1791-1804. By: W.P.A., Pub. 1938, Reprinted 2016, 164 pages, Index, ISBN #0-89308-879-X.

TN 177 $20.00

Washington County was created in 1777 from part of Wilkes and Burke Counties, North Carolina. It is the oldest county in the state and from it all of the other counties in Tennessee were carved out. Most of these early settlers were from North Carolina and Virginia.

Washington County, Tennessee Wills, 1777-1872. By: Golden F. Burgner, Pub. 1983, Reprinted 2012,162 pages, soft cover, Index, ISBN # 0-89308-285-6.

TN 64 $25.00

Washington county was formed in 1777 from part of Wilkes & Burke counties, North Carolina, and included all of the present state of Tennessee. It is the oldest county in the state and from it all of the other counties in Tennessee were carved out. Most of these early settlers were from North Carolina, Virginia.

White County, Tennessee Court *of* Pleas

& Quarter Sessions, 1835-1841. By: W.P.A., Pub. 1941, reprinted 2015, 473 pages, soft cover, Index, ISBN #0-89308-454-9.

TN 169 $48.50

White County was created in 1806 from Smith County. In these levying and expenditure of local taxes, selecting & summoning of juries, licenses being granted to operators of taverns, as well as deeds & bills of sale being acknowledge by the grantor. The Court also oversaw a wide range of matters involving estates, including probate of will, settlements of estates, and appraisement, as well as matters dealing with bastardy, and many other valuable bits of information.

Williamson County, TN. Marriage Records, 1800-1850. By: Wilena Roberts BeJach, Pub. 1957, Reprinted 2018, 296 pages, Index, ISBN #0-89308-909-5.

TN 111 $30.00

Williamson County was formed in 1799 from Davidson County, and until 1804 it extended to the Alabama line. Later counties cut out of this original Williamson County were: Bedford, Lincoln, Marshall, Maury, Rutherford, and Giles. This book contains over 5,000 marriages. All of which were copied from the original bonds and licenses. During this time frame, various factors such as: bad roads, long distances from courthouse, and weather would cause clergymen or justices of the peace who performed the ceremonies not to record the rites solemnized by them. Hence, we often find the bond but not the return by the official.

Wilson County, Tennessee Chancery Court Records, 1842-1892. By: Thomas Partlow, Pub. 2005, 261 pages, soft cover, Index, ISBN #0-89308-763-7.

TN 148 $38.50

Wilson County is a pivotal county in the early settlement of Tennessee and in the subsequent migration of people westward. It is surrounded by the counties of: Cannon, DeKalb, Rutherford, Smith and Sumner. Chancery court records have provided many a detailed breakthroughs in family research not found elsewhere. This book is valuable research and reference tool that often supplies that missing link of the family frequently naming fathers, mothers, children, grandchildren, brother, sisters, aunts and uncles, considering that these courts heard cases that covered land and inheritance. As these so-called friendly suits were heard in Chancery Court, estates were divided and settled in great detail, naming complete families and often naming states where members of the families settled. Many lost or destroyed Wills are reconstructed in great detail herein.

Wilson County, Tennessee Chancery Court Minutes, 1873-1905. By: Thomas Partlow, Pub. 2018, 342 pages, Index, ISBN #0-89308-720-3.

TN 159 $35.00

Wilson County is a pivotal county in the early settlement of Tennessee and in the subsequent migration of people westward. It is surrounded by the counties of: Cannon, DeKalb, Rutherford, Smith and Sumner. Chancery court records have provided many a detailed breakthroughs in family research not found elsewhere. This book is valuable research and reference tool that often supplies that missing link of the family frequently naming fathers, mothers, children, grandchildren, brother, sisters, aunts and uncles, considering that these courts heard cases that covered land and inheritance.

Wilson County, Tennessee Circuit Court Records 1810-1875. By: Thomas Partlow, Pub. 2020, soft cover, Index.

Vol. #1, 1810-1855: 137 pages, ISBN #0-89308-635-5.

TN 109 $18.50

Vol. #2, 1858-1875: 132 pages, ISBN #0-89308-818-8.

TN 110 $18.50

Circuit court records are another unique source for tracing those elusive family members. The type of records found within this book are: Petitions for divorce, breach of peace, assault & battery, guardianship, horse stealing, indictments for murders, indictments for larceny, bigamy charges, oaths relating to service in Revolutionary War, Deeds of gifts possession of counterfeit money, and many, many other interesting tidbits of information concerning persons of Wilson County that are not available elsewhere.

Wilson County, Tennessee Deeds, Marriages *and* Wills, 1800-1902. By: Thomas Partlow, Pub. 1987, 244 pages, soft cover, Index, ISBN #0-89308-605-3.

TN 101 $30.00

The county court clerk's office contains marriage records, guardian settlements, wills and inventories, and the minutes of the county court. The records date from 1800 down to the present. Fortunately, none of Wilson County's records are missing. An effort has been made to abstract all of these records from 1800 through 1900. This book is the completion of that effort. This book does include the first of the deed books of Wilson County, Deed Books A & B. Deeds are GREAT source for genealogical research due to the many and varied family members that are mentioned. Not only will the reader find the deed transaction itself, but often times such things as: marriages, relinquishment of dower, divisions of family farms among heirs, remarriages of widows are just a few of the matters you can anticipate finding within records of deeds.

Wilson County, Tennessee Deeds, 1793-1893. (4 Volumes) By: Thomas Partlow, Soft cover, 4 volumes.

Vol. #1, 1793-1829: Pub. 2019, 270 pages, ISBN #0-89308-540-5.

TN 86 $32.50

Vol. #2, 1829-1853: Pub. 1984, Hard Cover, 464 pages, ISBN #0-89308-541-3.

TN 87 $45.00

Vol. #3, 1853-1875: Pub. 2020,509 pages, ISBN #0-89308-833-1.

TN 157 $45.00

Vol. #4, 1875-1893: Pub. 2020, 526 pages, Index, ISBN #0-89308-910-9

TN 172 $48.50

Wilson County is a pivotal county in the early settlement of Tennessee, and in the subsequent migration of people westward. The earliest deeds in Wilson County are located in the register's office. Deeds are GREAT source for genealogical research due to the many and varied family members that are mentioned. Not only will the reader find the deed transaction itself, but often times such things as: marriages, relinquishment of dower, divisions of family farms among heirs, remarriages of widows are just a few of the matters you can anticipate finding within records of deeds.

Wilson County, Tennessee Trust Deed Books EE-NN, 1828-1868. By: Thomas Partlow, Pub 1997, 351 pgs, soft cover, Index, ISBN #0-89308-320-8.

TN 107 $38.50

Trust deeds are really mortgages. People are putting up their property both real and personal, as collateral for loans. This said, there are some deed transactions in these records. These records are tremendously important because they are the records dealing with the buying and selling of slaves in Wilson County. By using census records, as well as other records, including these trust deed books, it should be possible for many people to trace their ancestry back to the slave. To the authors knowledge these Trust Deed Books begin with "EE", because every effort was made and no earlier books were found in the County Court House.

Wilson County, Tennessee Genealogical Resource Material, 1827-1869. By: Thomas Partlow, Pub. 1997, Reprinted 2018, 358 pages, Index, ISBN #0-89308-524-3.

TN 108 $38.50

Wilson County is a pivotal county in the early settlement of Tennessee and in the subsequent migration of people westward. It is surrounded by the counties of: Cannon, DeKalb, Rutherford, Smith and Sumner. Wilson County records date back to the separation of the county from Sumner County in 1799. The records at the courthouse are probably as complete as any records to be found. This book is a companion book for the other books that have been done on Wilson County, covering the 1800's It primarily covers the period from 1827 to 1869. However, it does include events prior to 1827 and past 1869. This book is unique in that some of the records are in private hands and are not available to the public at large: in particular, the Chancery Court Records and the Tax Lists. The records contained in this book are: Power of Attorney Receipts, Fall Creek Baptist Church Minutes, Circuit Court Receipts 1849-1858, Circuit Court Minutes 1851-1860, Chancery Court Minutes 1834-1839, Tax Lists 1827-1829. The Tax lists are of particular value, in that they provide a county census for the years covered.

Wilson County, Tennessee Miscellaneous Records, 1800-1875. By: Thomas Partlow, Pub. 1982, Reprinted 2018, 230 pages, Index, ISBN #0-89308-283-X.

TN 65 $25.00

This book contains 6 Guardian Books for the years 1836-1875; the Minute books 1814-1829; 3 Will and Inventory Records books for 1853-1866; Soldiers Lists for the Revolutionary War and the War of 1812; and Cemetery records for Sugg's Creek and Mount Vernon cemeteries.

Wilson County, Tennessee, 1800-1899, The People *of*. By: Thomas Partlow, Pub.1983, Reprinted 2019, 148 pages, soft cover, Index, ISBN #0-89308-308-9.

TN 77 $20.00

This book contains Wilson County Court Minutes for most of the years from 1802-1875, County Court Judgements for 1809-1819, Quarterly Court Minutes for 1816-1848, Wills & Inventories for 1871-1878. It also has some church records and minutes of Big Spring Church. There are also Lebanon Democrat excerpts. Oaths of Loyalty and some obituaries. This book is a rare glimpse into the lives of those people who lived in Wilson County during the 1800's and no attempt has been made to conceal the truth as revealed in these records.

(Wilson County) Sugg's Creek Meeting House Church Book, 1769-1858. By: Thomas Partlow, Pub. 2022, 136 pages, Index, soft cover,

ISBN #978-1-63914-073-2.

TN 204 $18.50

Sugg's Creek Church lies within Wilson County, Tennessee and was established in 1800 as a Presbyterian Church. Many of its early members had just arrived from York County, South Carolina area. A number of these early transplanted South Carolinians now lie buried in the Sugg's Creek Cemetery. Information to be found with in this book: a short account of the organization of the first Presbyterian Church at Sugg's Creek Meeting House with a brief notice of the origin of the Cumberland Presbyterian Church at this place. Also, a record of names, births, baptisms, deaths, marriages, communions, removals and other necessary church records.

Wilson County, Tennessee Tax Lists, 1830-1832. By: Thomas Partlow, Pub. 2008, 180 pages, soft cover, Index, ISBN #0-89308-837-4.

TN 164 $25.00

Wilson County is a pivotal county in the early settlement of Tennessee and in the subsequent migration of people westward. It is surrounded by the counties of: Cannon, DeKalb, Rutherford, Smith and Sumner. Some of the least know records for the state of Tennessee are the Land Tax Lists. Within these land tax lists, you will discover not only the owner's name and acreage but with a little effort you will be able to follow a family through its land holdings. You can see when a person dies, when he sells out and leaves the county, when he passes his land down to his children. Of special interest, after the owners name sometimes a set of initials will appear. These can mean one of several things: they can be the initials of the person he purchased the land from, or they can mean the location of the land such as a creeks name or geographical feature. These tax lists can be extremely important because sometimes when there was not a will or a deed, the transaction appears in these lists and nowhere else.

Wilson County, Tennessee Wills, 1802-1850. By: Thomas Partlow, Pub. 1981, reprinted 1998, 222 pages, Hard Cover, Index, ISBN #0-89308-230-9.

TN 28 $30.00

Wilson County records date back to the separation of the county from Sumner County in 1799. The records at the courthouse are probably as complete as any records to be found. The abstracts are taken from the first thirteen Wills & Inventories books to be found at the courthouse. The index contains the names of some 8,500 names.

Marriages, Deaths, & Taxes

Early East Tennessee Taxpayers, 1778-1839. By: Pollyanna Creekmore, Pub. 1980, reprinted 2015, 328 pages, soft cover, Index, ISBN #0-89308-145-0.

TN 25 $35.00

The counties and year of their respective tax lists are as follows: Anderson 1801, Blount 1801, Campbell 1818, Carter 1796, Cocke 1839, Grainger 1799, Greene 1787 and 1805, Hawkins 1809-1812, Jefferson 1800, Knox 1806, Sullivan 1796, and Washington 1778.

Marriages *from* Early Tennessee Newspapers, 1794-1851. By: Rev. S. Emmett Lucas, Jr., Orig. Pub. 1978, reprinted 2005, 544 pages, Hard Cover, Index, ISBN #0-89308-092-6.

TN 19 $52.50

Until their publication by S.H.P., Inc., these marriage records from the EARLIEST Tennessee newspapers had been available ONLY at the Tennessee State Library and Archives in Nashville in their card files. These marriage notices cover the ENTIRE state of Tennessee for the most part, beginning with the earliest ones in 1794 in the Knoxville Gazette. The total number of such marriage notices is approximately 12,000 or more and contains such information as: name of bride's father, often times both bride and groom's place of residence (county and state); sometimes the groom's occupation; date of marriage and where it was performed and sometimes the officiating minister's name; ages of Bride and Groom. A brief resume of states other than Tennessee where such marriages were performed or the former home of either the bride or groom: AL, AR, CT, FL, KY, MS, MO, MD, LA, IA, IN, IL, NY, NC, NJ, OH, PA, SC, VT, WV, & VA to cite but a few. Newspapers from which both the Marriages & Obituaries have been taken: The Knoxville Gazette, The Daily Republican Banner, The Western Weekly Review (Franklin, TN.), The Politician and Weekly Nashville, The Nashville True Whig and Weekly Commercial Advertiser, National Banner, Impartial Review and Cumberland repository, Nashville.

Obituaries *from* Early Tennessee Newspapers, 1794-1851. By: Rev. S. Emmett Lucas, Jr., Orig. Pub. 1978, reprinted 2005, 432 pages, Hard Cover, Index, ISBN #0-89308-093-4.

TN 20 $42.50

As just described in the above book on Early Tennessee Marriage Notices, these Obituaries taken from the above Early Tennessee newspapers have been available ONLY at the Tennessee State Library & Archives in Nashville. These approximately 7,000 death notices contain date and place of death, sometimes the cause of death, survivors, age at time of death, etc.... A glance at these notices shows for instance: one person dying in 1807 aged 60; another dying in 1815 aged 88; another in 1832 aged 95. Thus, the reader can readily see that these Obituaries will often carry a person back well into the early 1700's.

Obituaries *from* Tennessee Newspapers, 1851-1899. By: Jill K. Knight, Pub. 1980, reprinted 2014, 476 pages, soft cover, Index, ISBN #0-89308-174-4.

TN 5 $43.50

This volume contains obituaries and other genealogical information from more than 60 Tennessee and North Alabama newspapers from 1851-1899. Many of these papers are from the author's personal collection of more than 80 bound sets and cannot be found in the State Library. However, many have been microfilmed. Some newspapers listed are not complete volumes, as often only one or two papers might have survived. Additional information included is of a genealogical nature is such information that might add to a complete picture of people who lived from 1851-1899. Out-of-State obituaries were often included in these papers. The majority of the obits are for the Civil war period, a time when some counties were occupied by Federal troops and their records were not kept with any regularity.

Biographical Sketches & Family Histories

Cumberland Region *of* Tennessee, Biographical Sketches *of the*. By: G.A. Ogle & Company, Publishers, Pub. 1898, reprinted 1995, 291 pages, Hard Cover, Index, ISBN #0-89308-191-4.

TN 22 $35.00

This almost unknown and overlooked book has been reprinted as to bring to the reader's attention and use some 228 biographical sketches of individuals who lived in the Cumberland Region of East Tennessee. Surnames for which biographies are to be found are: Alley, Anderson, Annis, Ashburn, Austin, Barber Baumgartner, Beene, Berry, Biley, Billingsley, Blocklock, Boyd, Brady, Brewer, Bright, Brown (2), Bull, Burnett, Cain, Carpenter, Center, Clark, Cotnam, Cummings, Dame, Davis (4), Dlakins, Dietzen, Dykes, Farmer, Flynn, Foster (2), Frater, Garrison, Gillenine, Gill, Gilliam, Gallreath, Griffith, Grissom, Griswold, Groupon (3), Greer (3), Gunn, Hall, Humby (4), Hamilton, Hargis, Harris, Hastons, Havron, Haynes (2), Heard, Hendrix, Henson, Hicks, Hinch, Hillis, Hodges, Hoodenpyle, Howland, Hudson, Hunter, Hutcheson, Janeway, Jenkins, Johnson (2), Jones, Justin, Kearley, Kell (2), Kelley, Kell (5), Keeling, Ladd, Lamb, Lay, Lockhart, Long, McDaniel, McElroy, McGlothen, McLarney, McNabb, McRee, McReynolds (4), Mabry, Mansfield (2), Marugg (2), Meyer, Minter, Morgan, Moore (2), Morrison, Moyers, Northcut (3), Norwood (2), Pankey, Paine, Parham, Parkins (2), Partin, Parker, Patton (3), Peck, Pearson, Peay, Pike, Prigmore, Proctor, Pryor (6), Orange, Overturf, Rankin, Real, Revfro, Richards, Riggle, Roberson, Roberts, Rogers (2), Rust, Safley, Sanders, Sexton, Schild (2), Scurggs, Schoolfield, Seamons, Shirley, Shoemate, Simmons (2), Skillern, Skelton (2), Silver, Smith, Smartt, Snodgrass, Sparkman (3), Spears, Stewart, Standifer, Stone, Swafford (2), Swan, Taylor (2), Tate (2), Thach (2), Thompson, Thurman, Thaxton, Turner, Weaver, Whitlock, Wiley, Willis, Witson, Woodlee (2), Worthington (2), Vick, Von Bergen.

(Eastern TN.) Leaves *from the* Family Tree. By: Penelope J. Allen, Pub.1982, reprinted 2010, 464 pages, 7" x 10" Hard Cover, Index, ISBN #0-98308-227-9.

TN 37 $75.00

This book is a collection of family histories primarily in East Tennessee which the author compiled and wrote for the Chattanooga Times Sunday Magazine from December 3. 1933 to March 21, 1937. A list of the families is found below: Abel, Anderson (2), Bean, Blizard, Brooks, Buchanan, Butler, Callaway, Campbell, Cate, Cleage, Cleveland, Clingan, Coffey, Craigmiles, Cravens, Darwin, Day, Donahoo, Doran-Donelly, Edwards (2), Everett, Fisk, Foster, Foust, Gamble, Gaut, Gillespie, Goodner, Greer (3), Guthrie, Hambright, Hildebrand, Hooke, Hughes, Igou, Johnson, Jones, Julian, Lauderdale, Lea, Leeper, Leuty, Lillard, Lowrey, Lusk, Matlock-Howard, Mayberry, McCarty, McDonald, McLaurine, McMillin, McNair, Meigs, Morgan, Parks, Patterson, Pettigrew, Pope, Ramsey, Randolph, Rankin, Roane, Robertson, Roddye, Ross, Rowles, Sevier, Shelton, Shugart, Smith-Morgan, Smith, Stewart, Still, Swann, Tate, Thurman, Trewhitt, Turney, Van Dyke, Vann, Waterhouse, Weatherly, Whiteside, and Yarnell. The persons within this book touch and or cover ALL parts of Eastern Tennessee. These family histories are quite detailed with many notations going back to the early to mid 1700's with many instances going back across the Atlantic Ocean. One can expect to find families going back 5-6 generations listing such things as: marriages, deaths, births, names of in-laws, occupations, land owned, Revolutionary War service, War of 1812 service, Civil War service, Indian skirmishes, residence and former residences, contributions to the community, education, church affiliations. Not only is this basically a Biographical Sketch book on persons from Eastern Tennessee but, the author has also included several other items of genealogical value such as: Tax Lists for the counties of Grainger-1805, Jefferson-1800, and Rhea-1808, along with church minutes from McMinn & Rhea Counties, Revolutionary pensioners & soldiers in the War of 1812 for Franklin county, 1805 Taxable Polls for Grainger County, Revolutionary Soldiers of McMinn County, Revolutionary Graves in Tennessee, Court Minutes of Rhea County 1821, SOME Jefferson County Baptisms-Births-Marriages-Deaths form church minutes 1818-1822, Warrants & Claims of land from persons living in Tennessee who served in the War of 1812 including the Creek War, a list of applications of widows & orphans for the War of 1812 pensions, and many, many other useful items of genealogical interest for the East Tennessee researcher.

Sketches *of* Prominent Tennesseans. By: William S. Speer, Orig. Pub. 1888, reprinted 1997, 728 pages, Hard Cover, Index, ISBN #0-89308-094-2.

TN 24 $48.00

This very rare and much sought out book is similar to many of the Biographical Sketch books done throughout the country of this era. With the only one exception, that this book covers the entire state and not a specific geographical region. These 259 biographical sketches list the important events in the life of the subject, his noteworthy contributions to the city and/or state, date of birth, names of parents, and sometimes his ancestors, name of spouse and her date and place of birth and name of her parents, and names of children and spouses of the Biographies'. Surnames for which biographies are to be found are too numerous to list due to space.

150 Prominent Tennesseans, Biographical Questionnaires *of.* By: John Trotwood Moore and Colleen Morse Elliott, Pub. 1982, 148 pages, soft cover, Index, ISBN #0-89308-222-8.

TN 35 $20.00

Surnames covered are: Allison, Amis, Baptist, Bass, Bates, Banter, Bennett, Boyle, Brister, Brown (2), Bryan, Butler, Byrns, Campbell, Capehart, Caperton, Chandler, Chappell, Choate, Clark, Clarke, Clayton, Cook, Cooper (2), Creswell, Croskey, Cunningham, Davis (2), De La Vergne, Depew, De Witt, Dorsey, Drinnon (2), Durham, Easterley, Easterly, Edwards, Ellis, English, Eskridge, Farrell, Finney, Flynn, Fort, Frazier, Gailor, Gant, Gardenhire, Garrison, Gilbert, Ginn, Griffin, Hake, Hamilton, Harper, Harrell, Harris, Harwell, Haston, Haynie, Hearn, Hewgley, Hill (2), Hughes, Jackson (2), Jamison, Jarratt, Jetton, Johnson, Keaton, Kelley, Kemper, Kenny, King (2), Kruesi, Larkins, Larsen, Lawrence, Littlefield, McDaniel, McDonald, McKenzie, McKnight, McLean, McMurray, McReynolds (2), Major, Malone, Marable, Marshall, Matthews, Maxey, Mitchell (2), Moffitt, Moore (2), Murrey, Musgrove, Nelson, Newman, Newton, Norment, Nuehols, Odel, Officier (2), O'Guin, O'Meara, Patton, Peek, Perry, Pile, Polk, Remine, Rice, Rowsey, Simmons, Sloan, Smith, Stalcup, Stewart, Swann, Sweet, Swink, Terry, Testerman, Tillman, Warren, Weems (2), West, White (2), Willett, Williamson, Wilson, Winsor, Wiseman, Yoakley, and York.

Goodspeed's
Biographical Sketches & Family Histories

History *of* Tennessee: The General History. By: Goodspeed Publishing Company, Pub. 1887, Reprinted 2020, 870 pages, NEW FULL NAME Index, ISBN #0-89308-123-X.

TN 6 $62.50

This is the general or historical portion of probably the Rarest and MOST VALUABLE set of books ever published on the state of Tennessee and its early families. This book is the missing 796 pages that originally appeared front of all 16 Tennessee Illustrated books by Goodspeed Publishing Company. Like most works of this kind, this edition contains a history of the state with its ties to early Tennessee; these are followed by varying appendices one of which contains a listing of both Federal and Confederate troops in service from Tennessee. This is an extremely detailed and complete history of the state covering such things as: The Mound Builders and the age of the Mounds, The Natchez, the Pioneers and Pioneer Days, The Indian Tribes throughout the State, Earliest Indian Occupation, French Trading Stations, Spanish Influence, The Settlement of Tennessee from the First Settlements of Tennessee including Brown's Settlement to Daniel Boone to Washington County, North Carolina, Affairs on the Cumberland to the settlement of Western TN, early Politics and extension of Frontier lines, The First Census (1795) of Tennessee, Tennessee's part in the Revolutionary War, Mexican War, the Seminole War, War of 1812 along with the Battle of Wahoo Swamp. Even a list of Troops sent to Mexico, there is considerable amounts of information and data on Tennessee's involvement in the Civil War, Tennessee's Federal Military History during the Civil War along with-it Confederate's History, Slavery, Biographical Sketches of: Blount, Bell, Brownlow, Carroll, Crocket, Forrest, Grundy, Haywood, Houston, Jackson, Johnson, Polk, Robertson, Sevier, White, and Zollicoffer. The NEW FULL NAME Index for this reprint has approximately 4,500 entries.

Carroll, Henry, *and* Benton Counties, Tennessee, History of. By: Goodspeed Publishing Company, Pub. 1887, reprinted 2015, 176 pages, soft cover, New Index, ISBN #0-89308-098-5.

TN 9 $22.50

This volume contains 175 biographical sketches of individuals along with genealogical data on some 500 other families/individuals from the above-mentioned counties. The index mentions approx. 3,500 persons.

Fayette *and* Hardeman Counties, History of. BY: Goodspeed Publishing Company, Orig. Pub. 1887, Reprinted 2017, 188 pages, New Index, Soft Cover, ISBN #0-89308-112-4.

TN 11 $22.50

It also contains biographical sketches of some 175 individuals in these counties and genealogical data on some 500 other families / individuals.

Gibson, Obion, Weakley, Dyer *and* Lake Counties, Tennessee, History of. By: Goodspeed Publishing Company, Orig. Pub. 1886, reprinted 1988, 352 pages, New Indx, Hard Cover, ISBN #0-89308-096-9.

TN 7 $37.50

It contains biographical sketches of some 750 individuals in these counties and genealogical data on some 3,000 other families / individuals.

Giles, Lincoln, Franklin *and* Moore Counties, Tennessee, History of. By: Goodspeed Publishing Company, Orig. Pub. 1886, reprinted 1997, 181 pages, New Index, Hard Cover, ISBN #0-89308-116-7.

TN 15 $30.00

This volume contains biographical sketches of some 332 individuals of these counties and genealogical data on some 1,400 other families / individuals.

Hamilton County, Tennessee, History of. By: Goodspeed Publishing Company, Pub. 1887, Reprinted 2018, 256 pages, New Index, soft cover, ISBN #0-89308-126-4.

TN 197 $27.50

This volume contains biographical sketches of some 250 individuals in these counties and genealogical data on some 1200 other families / individuals.

Henderson, Chester, McNairy, Decatur, *and* Hardin Counties, Tennessee, History *of.* By: Goodspeed Publishing Company, Pub. 1886, reprinted 2017, 130 pages, soft cover, New Index, ISBN #0-89308-097-7.

TN 8 $18.50

This volume contains 168 biographical sketches of individuals along with genealogical data on some 500 other families/individuals from the above mention counties. The index mentions approx. 3,500 persons.

Knox County, Tennessee, History of. By: Goodspeed Publishing Company, Orig. Pub. 1887, Reprinted 2017, 304 pages, New Index, Soft Cover, ISBN #0-89308-125-6.

TN 61 $30.00

It also contains biographical sketches of some 400 individuals in these counties and genealogical data on some 1000 other families / individuals.

Lauderdale, Tipton, Haywood *and* Crockett Counties, Tennessee, History of. By: Goodspeed Publishing Company, Orig. Pub. 1886, reprinted 1997 208 pages, New Index, Hard Cover, ISBN #0-89308-099-3.

TN 10 $30.00

This volume contains biographical sketches of some 365 individuals and genealogical data on some 1,500 other families / individuals.

Lawrence, Wayne, Perry, Hickman *and* Lewis Counties, Tennessee, History of. By: Goodspeed Publishing Company, Orig. Pub. 1886, reprinted 1979, 129 pages, New Index, Soft Cover, ISBN #0-89308-113-2.

TN 12 $20.00

This volume contains biographical sketches of some 222 individuals and genealogical data on some 1,000 other families / individuals.

Madison County, Tennessee, History of. By: Goodspeed Publishing Company, Orig. Pub. 1887, Reprinted 1979, 120 pages, New Index, Hard Cover, ISBN #0-89308-114-0.

TN 13 $25.00

This volume contains biographical sketches of some 120 individuals and genealogical data on some 400 other families / individuals.

Maury, Williamson, Rutherford, Wilson, Bedford, *and* Marshall Counties, Tennessee, History *of.* By: Goodspeed's Publishing Company, Orig. Pub. 1887, reprinted 2017, 536 pages, New Index, Soft Cover, ISBN #0-89308-629-0.

TN 106 $48.50

This volume contains biographical sketches of some 1,031 individuals in these counties and genealogical data of some 20,000 other families / individuals. A new index has been created to make this book more useful fo r the reader.

Montgomery, Robertson, Humphries, Stewart, Dickson, Cheatham, *and* Houston Counties, Tennessee, History of. By: Goodspeed Publishing Company, Pub. 1886, reprinted 2017, 728 pages, soft cover, New Index, ISBN #0-89308-117-5.

TN 16 $58.50

This volume contains biographical sketches of some 700 individuals in these counties and genealogical data on some 3,000 other families / individuals. The index mentions over 12,000 persons.

Shelby County, Tennessee, History of. By: Goodspeed Publishing Company, Pub. 1887, Reprinted 2018, 285 pages, New Index, soft cover, ISBN #0-89308-231-7.

TN 198 $30.00

This volume contains biographical sketches of some 250 individuals in these counties and genealogical data on some 1500 other families / individuals.

Sumner, Smith, Macon *and* Trousdale Counties, Tennessee, History of. By: Goodspeed Publishing Company, Orig. Pub. 1887, reprinted 2020, 216 pages, New Index, Soft Cover, ISBN #0-89308-115-9.

TN 14 $25.00

This volume contains biographical sketches of some 202 individuals in these counties and genealogical data on some 900 other families / individuals.

Thirty East Tennessee Counties, History of. By: Goodspeed Publishing Company, Orig. Pub. 1887, reprinted 2006, 526 pages, New Index, Hard Cover, ISBN #0-89308-188-4.

TN 18 $50.00

This volume contains biographical sketches of some 1,200 and genealogical data of some 30,000 other families / individuals for the following counties: Anderson, Blount, Bradley, Campbell, Clairborne, Cocke, Grainger, Greene, Hamblen, Hamilton, Hancock, Hawkins, James, Jefferson, Johnson, Knox, Loudon, McMinn, Meigs, Monroe, Morgan, Polk, Rhea, Roane, Sevier, Sullivan, Unicoi, Union, and Washington.

Miscellaneous Records

35,000 Tennessee Marriage Records *and* Bonds, 1783-1870. (3 Volumes) By: Silas E. Lucas, Jr & Ella L Sheffield, Pub. 1981, Reprinted 2018, Soft Cover, Index

Vol. #1, "A-F": 542 pages, Index, ISBN #0-89308-223-6.

TN 200 $48.50

Vol. #2, "G-N": 544 pages, Index, ISBN #0-89308-224-4.

TN 201 $48.50

Vol. #3, "O-Z": 516 pages, Index, ISBN #0-89308-225-2

TN 202 $48.50

The 3 Volume Set: ISBN #0-89308-226-0
TN 48 $125.00

These marriage bonds taken from almost every county in Tennessee between the period 1783 down to about 1870 have, until the publication of this set of books, only been available in the card file at the Tennessee State Library and Archives in Nashville, TN. Each book is arranged alphabetically by Groom with an accompanying bride's name index. Besides the names of the bride and groom, the reader will discover the issue date of the bond, the name of the bondsman and the county of residence.

North Carolina Land Grants *in* Tennessee, 1778-1791. By: Golden F. Burgner, Pub. 1981, reprinted 1990, 214 pages, soft cover, Index, ISBN #0-89308-205-8.

TN 33 $25.00

This book contains 5,486 land grants issued by the State of North Carolina in the State of Tennessee. The counties in which this land fell were: Davidson, Greene, Hawkins, Sullivan, Sumner, Tennessee, Washington, and the eastern, Middle and Western districts.

(MAPS 1790-1920) The Formation *of* Tennessee Counties. By: Austin P. Foster, Pub. 1923, Reprinted 1989, 124 pages, maps, Hard Cover, index, ISBN #0-89308-239-2.

TN 58 $28.50

The book is arranged alphabetically by county in 3 sections for the 3 major divisions of Tennessee, viz East Middle, and West. Data is given on the information of each county and the counties from which each was formed with dates and other pertinent data which will greatly assist the researcher in learning more about the formation and growth of Tennessee's 95 counties and will assist the Genealogist in his research. A series of maps have been added to this reprint. These important maps present modern county boundaries as they exist in each of the federal censuses from 1790 through 1920. Then, on each of these maps the old county boundary lines are superimposed over the modern ones to highlight the boundary changes at ten-year intervals. These maps are extremely helpful in researching the state of Tennessee for the periods given as most counties underwent many and varied boundary changes.

Some Tennessee Heroes *of the* Revolution. By: Zella Armstrong, Pub. 1933, reprinted 2022, 160 pages, soft cover, ISBN #978-1-63914-089-3.

TN 51 $22.50

Even though Tennessee was not formed until after the Revolutionary War, she did have settlers of her current boundaries that show up within the North Carolina Rolls. This book is based on the Invalid Lists of 1806, which only awarded pensions to those who were disabled by reason of the War and the Pension Lists of 1818, 1832 and 1840. The reader will discover valuable information on several hundred pensioners within while providing information such as: name, age, date and place of birth, residence, date of the pension application, service record, names of all family members, and place or places of migration to and from, or within the State of Tennessee. Of special interest, it should be noted that the 1840 Pension List includes widows' applications. These widows were required to submit proof of marriage and children. Because of this, their applications provide a rich source of genealogical source material. This book has data on several hundred Revolutionary War veterans while documenting several thousand related family members.

Tennessee Soldiers *in the* Revolution. By: Penelope Johnson Allen, Pub. 1935, Reprinted 2022, 72 pages, soft cover, ISBN #978-1-63914-088-6.

TN 55 $15.00

This book is a roster of those North Carolina frontiersmen who were patriots to the cause of independence. This listing of Revolutionary soldiers taken from the Revolutionary Army Accounts of North Carolina in the State Archives at Raleigh, showing claims against North Carolina for service by men of the two western-most counties of Washington and Sullivan, which later became a part of Tennessee. The author has also included data on wills of Washington County, marriages of Blount and Davidson counties, and a final section on Revolutionary grants in Davidson County.

Twenty-Four Hundred Tennessee Pensioners, Revolution *and* War *of* 1812. By: Zella Armstrong, Pub. 1937, reprinted 2022, 122 pages, soft cover, ISBN #978-1-63914-090-9.

TN 56 $18.50

Even though Tennessee was not formed until after the Revolutionary War, she did have settlers of her current boundaries that show up within the North Carolina Rolls. The book is an alphabetical list of 2,400 Tennessee pensioners. It was compiled from the Pension Lists of 1816, 1818, 1828, 1832, and the U.S. Census of 1840. Information to be found within: name, age, residence, service, and the source of the data. The reader will also discover that the Widows drawing on their husbands' claims are listed.

Tennesseans *in* Texas: as Found *in the* 1850 Census. By: Helen & Timothy Marsh, Pub. 1986, 416 pages, Hard Cover, Index, ISBN #0-89308-561--8.

TN 94 $45.00

This was compiled as the result of a detailed study of the 1850 Federal Census of Texas, giving the birthplace and deaths of the inhabitants living in Texas in 1850.The book is arranged alphabetically by county for those persons who showed Tennessee as their birth state. Since the person showing Tennessee as the birth state is shown with the other members of his or her household, it becomes easy for one to see the migration patterns that many of these people took upon leaving Tennessee before their arrival in Texas.4

The Tennessee Civil War Veterans Questionnaires (Volumes 1-5). By: Gustavus W. Dyer & John T. Moore, Orig. Pub. 1985, 5 volumes 2,473 pages, Hard Cover, ISBN #0-89308-221-X.

Vol. #1, Contains Federal Veterans (161 veterans) and Confederate Veterans "A-B" (204 veterans): 472 pages, ISBN #0-89308-216-3

TN 40 $50.00

Vol. #2, Contains Confederate Veterans "C-F" (307 veterans): 479 pages, ISBN #0-89308-217-1.

TN 41 $50.00

Vol. #3, Contains Confederate Veterans "G-K" (325 veterans): 487 pages, ISBN #0-89308-218-X

TN 42 $50.00

Vol. #4, Contains Confederate Veterans "I-Q" 317 veterans): 510 pages, ISBN #0-89308-219-8

TN 43 $50.00

Vol. #5, Contains Confederate Veterans "R-Z" (373 veterans): 525 pages, ISBN #-89308-220-1

TN 44 $50.00

The 5 Volume Set: ISBN #-89308-221-X
TN 39 $250.00

Veterans of the Civil War have long been dead and with their passing were stories and memories of people and places...Memories of lives offered for their homeland. This set of books, Tennessee Civil War Questionnaires, helps to preserve some of this history. It is the publication of responses to questionnaires that were sent to Tennessee Civil War veterans in 1914-1915 and again in 1920. Veteran who responded included not only those who served in Tennessee units and were still living in other states..... and some men who enlisted in other states and who had moved to Tennessee by the time of the survey. Although the questionnaires differed somewhat in the order of information requested, the responses generally included the veteran's place of residence, age, place of enlistment, unit, education, occupations, further information about the origin of his family, his personal property, and land owned before the war by the veteran and his father. In addition, the veterans gave their opinion of social conditions before the war including slavery, an account of their war experiences, and their occupation after the war. They were also asked to list names of their Civil War comrades. These interviewed veterans came from all social classes, and their answers varied from short and barely literate annals of the poor farmer to perceptive assessments of pre-war social conditions and detailed autobiographies of well-educated sons of planters, artisans and merchants. This cross-section of human experience makes the material useful to historians as well as to the genealogists pursuing information about lives of specific ancestors. Both the Federal and Confederate sections have full-name indexes of more than 1,600 veterans, their family members and associates.......

TEXAS

An Abstract *of the* Original Titles *of* Record *in the* General Land Office *of* Texas. By: Mary Lewis Ulmer, Pub. 1838, Reprinted 2022, 186 pages, soft cover, ISBN #978-0-89308-849-8.

TX 8 $22.50

This book is one of the most important and most useful books on early Texas. It contains a listing by colony, alphabetically, of every settler granted land in Texas between 1791 and 1836. Upon this list all land titles in Texas were based, and the land ownership established. In addition, following the names of the grantees, there are columns giving date of titles, quantity of land received, location of the land, and remarks, such as "Sam Houston and Phil Sublett, Agents." This is one of the fundamental sources of information on the settlement of Texas, moistly for the period ending in 1835. The period actually covered is from the Spanish period through the Mexican grants and the opening of Texas to foreign settlement, principally by Anglo-Americans, to the Declaration of Independence. The date of the earliest grant is October 18,1791 to Edward Murphy, official Indian trader at Nacogdoches and the last one, February 27,1836 to William F. Gray of Austin's Colony.

Biographical Souvenir *of the* State *of* Texas. By: F.A. Battle & Company, Pub. 1889, Reprinted 2017, 960 pages, Index, Hard Cover, ISBN #0-89308-119-1.

TX 1 $85.00

This book, representative of many of the Biographical sketch books done in the late 19th century, is a set of 1740 Biographical sketches on many early Texas families. It is liberally illustrated with photographs and finely executed steele engravings of some of the men and women whose lives are sold in this volume. Many of the families have their genealogies carried well back into the mid-1700's. To see a complete listing of surnamesof these biographies, go to our website to find thois book and look at its description.

Early Texas Birth Records, 1838-1878. By: Jane Sumner, Alice Gracy, and Emma S. Gentry, Orig. Pub. 1978, reprinted 2002, 150 pages, Hard Cover, Index, ISBN #0-89308-130-2.

TX 6 $28.50

Many persons believe that birth records in Texas were not kept until 1903. However, the Texas Constitution Convention of 1869 called for the registration of births, deaths and marriages in every organized county and such was set up by legislative action in 1873 and repealed in 1876. A few counties continued to keep birth records of which the number was 43 counties. Of these, 25 counties had their original books. Often when registering a child born during the years 1873-1878, the parents would list all of their previous children, hence there are many quite early dates, as early as 1838.

East Texas Newspapers 1839-1856, Abstracts of Early. By: Linda Cheves Nicklas, Pub. 1994, Reprinted 2017, 168 pages, Index, ISBN #0-89308-503-0.

TX 17 $20.00

This new title of newspaper abstracts covers papers in Clarksville, Marshall, Nacogdoches, and San Augustine. Texas did not require the filing of death certificates until 1903 and hence for someone trying to locate the death of a family member for early to mid-19th century deaths. The author has attempted to locate all death notices found in these papers, as well as marriage notices which generally gave additional information not available elsewhere, such as parents' names, state of origin and full name of the parties. Also included is data of historical interest, such as the establishment of new towns and steamship travel. A number of EAST TEXAS counties have suffered devastating losses of records due to courthouse fires. In cases of "burned" counties, not only were marriages included, but so is other information ordinarily found in county records, such as probate notices.

East Texas, Memorial *and* Genealogical Records *of.* By: Goodspeed Publishing Company, Pub. 1895, reprinted 1982, over 465 pages, Hard Cover, Index, ISBN #0-89308-300-3.

TX 14 $42.50

This book contains approximately 200 Biographical Sketches of these early citizens.

El Paso Newspapers *to* 1885, Births, Deaths, *and* Marriages in. By: Jane Beard, Pub. 1982, Reprinted 2018, 248 pages, INDEX, soft cover, ISBN #0-89308-171-X.

TX 7 $30.00

This book contains all the genealogical information given for births, deaths and marriages that appeared in these early newspapers for the states of Arizona, New Mexico, Texas and Oklahoma (Indian Territory). If they occurred elsewhere but had a connection with this area, they were included. Many people came from other states, particularly the Northern states from Illinois east, for their health. Many died here, some went home to die, but their death was reported in this area. Some came to die and stayed to live. Many Americans died in New Mexico and have been included along with some who died in other Central and South America countries. If you had a relative who "went West" and disappeared before 1886, this book could be of GREAT HELP.

Galveston, Texas 1846-1871, Ships Passenger List *of the* Port *of.* By: The Galveston Co. Genealogical Society, Pub. 1984, 272 pages, Hard Cover, Index, ISBN #0-89308-343-7.

TX 12 $30.00

This is the only early ships' passenger list that has survived for Texas. Information you will find includes name of vessel, name of master, port of departure, name of passenger, age, sex, occupation, origin, and destination. This book contains more than 9,000 names and is a very valuable tool for this time period.

Galveston, Texas, Baptismal, Confirmation, Marriage *and* Death Records, 1860-1952, St. Joseph Catholic Church. By: Galveston County Gen'l Society, Pub. 1984, Reprinted 2018, 272 pages, INDEX, soft cover, ISBN #0-89308-344-5.

TX 13 $35.00

If you have German ancestors that came to Texas or through Texas to the Midwest, in the mid-1800's, this book is a MUST. Many Germans came to the Republic of Texas on German land contracts through the Ports of Galveston and stayed to raise their families. By 1855, they had been joined by others, making German's population close to one-half German. It was at this time that the Catholic Diocese tried to build a church in Galveston so services could be held in German. This book has confirmations, communions, marriages, births and deaths from 1860 to 1952. There are approximately 13,500 names in this four-part-book.

Hopkins County, Texas, Early History *of.* Biographical Sketches and Incidents of the early Settled Families. By: E.B. Fleming, Pub. 1902, reprinted 2023, 184 pages, soft cover, ISBN #0-89308-186-8.

TX 22 $22.50

Hopkins County was created in 1846 from Red River County. It lies in the extreme northeastern corner of the state. This book starts out with history of the state and then moves to early life in the county. But the bulk of this book is devoted to biographical sketches of its early settlers. Surnames of biography's: Attaway, Bailey (2), Barclay, Blackwell, Branom, Brumley, Calvert, Campbell, Cargile, Chapman (2), Clifton (2), Collins, Conly, Coyle, Fanning, Garrett, Glover, Green, Hargrave (3), Harper, Hogsett, Holderness, Hopkins, Houston, King, Landers, Lindley (3), Lollar, Martin, Mayes, Melson, Millhollin, Minter, Mooney, Nance, Odom, Petty, Pierce, Preston, Ransom, Russell, Simms (2), Smith, Sparks, Spencer, Stacy, Stout, Sturdivant, Vaden, Waggoners, Weaver (2), White, Williams, and Youngblood.

Houston County, Texas, History *of.* By: By: Armistead A. Aldrich, Pub. 1943, Reprinted 2021, 226 pages, ISBN #978-1-63914-014-5.

TX 20 $25.00

This book is not too different from other county history books of this era. With such topics as County creation, Courthouses, Newspapers, schools, Churches, Spanish Mission & Edens-Madden Massacre - all important in the development of the county - are carefully discussed. This type of county history book can help one develop ideas or paths to those missing ancestors by showing the customs and traditions of the local residents. A particular useful feature of this book is the extensive biographical information included. Almost half of this book is devoted to 73 biographical sketches. Surnames of biographical sketches are: Adair, Adams, Aldrich (6), Allbright, Baker, Barbee, Bayne, Beasley, Beeson (2), Berry, Box, Bracken, Bromberg, Burnett, Coleman, Collins (6), Cooper, Corley, Daniel, Davis (2), Dickerson, English (2), Gossett, Gause, Gillespie, Hall (3), Hallmark, Heflin, Hunter, Ingram, Johnson, Jowers, King (2), Kyle, LeGory, Long, Lundy, Madden, Mainer, Masters, McConnell, McLean, Meiwether, Miller, Monroe, Moore, Murchison (2), Nunn (2), Page, Patton, Pence, Randolph, Read, Rice, Smith, Stidham, Stokes, taylor, Thomas, Thompson, Tunstall, Wall, Williams, Woldert, Wortham, Worthington & Zavala.

Indian Wars *and* Pioneers *of* Texas, 1822-1874. By: John Henry Brown, Orig. Pub. 1880, Reprinted 2020, 1110 pages, NEW INDEX, Hard Cover, ISBN #0-89308-120-5.

TX 2 $85.00

This book is a MUST for the student of Texas history and especially for students of early American Indians and the wars fought between them and the white man. It begins with the Cherokee Indians and their 12 Associate Bands; from this early beginning it goes into the Cherokee and Tehuacana Fight of 1830; the first settlement in Gonzales in 1825 and its attack by Indians in 1826; the Battle of San Saba in 1831; scalping of Wilbarger and the death of Christian and Strother in 1833; attempted settlement of Beale's Rio Grande Colony in 1834; Fall of Parker's Fort in 1836; breakup of Bell County in 1836; Erath's Fight; Texas Independence; Cordova's rebellion, 1838-9; and page after page of detailed and exciting early history of Texas and the West. One of the most important aspects of this volume are the Biographical Sketches of over 536 individuals and their family history, with the names of over 6,500 other individuals.

Pioneer Women *in* Texas. By: Annie Doom Pickrell, Pub. 1929, reprinted 2022, 488 pages, Index, ISBN #978-1-63914-064-0.

TX 21 $45.00

Until the publication of this book, biographies of Texas women were almost non-existent. These biographical sketches have been prepared in the hope of preserving for future generations a correct idea of the lives and characteristics of the women who lived in Texas prior to 1845. The sketches have been woven from facts contributed by descendants or friends of each woman under discussion, and each sketch has been approved by those who have contributed. These biographies are rich in family, social and religious life of frontier Texas. They present a picture of daily pioneer activities, descriptions of homes and clothing, and religious and social activities that show the reader what life in everyday Texas was all about. Surnames of biographies: Askew, Bell, Billingsley, Bolling, Brown (2), Bunton, Burleson (2), Bolling, Caldwell, Carter, Chaffin, Childers, Cloud, Cole, Coulson, Cunningham, Daniels, Dardin, Doom, Duggan, Dyer, Fenn, Fisher, Flack, Gowan, Hamilton (2), Hemphill, Henry, Henderson, Houston (2), Hornsby, Hubert, Jones, Johnson, Kennerly, Kimbrell, Kleberg, Kyle, Linn, Litton, Lungkwitz, McClelland, McCormick, McCrocklin, McMahon, Mitchell, McCoy, Nail, Nichols, Rabb, Rice, Roberts, Rogers, Robertson, Runge, Scott, Sellers, Sevier, Sinks, Smith, Smyth, Thomson, Townsend, Troutman, Vaughn, Waller, Washington, Williams (2), Winfield, Winn, Yoast, and Van Zandt.

Southwest Texas, Memorial *and* Genealogical Records *of*. By: Goodspeed Publishing Co., Pub. 1884, Reprinted 1994, 688 pages, Hard Cover, New Index, ISBN #0-89308-122-1.

TX 4 $50.00

This is probably the RAREST of all the volumes done by the Goodspeed Publishing Co. on any of the states they compiled book on. This volume is similar to their other volumes in that it first gives a history of the state from earliest times; is followed by county histories included in the volume; and the Biographical sketches of individuals. This volume contains approximately 925 Biographical sketches with genealogical data on some 3,600 other families / individuals, with many of the families being carried well back into the mid 1700's.

The Spanish Archives *of the* General Land Office *of* Texas. By: Virginia H. Taylor, Pub. 1955, Reprinted 2020, 286 pages, Index, ISBN #0-89308-179-5.

TX 3 $30.00

This book contains a wealth of information about early settlers who came to Texas prior to 1836 and is arranged alphabetically by surname, giving the amount of land grant, the Colony or Commissioner where the land was located and the present-day location. The date of the Title gives a valuable clue as to when the settler arrived in Texas.

Tennesseans *in* Texas: as Found in the 1850 Census. By: Helen & Timothy Marsh, Pub. 1986, 416 pages, Hard Cover, Index, ISBN #0-89308-561--8.

TN 94 $45.00

This was compiled as the result of a detailed study of the 1850 Federal Census of Texas, giving the birthplace and deaths of the inhabitants living in Texas in 1850.The book is arranged alphabetically by county for those persons who showed Tennessee as their birth state. Since the person showing Tennessee as the birth state is shown with the other members of his or her household, it becomes easy for one to see the migration patterns that many of these people took upon leaving Tennessee before their arrival in Texas.

Early Travis County, Texas Records. By: Jane Summer, Pub. 1978, Reprinted 2018, 202 pages, INDEX, soft cover, ISBN #0-89308-129-9.

TX 5 $25.00

Selected, condemned, planned and designated by the Congress of the Republic of Texas, as the capital city for the Republic of Texas. Fifty-nine men signed the Declaration of Independence of the Republic of Texas on March 2, 1836. One was a native of England, One of Scotland, one of Ireland, one of Canada, 13 of Virginia, 10 of Tennessee, 8 of North Carolina, 5 of Kentucky, 4 of South Carolina, 4 of Georgia, 2 of New York, 2 of Pennsylvania, one of New Jersey, one of Mississippi, and 2 of Texas, native born in San Antonio de Bexar and educated in universities in Spain, and Lorenzo de Zavala born in Spain 1788, educated there, and died 1836 while holding the office of vice-president ad interim of the constitution at convention held March 1836. These and their counterparts who came later were ambassadors, empresarios, consulates of other nations, as well as other foreign dignitaries. They came to the new nation with its vast areas of varied soils and timber. They brought with them their families and their fortunes. This is the history of these people as shown by the records in the Travis County Court House. The deeds from the County Clerk's office, Wills and probate from the County Court, and lawsuits from the District Courts of Travis County, TX. Texas was a republic for 10 years only, but the records continued uninterrupted by the change from Republic to State, and through the differences of the war between the states.

War *of* 1812 Veterans *in* Texas. (REVISED & UPDATED). By: Mary F Smith, Pub. 1979, Revised & Reprinted 1994, 468 pages, Hard Cover, New Index, ISBN #0-89308-690-8.

TX 15 $42.50

This book encompasses 650 men, known to have set foot on Texas soil at some time during their lives, who rendered military or public service during the War of 1812 period - from 1784 when the American. Revolution ended to 1815 when the Treaty of Ghent ending the War of 1812 was ratified. Information, when available, includes the places and dates of birth and death; place and date of marriage and the name of the celebrant of the ceremony; the names of all wives; children's dates of birth and names of their spouses; place of enrollment for service and places of residences in Texas and those before arriving; the names of veteran's immediate superior; cross references to the pension and bounty land file records in the National Archives, which include the names of relatives, friends and neighbors who served as witnesses. Appendix I is a special list of more than 100 widows with madden names given, showing the place and date of death of husband who did not himself enter Texas. Appendix II lists sources offering further information. This newly revised edition contains some 50 additional Veterans who Mrs. Smith has researched and found since the first edition in 1979. This reference work is important for Texas research and equally valuable for historical and genealogical research on non-Texas families; witnesses, for example, were living all across the present-day United States, from Maine to California - the scope is truly national.

VIRGINIA

1790 Census *of* Virginia, Heads of Families at the First Census of the U.S. taken in the year 1790: Records of the Enumeration: 1782 to 1785. Pub. 1908, Reprinted 1995, 189 pages, Hard Cover, Index, ISBN #0-89308-614-2.

VA 108 $32.50

Since the original returns for the state were destroyed in the War of 1812, taxpayer's lists were reconstructed by the Bureau of the Census.

Accomack County, Virginia, Revolutionary Soldiers *and* Sailors *of*. By: Stratton Nottingham, Pub. 1927, Reprinted 2019, 102 pages, Index, ISBN #0-89308-773-4.

VA 56 $15.00

The revolutionary records contained in this volume were compiled from the Court Records (1770-1854) of Lancaster County, VA. The records include the recommendation of the Court of those qualified to serve as officers in the County Militia, a record of their qualifications, certification of heirs of a deceased soldier or sailor, tracing the descent for three and sometimes four generations, movements of troops, public service claims & etc... The records also include the date of birth and death of many of the soldiers, also a number of marriages for which there are no bonds or other records. This volume also includes the Muster Rolls and Pay Rolls of the 92nd Regiment of VA. Militia, Lancaster County, War of 1812, of those entitled to Land Bounty.

Albemarle County *in* Virginia. By: Rev. Edgar Woods, Pub. 1901, reprinted 2023, 412 pages, Index, soft cover, ISBN #0-89308-878-1.

VA 190 $40.00

Albemarle County was created in 1744 from the western part of Goochland County. The first five chapters unfold the early history of the county, while the bulk of this book is devoted to biographical sketches of early families. Surnames to be found within this section of the book: Abell, Alphin, Anderson, Ballard, Barclay, Barksdale, Bibb, Bishop, Black, Bowcock, Bowen, Bramham, Brand, Brockman, Brooks, Brown, Burch, Burnley, Busters, Carr, Carter, Clark, Clarkson, Cochran, Cocke, Cole, Coles, Craven, Dabney, Davis, Dawson, Dedman, Dickerson, Dollins, Douglas, Dowell, Duke, Dunkum, Durrett, Dyer, Eades, Early, Eubank, Everett, Fagg, Farish, Farrar, Ficklin, Field, Fitch, Fretwell, Fry, Gantt, Garland,

Garrett, Garth, Gentry, Gilmer, Gooch, Goodman, Goolsby, Gordon, Goss, Grayson, Hamner, Hancock, Hardin, Harper, Harris, Harrison, Hart, Harvie, Hays, Henderson, Hening, Hopkins, Hudson, Hughes, Irvin, Jameson, Jarman, Jefferson, Jones, Jouett, Kelly, Kerr, Key, Kinkead, Kinsolving, Leake, Levy, Lewis, Lindsay, Lynch, McGehee, McKennie, Macon, Magruder, Marks, Martin, Massie, Maupin, Maury, Mayo, Meriwether, Michie, Mills, Minor, Monroe, Moon, Moore, Moorman, Morris, Neilson, Nelson, Nicholas, Old, Oldham, Page, Patrick, Perry, Peyton, Phillips, Pilson, Piper, Price, Quarles, Railey, Ramsay, Randolph, Rea, Rives, Rodes, Rogers, Sampson, Schenk, Scott, Shelton, Simms, Smith, Southall, Sowell, Staples, Stevenson, Stockton, Suddarth, Sumter, Sutherland, Taylor, Terrell, Thomas, Thompson, Thurman, Timberlake, Tompkins, Tooley, Turner, Twyman, Waddell, Walker, Wallace, Watson, Watts, Wayt, Wertenbaker, Wheeler, White, Wilkinson, Wingfield, Winn, Wood, Woods, Woodson, Yancey, & Yergain. the remaining portions of the book are appendices of: Frontier Militia, revolutionary Soldiers, military organizations of the county, county officers, emigrants from Albemarle to other states and a necrology from 1744-1890.

Albemarle County Virginia, 1783-1852, Guardians' Bonds *of.* By: Mary Catherine Murphy, Pub. 1968, Reprinted 2018, 234 pages, Index, ISBN # 0-89308-939-7.

VA 178 $28.50

Albemarle County was created in 1744 from Goochland County. Information that will be found within: Name or Orphan, Name of deceased parent, Name and relationship of Guardian; amount & date of bond.

Albemarle County *and* Charlottesville, Virginia, 1781-1929, Marriages of. By: William L. Norford, Pub. 1956, reprinted 2023, 286 pages, soft cover, ISBN #978-1-63914-124-1.

VA 170 $32.50

Albemarle County was created in 1744 from the western part of Goochland County. These marriages are listed in alphabetical order covering Albemarle County for 1781-1929 and the city of Charlottesville for 1888-1929.

Alleghany County Virginia, A Centennial History *of.* By: Oren F. Morton, Pub. 1923, Reprinted 2018, 236 pages, Index, soft cover ISBN # 0-89308-926-5.

VA 164 $25.00

Alleghany County was created in 1822 from Bath and Botetourt counties. This book is not too different from other county history books of this era. With such topics as trade and transportation, labor, farming, politics, and race relations - all important in the development of the county - are carefully discussed. This type of county history book can help one develop ideas or paths to those missing ancestors by showing the customs and traditions of the local residents. A particular useful feature of this book are the hundreds of mini biographies inter dispersed throughout the book. Family & Biographical Sketches: Aritt, Armentrout, Armstrong, Beards, Bell, Bennett, Bowyer, Callaghan, Carpenter, Carson, Carter, Damron, Dresslers, Ervine, Fridley, Fudge, Gillespies, Gilliland, Hansbarger, Helmintoller, Helper, Holloway, Holley, Huddleston, Jackson, Johnson, Kimberlin, Kincaids, King, Knox, Landes, Leighton, Lemon, Lockhart, McAllister, Mallow, Mann, Massie, Milhollen, Morris, Morton, Parrish, Pennell, Persingers, Persinger, Rvercomb, Robinson, Scott, Skeen, Stull, Taylor, Warren, Wolfe, and Wright. You will also discover several lists: 1782 personal property books, 1840 Residents, Marriages recorded in Botetourt 1778-1795, Marriages recorded in Bath 1790-1800, Marriages recorded in Alleghany 1825-1857.

Amherst County, Virginia 1761-1807, *and* Albemarle County, Virginia 1748-1763, The Deeds *of.* By: The Rev. Bailey Fulton Davis, Pub. 1979, reprinted 2014, 560 pgs, Index, ISBN #0-89308-147-7.

VA 1 $52.50

Albemarle County was created from Goochland County in 1744. In turn, Albemarle County was divided to created 3 new counties: Amherst, 1761; Buckingham, 1761; and Fluvanna, 1777. All deeds for both counties begin with the first recorded book for that county, even though there is a 4-year discrepancy for the county of Albemarle.

Amherst County, Virginia Deeds, 1807-1852. (Vol. #2) By: Rev. Bailey Davis, Pub. 1985, Reprinted 2016, 384 pages, Index, ISBN # 0-89308-301-1.

VA 36 $40.00

Amherst County was created from the southwestern portion of Albemarle County in 1761. These deeds include many bills of sale; trust deeds; powers of attorney; dower right releases; names of counties and states where the grantor has taken up residence or plans to reside; leases; damage suits; inquisitions into death; deeds of gifts; bonds and contracts.

Amherst County, Virginia 1827-1852, Books S-Z, Vol. #3., The Deeds of. By: The Rev. Bailey Fulton Davis, Pub. 1985, 420 pages, Hard Cover, Index, ISBN #0-89308-363-1.

VA 48 $37.50

Amherst County was created from the southwestern portion of Albemarle County in 1761. These deeds cover from the years 1827-1852.

Amherst County, VA. *in the* Revolution. Including Extracts *from the* "LOST ORDER BOOK" 1773-1782. By: Lenora H. Sweeny, Pub. 1951, reprinted 2020, 230 pages, Index, Soft Cover, ISBN #0-89308-269-4.

VA 27 $28.50

Located on the eastern slope of the Blue Ridge Mountains, Amherst County was created from the southwestern portion of Albemarle County in 1761. Originally, its boundary lines were much larger, included in its boundaries was Nelson County which was Nelson County which was carved off in 1808. It is surrounded by the present-day counties of: Appomattox, Bedford, Botetourt, Buckingham, Campbell, Nelson, and Rockbridge.

Thought to have been destroyed or carried off during the Civil War, the Amherst Order Book covering the Revolutionary time frame was discovered by the author during one of her many trips to the courthouse while doing research. Not only was the: Lost Order Book" 1773-1782 used to complete this book but other sources as well including Muster & Pay Rolls. Included in the discussion of Amherst's participation in the Revolution are many lists of which some are: The First Rifle Company, Officers of the Militia before and during the Revolution, Revolutionary soldiers from Amherst County comprising then the territory of the present-day county of Nelson, and many, many lists of muster & payrolls from various companies serving duty from Amherst County. The author has even included disbursements to wives, widows & orphans of Revolutionary soldiers and also, claims for property impresses or taken for public service. Another interesting feature of this "Lost Order Book" 1773-1782 is a list of the names of soldiers who proved they had served in the French & Indian War and thus qualified to obtain bounty land allowed by the proclamation of the King of Great Britain in 1763. Of Special interest, the author has included over 200 applications of Amherst soldiers for Pensions. These applications many times give such information as: date & place of birth, date of death, current residence at time of filing, date of enlistment, his service record, date of marriage, names of spouse & children, along with their birth dates and marriage dates, names of his & his wife's parents, names of fellow soldiers he served with, even neighbors that lived beside him before taken duty, and date placed on pension roll.

Amherst County, Virginia Wills 1761-1865. By: The Rev. Bailey Fulton Davis, Pub. 1985, reprinted 1998, 472 pages, Soft Cover, Index, ISBN #0-89308-302-X.

VA 35 $45.00

Amherst County was created from the southwestern portion of Albemarle County in 1761. These wills cover from the very beginning of the county all the way through to 1865.

(Augusta Co.) Chronicles *of the* Scotch-Irish Settlement *in* Virginia. Extracted *from the* Original Records *of* Augusta County, 1745-1800. (3 Volumes). By: Lyman Chalkley, Pub. 1912, reprinted 2023, 3 volumes, 2000 pages, Index, soft cover.

This monumental 3 volume set of books consists of abstracts of court records pertaining to the Scotch-Irish pioneers who first breached the mountain barrier sealing off the Atlantic seaboard from the country west of the Blue Ridge. However, it's referred to, its value as a reference work is unsurpassed, genealogists and historians alike regard it as the basic record of the first settlement of the country beyond the Blue Ridge Mountains. In 1745, when Augusta County, Virginia was erected, its boundaries extended from the Alleghenies to the Mississippi River, and from the northern part of Tennessee to the Great Lakes. This means that all of the states of Ohio, Illinois, Indiana and West Virginia were created from this one Virginia County along with the Virginia counties of: Bath, Botetourt, and Rockingham.

Vol. #1: 620 pgs, ISBN #978-1-63914-096-1

VA 195 $50.00

Data to be found within this volume: Abstracts of court order books (1745-1799), plus notes from county court judgments, original papers on suits (1745-1825), and petitions filed in court from 1745 on. Each volume is indexed, and the combined total of names is over 50,000.

Vol. #2: 656 pgs, ISBN #978-1-63914-097-8.

VA 196 $55.00

Data to be found within this volume: Records of the circuit and district courts, marriage bonds, licenses and returns (1748-1800), land entries (1744-1751), guardians' bonds (1782-1801), administrators' bonds (1776-1810), tax delinquents (1748-1804), proceedings of the Vestry of Augusta Parish (1746-1799), and records of military service in colonial wars and the Revolution. Each volume is indexed, and the combined total of names is over 50,000.

Vol. #3: 242 pgs, ISBN #978-1-63914-098-5.

VA 197 $27.50

Data to be found within this volume: Will abstracts (1745-1818) and deed abstracts (1745-1792). Each volume is indexed, and the combined total of names is over 50,000.

(Augusta Co.) Annals *of* Southwest

Virginia, 1769-1800. By: Lewis P. Summers, Orig. Pub. 1929, reprinted 2020 in 2 volumes, 1780 pages, soft cover, Index, ISBN #0-89308-474-3.

VA 110 $125.00

In 1769 Augusta County was divided and all territory south of Mary's River was included in the new county of Botetourt. This area was early settled by Scotch, Irish, Dutch, German, Swiss, and some English settlers. The records contained herein are: Botetourt County - minutes of the County Court; first survey of land; marriage licenses; lists of ministers; briefs of deeds and briefs of wills. Fincastle County - minutes of the County Court; first surveys of land; briefs of deeds and wills. Montgomery County - minutes of the County Court; first surveys of land; marriage licenses; briefs of deeds and wills. Washington County - minutes of the County Court; first surveys of land; marriage licenses; briefs of deeds and wills. Wythe County - minutes of the County Court; marriage licenses. Also contained are Revolutionary soldiers of Southwest Virginia; a list of regiments at the battle of Point Pleasant; French Indian War Land Grants by Proclamation of the King of England, 1763; Cherokee expedition of 1776; Forts in Southwest VA., and soldiers stationed therein. These set of books contains the names of more than 25,000 persons.

Bristol Parish, Virginia 1720-1789, The Vestry Book *of.* By: CG Chamberlayne, Pub. 1898, Reprinted 1994, 428 pgs, Hard Cover, Index, ISBN #0-89308-496-4.

VA 106 $40.00

Bristol Parish was established in 1643 and covered the area of Charles City, South of the James River. Bristol Parish covers the area later comprised of Dinwiddie, Henrico, and Prince George Counties. This rare book contains all of the vestry meetings and minutes of the vestry from October 1720 through April 1789, being complete except for the period October 20, 1722, through November 11, 1723. The earliest recorded date in the Register of Births, Baptisms and Deaths is April 12, 1685, through March 9, 1798. For many years the register Book was thought to have been lost but was discovered in Petersburg in 1894. In preparing this book the author expended great care in following the original book in every eccentricity of spelling and abbreviation and in all mistakes. THE VESTRY BOOK itself contains the names of approximately 5,000 individuals either as Vestry members or as those who had been appointed to procession land of property owners; apprentice young people to other in the parish for training in crafts or livelihoods; binding out young slaves for training; clothing and feeding and general care and welfare of the poor in their midst. THE PARISH REGISTER which lists the birth, baptisms, and deaths contains the names of over 7,139 individuals including slaves and their owners, mulattos and their mothers and the whites. This book contains some very rich genealogical data especially for the person with BLACK ROOTS.

Bristol Parish, A History *of.* (With Genealogies of Families Connected there with and Historical Illustrations) By: The Rev. Philip Slaughter, Pub. 1879, Reprinted 1994, 238 pages, Hard Cover, New Index, ISBN #0-89308-495-6.

VA 107 $32.50

The first half of this history pertains to the general history of this parish with a special emphasis upon the early Episcopal clergy who were Rectors of the Parish Church. The second half of the history deals with GENEALOGIES of the many early families; a listing of members of the various Vestries; as well as some abstracts from some Baptismal registers. Family genealogies include the following families: Atkinson, Bolling, Bland, Claiborne, Eppes, Field, Gilliam, Grammer, Haxall, Kennon, May, Munford, Murray, Peterson, Pegram, Ramsey, Randolph, Robertson, Skipwith, Walker, Withers, and Worsham. Other families interrelated to those for whom genealogies are given include: Archer, Backer, Bassett, Beverly, Burwell, Byrd, Cary, Coalton, Cocke, Coleman, Dupuy, Fitzhugh, Gordon, Grymes, Harrison, Isham, Jefferson, Kennon, Lay, Lee, Meade, Peyton, Seemes, Sherrard, Sinclair, Starke, Tanner, Thweatt, Tucker, Walke, Walker, Whittle, and Wilmer.

Brunswick County, Virginia 1750-1810, Marriage Bonds *and* Ministers' Returns *of.* By: Catherine Lindsay Knorr, Pub. 1953, Reprinted 1982, 146 pages, map, Index, ISBN #0-89308-261-9.

VA 24 $18.50

Brunswick County was created in 1720 from Prince George County, VA even though the government was not organized u ntil 1732. Later its boundaries grew due to land being added via Isle of Wight & Surry counties.

Burned Record Counties *of* Virginia, Some Marriages *in the.* By: Virginia Genealogical Society, Pub. 1972, reprinted 2009, 104 pages, Index, ISBN #0-89308-266-X.

VA 30 $15.00

This compilation is based on a search of the few original sources available for Hanover, Dinwiddie, Charles City, Nansemond, Elizabeth City, Buckingham, Stafford, King and Queen, and Gloucester counties, Virginia. Approximately 1,500 marriages are recorded.

Burned Record Counties, Virginia Tithables *from.* By: R F. Woodson and I B. Woodson, Pub. 1970, Reprinted 2018, 122 pages, ISBN #0-89308-306-2.

VA 39 $20.00

Counties being covered are: Buckingham, Gloucester, Hanover, James City, and Stafford.

Charles City County, Virginia Court Orders, 1655-1696. By: Beverley Fleet, Pub. 1941, Reprinted 2019, soft cover, Index, ISBN #0-89308-369-0.

Vol. #1, 1655-1661: 244 pages, ISBN #0-89308-368-2

VA 159 $27.50

Vol. #2, 1661-1696: 242 pages, ISBN #0-89308-369-0.

VA 160 $27.50

Charles City County was created in 1634 and is the parent county to the counties of: Prince George, Brunswick, Dinwiddie, Amelia, Greenville, Lunenburg, Nottoway, Prince Edward, Mecklenburg, Halifax, Bedford, Charlotte, & Pittsylvania counties.

Colonial Caroline, A History *of* Caroline County, Virginia. By: Thomas Elliott Campbell, Pub. 1954, Reprinted 2018,578 pages, Index, ISBN # 0-89308-905-2.

VA 64 $48.50

Caroline County was created from Essex, King & Queen and King William Counties in 1728. Settlers began showing up around 1655 and many of her early settlers were Huguenots. During the Revolution, Caroline was the third most populous county within Virginia. This book is a well-documented and detailed history of the county. But what the genealogists will savor are all of the records he included that cover such items as: land/crown grants covering St. Mary's, Drysdale, St. Margaret's Parishes, Head Righters, Indentured Servants, Slaves being registered and crimes by slaves, lists of office holders, lists of jurors, lists of persons exempt from taxes, lists of persons in the Militia as well as those serving as soldiers & sailors in the Revolutionary War, lists of persons petitioning for hardship allotments, Tobacco planters and their role, list & descriptions of merchants from the three parishes, list and description of Grist Mills and their involvement, lists of tavern owners & location of the tavern, Cases involving adultery & separations along with bastardy children, Churches and their involvement with the community including those charged with persecution and those receiving welfare, various criminal cases from felony all the way down assault & batteries, Apprenticeships, briefs of Wills 1732-1778, Guardians and their wards 1740-1781 and many, many useful items to help find and document that elusive ancestor. This index to this book has approximately 12,000 entries.

Charlotte County, Virginia 1764-1815, Marriage Bonds *and* Ministers' Returns *of.* By: Catherine L. Knorr, Pub. 1958, Reprinted 1982, 170 pages, map, soft cover, Index, ISBN #0-89308-262-7.

VA 25 $17.50

Charlotte was formed in 1764 from Lunenburg. it is surrounded by Mecklenburg, Lunenburg, Prince Edward, Appomattox, Campbell, and Halifax.

Chesterfield County, Virginia 1771-1815, Marriage Bonds and Minister's Returns of. By: Catherine L. Knorr, Pub. 1958, reprinted 1992, 170 pages, soft cover, Index, ISBN #0-89308-250-3.

VA 13 $20.00

Part of Henrico Parish from the earliest days of the Colony to 1642-1643 when Bristol Parish was formed. In 1735, it was granted its own exclusive parish named Dale, and in 1749 the official county was formed. It is surrounded by Henrico, Charles City, Prince George, Dinwiddle, Albemarle, Powhatan, and Goochland.

Culpeper County, Virginia 1763-1764, Abstracts *from the* Court Minute Book *of.* By: A.M. Prichard, Pub. 1930, Reprinted 2009, 74 pages, Index, ISBN #0-89308-792-0.

VA 125 $12.50

Culpeper county was created in 1749 from Orange County, VA and in turn it became the parent county to Madison & Rappahannock. The order or minute books of the court before 1790 are all missing except for the years that this book covers.

Culpeper County, Virginia, Genealogical *and* Historical Notes *on.* Embracing a revised and Enlarged Edition of Dr. Phillip Slaughter's History of St. Mark's Parish. By: R.T. Green, Pub. 1900, reprinted 1996, 322 pages, Hard Cover, Index, ISBN #0-89308-468-9.

VA 79 $35.00

Culpeper County was created from the northern part of Orange county in 1749. Culpeper County itself gave birth to two new counties: 1793 to Madison and 1833 to Rappahannock. This book starts out with the organization of the Parish, which then leads into the Vestry Minutes of the Parish. In addition, among other information provided including the Germanna Settlement, are lists of Colonial Militia, Revolutionary War Pensioners, Civil War musters, marriage records from 1781 to 1825 and will abstracts from 1749 to 1821. A major portion of this book is devoted to detailed genealogies of many of the early families of the county such as: Ashby, Ball, Barbour, Broaddus, Brown, Browning, Bryan-Lillard, Carter, Cave, Clayton, Coleman, Conway, Cooke, Field, Fry, Garnett, Glassell, Green, Grinnan, Henry-Winston, Hill, Jones, Lamon, Lillard-Bryan, Littlepage, Madison, Mason, Micou, Pendleton, Rice, Slaughter, Somerville, Spotswood, Stevens, Stevenson, Strother, Taylor, Thom, Thomas, Thompson, Williams, Winston-Henry, Woodville, and Yancey, all of which are filled with extremely detailed genealogies and dates with some going back as many as five generations.

Culpeper County, Virginia 1781-1815, Marriages of. By: Catherine Lindsay Knorr, Pub. 1954, reprinted 1982, 136 pages, map, soft cover, Index, ISBN #0-89308-253-8.

VA 16 $18.50

Culpeper County, Virginia, Records *of.* By: Dorothy F. Wulfeck, Pub. 1965, Reprinted 2018, 198 pages, Index, soft cover, ISBN #0-89308-791-2.

VA 121 $20.00

Culpeper was created in 1749 from Orange County which in turn was created from Spotsylvania which was created from Essex. This volume includes the abstracts of Wills from 1770-1791 and the index for book "G" 1813-1817. Book "G" is lost so the index to the original book will help place an individual in the county at a given time frame. The reader will also discover abstracts of Old Miscellaneous Papers 1827-1870 which were discovered in the Clerk's office. Also included are Court Suits from 1815-1839, along with some Tombstone Inscriptions.

Cumberland County, Virginia 1749-1840, Marriages *of.* By: Katherine Elliott, Pub. 1969, reprinted 1983, 198 pages, soft cover, Index, ISBN #0-893208-382-X

VA 67 $22.50

The marriage records in this volume have been taken from the marriage bonds now surviving minister's return of marriages performed, consents of parents or guardians now extant, marriages recorded in the original Douglas Register pertaining to Cumberland County, and other sources considered authentic. Some marriage records by inference taken from wills, deeds, and other records have been included. Notes have been included which seemed to be pertinent or of value. This volume lists the names of the grooms in alphabetical order, with separate indices for the brides and other names appearing such as surely, witnesses and names appearing in consents. This book contains approximately 2,000 marriages.

Cumberland County, Virginia Will Books 1 & 2, 1749-1792. Will abstracts of. By: Katherine Reynolds, Pub. 1984, 104 pages, soft cover, Index, ISBN #0-89308-430-1.

VA 41 $17.50

Cumberland County was created in 1749 from the portion of Goochland County south of the James River. Its boundaries at that time were Albemarle County (after 1761 Buckingham County) on the west, Amelia County (after 1754 also Prince Edward County) on the south, Chesterfield County on the east and Goochland County on the north. In 1777 the county was divided; its eastern portion of Buckingham County along the James River was added to Cumberland County. Since that time, there have been no changes in its boundaries.

(Dinwiddie Co.) Virginia Marriages *in* Rev. John Cameron's Register *and* Bath Parish Register. By: Virginia Genealogical Society, Pub. 1963, Reprinted 2020, 56 pages, Index, ISBN #0-89308-264-3.

VA 28 $17.50

Marriages included in this book are from the areas of Dinwiddie, Prince George, and Nottoway counties. Prince George and Dinwiddie are burned counties with few surviving records. The records of Nottoway County are all extant except that they have no marriages. These marriages pick up where The Vestry Book and Register of Bristol Parish, VA., 1720-1789 leave off.

Essex County, Virginia, Records *of.* Beverly Fleet, Pub. 1940, reprinted 2004, 242 pages, soft cover, Index, ISBN #0-89308-790-4.

VA 120 $32.50

Essex County was created from OLD Rappahannock County in 1692. This volume is a consolidation of 2 volumes of books into one user friendly volume that Mrs. Fleet published back in 1940. This book includes Wills & Deeds from 1711-1717.

(Fairfax County) The History *of* Truro Parish *in* Virginia. By: Phillip Slaughter, Orig. Pub. 1907, reprinted 2014,180 pages, soft cover, Index, ISBN #0-89308-862-5.

VA 140 $25.00

Truro Parish lies in the heart of what is call 'The Northern Neck" of Virginia and precisly in Fairfax County. The title says history but it should say Vestry Book, the author has transcribed the vestry book which was thought to be lost until the author found it. These records cover the time frame 1732-1785. When the parishes were formed by the General Assembly of Virginia, the Vestries were assigned some of the civil administrative functions and all such civil functions were official in nature and the records of actions taken were recorded in the vestry books. Such records contained in the Vestry book among other things are things like: upkeep of bastard children; payment for the upkeep of the ferry; prosecution of fornicators; appointment of road work crews; apprentice young people to others in the parish for training in crafts or other livelihoods; providing clothing, food and shelter for the poor and elderly; burial of the dead and many, many other similar duties.

Fauquier County, Virginia Wills, Administration *and* Marriages 1759-1800. By: J. Estelle King, Pub. 1939, Reprinted 2016, 174 pages, soft cover, Index, ISBN #0-89308-834-X.

VA 126 $23.50

Fauquier County was created in 1759 from Prince William County, VA. It was an important migration path for early settlers moving into Ohio, Tennessee, North & South Carolina. Many of her early settlers were from Pennsylvania, including Germans, Quakers, Welch and Scot Irish. This book contains not only wills of individuals, but also Administrations and marriages. The names of approximately 5,500 persons are found in these legal records of this important county.

Fredericksburg, Virginia 1782-1850, Marriage Bonds & Ministers' Returns of. By: Catherine Knorr, Pub. 1954, reprinted 2013, 116 pages, soft cover, Index, ISBN #0-89308-254-6.

VA 17 $18.50

Fredericksburg was created in 1727 and is located in the county of Spotsylvania. Due to the city's importance to trade during the American Revolution, it was severed form Spotsylvania in 1782 and given its own court system. This is the time frame when the marriages within this book begin. Of special note, these marriages cover a greater area than the city's corporate limits. Many Caroline & Stafford County residents got their marriage bonds in Fredericksburg. Let it be known that Fredericksburg was a unique and special trade center for this area of Virginia. The author has also included tombstone inscriptions from St. George Cemetery 1752-1920.

Gloucester County, Virginia, Colonial Records *of.* By: Polly C. Mason, Pub. 1946, Reprinted 2016, 166 pages, paper, Index, ISBN #0-89308-248-1.

VA 60 $22.50

Gloucester County was created from York County in 1651. Gloucester County Courthouse suffered two burnings, one in 1820 and the second in 1865. Most of the records were presumed destroyed or lost forever due to these fires. The author had discovered numerous files and records concerning this county located within the numerous volumes of records concerning the Colony of Virginia, the clerk's office in Yorktown (York County), and various other county courthouses of Virginia. Records within this book are: Land Patents 1642-1790, Rent Rolls 1704/5, Tax Lists 1770-1782, Mathews County Tax Lists 1774-1791, members of the Burgesses Council and Court, and Land Patents for Gloucester in King & Queen County, VA. The Index mentions approximately 6,500 persons.

Gloucester County Virginia, 1677-1793, The Vestry Book *of* Petsworth Parish. By: Churchill Gibson Chamberlayne, Pub. 1933, Reprinted 2019, 446 pages, Index, ISBN #0-89308-244-9.

VA 187 $40.00

Considering the fact that Gloucester County is a "BURNED" county prior to 1865, makes this book one of only a few sources of information about this county during this colonial period. This BURNED County was formed from York County in 1654 and is the parent county of: Hanover, King William, and King & Queen counties. When the parishes were formed by the General Assembly of Virginia, the Vestries were assigned some of the civil administrative functions and all such civil functions were official in nature and the records of actions taken were recorded in the vestry books. Such records contained in the Vestry book contained among other things such things as: upkeep of bastard children; payment for the upkeep of the ferry; prosecution of fornicators; appointment of road work crews; apprentice young people to others in the parish for training in crafts or other livelihoods; providing clothing, food and shelter for the poor and elderly; burial of the dead and many, many other similar duties.

(Goochland Co.) The Douglas Register: being a detailed Register of Marriages, Births and Deaths together with other interesting notes as kept by the Rev. William Douglas, 1750-1797. By: William MacFarlane Jones, Pub.1928, reprinted 2023, 408 pages, soft cover, ISBN #978-1-63914-110-4.

VA 180 $40.00

Goochland County was created in 1728 from Henrico County. The Douglas Register is an extremely valuable set of records covering births, marriages, and deaths from 1750 to 1797. The registers are for St. James Northam Parish (Dover Church) and King William Parish both of Goochland County. These entries under the headings of births, marriages, and deaths are arranged in alphabetical order covering several thousand persons for Fluvanna, Goochland, Louisa, Orange, and Spotsylvania Counties. The author has also included lists of Huguenot settlers at Manakin-Town (King William Parish) and an index of Goochland County wills, 1728-1840, containing approximately 1,000 names with references to dates and locations.

Greenville County, Virginia 1781-1825,

Marriages Bonds *and* Ministers Returns of. By: Catherine Lindsay Knorr, Pub. 1955, reprinted 1983, 106 pages, map, soft cover, Index, ISBN #0-89308-251-1.

VA 14 $15.00

Greenville County was created from the Eastern portion of Brunswick County in 1781 and in 1802 its boundaries grew to the addition of land via Sussex County, VA.

Halifax County, Virginia, History of. By: Wirt Johnson Carrington, Pub. 1924, Reprinted 2016, 560 pages, New Index, Hard Cover, ISBN #0-89308-497-2.

VA 105 $52.50

According to most scholars and historians, this is probably the best and most complete history of Halifax County to be found. Halifax County was formed in 1752 from Lunenburg County. The territory at that time included present Pittsylvania, Henry, and Patrick Counties. It is surrounded by Mecklenburg, Charlotte, Campbell, Pittsylvania Counties and the state of North Carolina. This whole area of Southside Virginia is one of the most important areas of the state during this pre-1800 time period because of the major migrations across this portion of Virginia into North Carolina and South Carolina, as well as into other states to the west. This book begins with the formation and origins of the county, followed by miscellaneous extracts from Court records such as Deeds. Next comes a history of the town of South Boston after which a chapter is devoted to the "Road to the Wilderness" begun by DANIEL BOONE from Watauga through the wilderness of Kentucky via the Cumberland Gap. This is followed by other general history common to books of this type with a study of the rich, aristocratic, slave-owning whites. The major portion of this book is devoted to detailed genealogies of many of the early families of the county such as: Adams, Atkisson, Boynham, Barksdale, Belt, Booker, Boyd, Bruce, Calloway, Carlton, Carrington, Chastain, Chalmers, Chappell, Christian, Clark, Coleman, Craddock, Crews, Drinkards, Easley, Edmundson, Edmunds, Faulkner, Flournoy, Fourqueam, Green, Hart, Henry, Hodges, Hudson, Hurt, Irby, Jeffress, Jordan, lacy, Lawson, Leigh, Logan, Lovelace, Medley, Morton, Owen, Palmers, Penick, Ragland, Scott, Stebbens, Stokes, Wade, Watkins, Willingham, Wimbish, and Yuille, all of which are filled with extremely detailed genealogies and dates. Chapter 10 deals with a section of abstracts of Wills of many of the early families, many of whom are not listed in the prior chapter of genealogies. Another chapter is devoted to Churches (Episcopal), and this is followed by Chapter 12 which contains: the marriages from 1753-1800 and 1800-1850 arranged alphabetically by groom.

Halifax County, Virginia 1756-1800, Marriages *of*. By: Catherine Lindsay Knorr, Pub. 1957, reprinted 2013, 142 pages, soft cover, Index, ISBN #0-89308-259-7.

VA 22 $18.50

Halifax County was formed in 1752 from Lunenburg County. The territory at that time included present Pittsylvania, Henry, and Patrick Counties. It is surrounded by Mecklenburg, Charlotte, Campbell, Pittsylvania Counties and the state of North Carolina. This whole area of southside Virginia is one of the most important areas of the state during this pre-1800 time period because of the major migrations across this portion of Virginia into North Carolina and South Carolina, as well as into other states to the west.

(Hanover County) Our Quaker Friends *of* Ye Olden Time: Being in Part a Transcript of the Minute Books of Cedar Creek Meeting, Hanover County, and the South River Meeting, Campbell County, Virginia. By: James P. Bell, Pub. 1905, reprinted 2023, 288 pages, Index, soft cover, ISBN #978-1-63914-108-1.

VA 200 $30.00

Hanover County was created in 1721 from New Kent County and Campbell County, Virginia was created in1782 from Bedford County. This book is an invaluable transcript of the Minute Books of Cedar Creek Meeting, Hanover County, Virginia and the South River Meeting, Campbell County, Virginia. These records of Quaker births, deaths, marriages, disownments, and removals cover several thousand persons.

Hanover County, Virginia Chancery Wills *and* Notes. By: William R. Cocke III, Pub. 1940, reprinted 1998, 224 pages, soft cover, Index, ISBN #0-89308-287-2.

VA 8 $30.00

Here is a book that any researcher "MUST" have if he or she is researching in this "BURNED" county. Hanover County was created in 1721 from New Kent County and in turn the western portion of Hanover County was carved off to give way to Louisa County in 1742. Over 250 families are mentioned at some length in this book. There are 147 Wills or abstracts contained therein, many of them brought to light for the first time after painstaking research by the author. In the treatment and presentation of these "Notes", which are abstracts of bills & petitions, deeds, power of Attorney, administrators accounts, depositions, receipts and letters mentioning approximately 7,000 individuals. The objective was to extract every detail of genealogical, biographical and historical importance and to arrange when convenient alphabetically in relation to families, and chronologically as regards to genealogy. References are made to the title or style of the suit, year of institution, and ended file number.

Virginia Migrations: HANOVER COUNTY, 1723-1871. (Volumes #1 and #2) By: Eugenia G. Glazenbrook & Preston G. Glazenbrook, Pub. 1943, Reprinted 2019, 296 pages, Index, soft cover, ISBN #0-89308-086-1.

VA 184 $30.00

Here is a book that any researcher "MUST" have if he or she is researching in this "BURNED" county. Hanover County was created in 1721 from New Kent County and in turn the western portion of Hanover County was carved off to give way to Louisa County in 1742.

(Hanover County) Vestry Book *of* St. Paul's Parish, Hanover County, Virginia 1706-1786. By: C. G. Chamberlayne, Orig. Pub. 1940, reprinted 2014, 694 pages, soft cover, Index, ISBN #0-89308-829-3

VA 141 $52.50

Here is a book that any researcher "MUST" have if he or she is researching in this "BURNED" county. Hanover County was created in 1721 from New Kent County and in turn the western portion of Hanover County was carved off to give way to Louisa County in 1742. When the parishes were formed by the General Assembly of Virginia, the Vestries were assigned some of the civil administrative functions and all such civil functions were official in nature and the records of actions taken were recorded in the vestry books. Such records contained in the Vestry book among other things are things like: upkeep of bastard children; payment for the upkeep of the ferry; prosecution of fornicators; appointment of road work crews; apprentice young people to others in the parish for training in crafts or other livelihoods; providing clothing, food and shelter for the poor and elderly; burial of the dead and many, many other similar duties.

Henrico County, Virginia 1680-1808, Marriages *of*. By: Joyce H. Lindsay, Pub. 1960, reprinted 1995, 96 pages, soft cover, Index, ISBN #0-89308-364-X.

VA 99 $15.00

Henrico Parish, 1730-1773, The Vestry Book *of*. By: Dr. R.A. Brock, Orig. Pub. 1904, reprinted 1995, 204 pages, Hard Cover, New Index, ISBN #0-89308-618-5.

VA 89 $32.50

When the Parishes were created by the general Assembly of Virginia, the Vestries were assigned some of the civil administrative functions and all of such civil functions were official in nature and the records of actions taken were recorded in the vestry book. This book serves as a unique as well as double purpose in that it contains two different sets of records: the minutes of the vestry (civil functions) and also the order for Processing. The later was the surveying of land to attempt to eliminate lawsuits over boundary lines. This book is filled with hundreds of early inhabitants. In the last portion of this book are "Notes" from the author. These notes contain genealogies of some 30 founding families and individuals.

Henrico County, Virginia, Records, Vol. 21. By: Beverly Fleet, Pub. 1944, reprinted 1984, 104 pages, soft cover, Index, ISBN #0-89308-371-2.

VA 94 $15.00

This book contains: Sheriff's Bonds for 1735; Account Book abstracts for 1736; abstracts of Deeds and Wills 1725-1737.

Henry County, Virginia, History *of*. By: Judith A. Hill, Pub. 1925, reprinted 1995, 332 pages, Hard Cover, New Index, ISBN #0-89308-616-9.

VA 93 $38.00

Henry County was formed in 1776 from Pittsylvania County. This book contains considerable amounts of data about the early colonial times, Civil War, schools, churches, communities, etc.. with biographical sketches of its most prominent citizens and genealogical histories of half a hundred of its oldest families. Also, abstracts of Henry County Legislative Petition from 1779 to 1857 are given along with marriages from 1776-1800. The major portion of this book that is devoted to these biographies or family histories include such surnames as: Aaron, Allen, Anderson (3), Baker, Bailey (2), Barrow, Bassett, Brown (3), Bouldin, Booker, Bryant, Cahill, Callaway, Clanton, Clark, Craighead, Dandridge, Davis, Deschazo, Dillard (3), Dillion-Campbell-Hodges, Drewry, Dupuy, Dyer, Eggleton, Estes, Finney, Fontaine, Ford, Frye, Gravely, Gribbs (2), Hamilet, Hamilton (2), Hairston (2), Henry, Hill (2), Jones (4), Kearfoot, King (3), Koger, Lavinder, Matthews (3), Marshall, Martin, Mitchell, Morris (2), Mullins, Nance, Napier, Pannill, Pendelton, Penn (2), Price, Prillaman, Purcell, Rangeley, Reamey (2), Redd, Reed, Richardson, Rowland, Salmon, Schoolfield, Sheffield, Shelton, Smith (2), Spencer, Stanley, Starling, Stovall, Stultz (2), Taylor, Thomas, Townes, Traylor (3), Turner, Waller (2), Wells, Weems, Woods, Wooten, and Wray.

Henry County, Virginia Abstracts *of* Deed Books 1 & 2, Feb. 1776 - July 1784. By: Lela C. Adams, Pub. 1975, reprinted 1992, 188 pages, soft cover, Index, ISBN #0-89308-358-5.

VA 43 $20.00

In 1776, Patrick County was cut off of Pittsylvania County and was named for Patrick Henry. When first formed, Henry County embraced the whole of what is now Patrick County and the greater portion of present Franklin County, VA. These deeds include many bills of sale; trust deeds; powers of attorney; dower right releases; names of counties and states where the grantor has taken up residence or plans to reside; leases; damage suits; inquisitions into death; deeds of gifts; bonds and contracts.

Henry County, Virginia Abstracts *of* Deed Books 3 & 4, Aug. 1784 - June 1792. By: Lela C. Adams, Pub. 1978, Reprinted 1984, 136 pages, soft cover, Index, ISBN #0-89308-359-3.

VA 44 $18.50

Henry County, Virginia Abstracts *of* Deed Books 5 & 6, Oct. 1792 - Dec. 1805. By: Lela C. Adams, Pub. 1983, reprinted 1989, 232 pages, soft cover, Index, ISBN #0-89308-360-7.

VA 45 $20.00

Henry County, Virgina Marriage Bonds *and* Minister Returns, 1778-1849. By: Virginia A. Dodd, Pub. 1953, reprinted 2004, 132 pages, soft cover, ISBN 0-89308-759-9.

VA 113 $18.50

Henry County was created from Pittsylvania County in 1776.

Henry County, Virginia 1778-1780, Tax Lists *of*. By: Lela C. Adams, Pub. 1973, reprinted 1989, 34 pages, soft cover, Index, ISBN #0-89308-361-5.

VA 47 $12.50

Henry County Virginia Will Abstracts, Vol. 1 & 2, 1777-1820. By: Lela C. Adams, Pub. 1984, 120 pages, soft cover, Index, ISBN #0-89308-544-8.

VA 103 $17.50

These Wills include many bills of sale; trust deeds; powers of attorney; dower right releases; names of counties and states where the grantor has taken up residence or plans to reside; leases; damage suits; inquisitions into death; deeds of gifts; bonds and contracts.

Isle *of* Wight County, Virginia, Seventeenth Century. By: John B Boddie, Pub. 1938, Reprinted 2018, 778 pages, Index, Hard Cover, ISBN #0-89308-498-0.

VA 104 $58.50

This book being the standard history of Isle of Wight County begins with a brief chapter on the native inhabitants and moves quickly to describe early white settlers, including the Cavaliers and the Quakers. Edward Bennett, "Elder of the Ancient Church and merchant of London", was among the earliest settlers; he received a patent for land in Virginia in 1621 "conditioned on the settling of 200 immigrants. Contains about 60 pages of genealogical sketches. Many of the early families came from the southwest of England while others were from London and its surrounding counties. An additional 50 or so pages are given to the history of the Bennett and Boddie families of Virginia and the Carolinas. The court records cover the Isle of Wight Book A (apparently a collection of various records although it appears to be mostly wills); Will and Deeds Book I, 1662-1686; Deed Book I, 1688-1704; Land Grant spanning 1628 to 1705; Quit Rent, 1704; and a roster of county officers for Isle of Wight and surrounding counties. The index covers names and subjects.

Isle *of* Wight County, Virginia 1628-1800, Marriages *of*. By: Blanche Adams Chapman, Pub. 1933, Reprinted 2017,144 pages, soft cover, Index, ISBN #0-89308-918-4.

VA 153 $17.50

Isle of Wight County was created in 1637 and was later carved up to create Southampton County. This book should be considered a companion to the Wills & Inventories book also, as the marriages were not included within it. This book is an exact reproduction of the original.

Isle of Wight County, Virginia, Wills & Administrations. 1719-1760. (Vol. #2) By: Blanche Adams Chapman, Pub. 1938, Reprinted 2019, 254 pages, Index, ISBN #0-89308-467-0.

VA 151 $25.00

Isle of Wight County was created in 1634 shortly after the settlement of Jamestown. Settlers from England began showing up at his time. This book should be considered a companion book to "Seventeenth Century of Wight County, Virginia", as picks-up the wills that were not included within it.

James City County, Virginia 1634-1659, Vol. 4. By: Lindsay O Duvall, Pub. 1957, reprinted 1978, 96 pages, soft cover, Index, ISBN #0-89308-065-9.

VA 5 $17.50

James City County was created in 1634 and was one of the eight original shires. It is considered the mother county of the state, and with in it lie the first church & parish. It is the parent county in whole or part to: Charles City, New Kent, Surry, & York, counties. This county has sufferd great loss of records due to the Civil War.

King George County, Virginia 1777-1798, The Register *of* St. Paul's Parish 1715-1776 *and* Stafford County 1715-1776. By: George H.S. King, Pub. 1960, reprinted 1985, 192 pages, Hard Cover, Index, ISBN #0-89308-578-2.

VA 71 $27.50

King George County has suffered many missing records and the wills were thought to be part of the missing records until the author discovered them and returned them in 1977 after he transcribed them. This book is arranged alphabetically by surname in chronological order.

King George County, Virginia Wills, 1721-1752 *and* Miscellaneous Notes. By: George H.S. King, Pub. 1978, Reprinted 2021, 346 pages, Index, Soft Cover, ISBN #0-89308-578-2.

VA 72 $38.50

King George county was created in 1721 from Richmond County, VA. In 1777, King George & Stafford County changed portions of the boundaries with each other. And in 1778, King George again had property transferred to and from Westmoreland County, VA.

(King & Queen County) The Vestry Book *of* Stratton Major Parish, Virginia 1729-1783. By: C.G. Chamberlayne, Pub. 1931, reprinted 2021, 262 pages, soft cover, Index, ISBN #0-89308-793-9.

VA 130 $30.00

King & Queen County was created in 1691 from New Kent County, VA. In turn King & Queen County is the parent county in part and/or in whole to: Caroline, King William, and Spotsylvania. King & Queen County has suffered 2 major fires which have destroyed most of its records. With this said, any book covering this BURNED county should be considered must. In preparing this book the author expended great care in following the original book in every eccentricity of spelling and abbreviation and in all mistakes. The VESTRY BOOK itself contains the names of approximately 3,500 individuals either as Vestry members or as those who had been appointed to procession land of property owners; apprentice young people to other in the parish for training in crafts or livelihoods; binding out young slaves for training; clothing and feeding and general care and welfare of the poor in their midst.

King William County, Virginia *from* Old Newspapers *and* Files. By: Elizabeth Ryland, Pub. 1955, reprinted 2004, 151 pages, soft cover, Index, ISBN #0-89308-798-X.

VA 98 $25.00

King William County was created in 1702 from King & Queen County, VA. These newspaper abstracts cover from 1736-1841. These abstracts not only cover Marriages & Deaths but many other interesting genealogical tidbits such as: property/land sells, runaway slaves, missing property, business transactions, indenture servant sells and more.....

Old King William Homes *and* Families: An Account of Some of the Old Homesteads and Families of King William County, Virginia, from Its Earliest Settlement. By: Peyton Neale Clarke, Pub. 1897, reprinted 2023, 216 pages, Index, soft cover, ISBN #978-1-63914-107-4.

VA 199 $25.00

King William County was created 1702 from King and Queen County. In 1720 Spotsylvania County was formed from parts of King William, King and Queen, and Essex counties, and in 1727 parts of King William County were carved off to create Caroline County. This book is divided onto two parts. The first part gives the names many homes located in the county with a small history of the dwelling, covering such things as: current owner, past owner, description of the building, owner's occupation, and etc... The second part consists of genealogical sketches of some seventy-five early families and their descendants. Surnames of these biographies: Allen, Atkinson, Aylett, Baylor, Bolling, Braxton, Brecknock, Brown, Butler, Byrd, Claiborne, Cole, Coleman, Conway, Corr, Dandridge, Dickey, Dunbar, Edwards, Ellett, Fontaine, Fowke, Freeman, Gregory, Griswold, Henry, Hill, Hundley, Johnson, King, Kinkead, Lewis, Lipscomb, Littlepage, Lynn, McElwee, Moncure, Morancy, Neale, Newman, Pemberton, Peyton, Pollard, Quarles, Robins, Robinson, Shawhan, Taliaferro, Tatum, Teackle, Thornton, Trimble, Walker, Waller, and West. The author also, has included a lengthy history of the Edwards family, the descendants of Ambrose Edwards of Cherry Grove. The Index mentions approximately 3,000 persons.

Lancaster County, Virginia Records 1652-1655 (Vol. #22). By: Beverley Fleet, Pub. 1938, Reprinted 2015, 112 pages, Index, ISBN #0-89308-396-8.

VA 117 $15.00

Lancaster county was created in 1651 from Northumberland & York counties, VA. It in turn was divided to create Old Rappahannock and Middlesex Counties. Many of these Lancaster families moved to the Northern Neck or other parts of Virginia. This book contains the COURT ORDERS for the years 1652-1655. Of special note, this book ends where Duvall's volume begins (No over-lapping time frame).

Lancaster County, Virginia Court Order and Deeds, 1656-1680. By: Lindsay O. Duvall, Reprinted 2014, 112 pages, Index, ISBN #0-89308-063-2.

VA 3 $15.00

Lancaster county was created in 1651 from Northumberland & York counties, VA. It in turn was divided to create Old Rappahannock and Middlesex Counties. Many of these Lancaster families moved to the Northern Neck or other parts of Virginia. The Deeds within this book cover the years 1666-1680. While the court orders pick up where Mr. Fleet's book leaves off at 1656 and continue on through 1680. The Index mentions approximately 3,000 persons.

Lancaster County, VA., 1701-1848, The Marriage License Bonds *of.* By: Stratton Nottingham, Pub. 1927, Reprinted 2014, 108 pages, Index, ISBN #0-89308-867-5.

VA 92 $15.00

Lancaster county was created in 1651 from Northumberland & York counties, VA.

Lancaster County, Virginia Record Book #2, 1654-1666. By: Beverley Fleet, Pub. 1941, Reprinted 2019, 142 pages, Index, ISBN #0-89308-161-2.

VA 54 $17.50

Lancaster County was created in 1651 from Northumberland County. Records that are found within: Power of Attorney, Deeds, Wills, Depositions, Land Grants, Inventory of Estates, Slave Runaways, and many other useful things for the researcher......

Lancaster County, Virginia, Revolutionary Soldiers & Sailors. By: Stratton Nottingham, Orig. Pub. 1930, reprinted 2011, 78 pages, soft cover, Index, ISBN #0-89308-735-1.

VA 95 $12.50

The revolutionary records contained in this volume were compiled from the Court Records (1770-1854) of Lancaster County, VA. The records include the recommendation of the Court of those qualified to serve as officers in the County Militia, a record of their qualifications, certification of heirs of a deceased soldier or sailor, tracing the descent for three and sometimes four generations, movements of troops, public service claims & etc... The records also include the date of birth and death of many of the soldiers, also a number of marriages for which there are no bonds or other records. This volume also includes the Muster Rolls and Pay Rolls of the 92nd Regiment of VA. Militia, Lancaster County, War of 1812, of those entitled to Land Bounty.

Lancaster County, Virginia Wills 1653-1800, Abstracts *of.* By: Ida J. Lee, Pub. 1959, reprinted 2004, 246 pages, New Index, soft cover, ISBN #0-89308-758-0.

VA 112 $30.00

Until now, this book has been very area. cult to use for the researcher due to its lack of an index. We have made a NEW INDEX, that contains the names of approx. 6,000 individuals, especially for this reprint. This book should help those who had relatives living in the Eastern portion of the State with emphasis around the Chesapeake Bay area.

Louisa County, Virginia Marriages, 1766-1815. By: Kathleen Booth Willimas, Pub. 1959, Reprinted 2016, 150 pages, Index, ISBN #0-89308-881-1.

VA 157 $20.00

Louisa County was created in 1742 from Hanover County, VA. The marriages are listed alphabetically by Groom a with an index of approximately 1,500 brides.

Lower Norfolk County, Virginia Wills *and* Deeds, 1651-1654. By: Beverley Fleet, Pub. 1948, reprinted 2021, 108 pages, Index, soft cover, ISBN #0-89308-388-7.

VA 161 $17.50

Lower Norfolk County was created in 1637 from New Norfolk which in turn was created from Elizabeth City in 1636. This book is a reprint of of Volume #31 of the Virginia Colonial Abstracts series that the author published back in the early to mid 1900's.

Cumberland Parish: Lunenburg County, Virginia 1749-1816 *and* Vestry Book 1749-1816. By Landon C. Bell, Pub. 1930, Reprinted 2019, 638 pages, Index, soft cover, ISBN #0-89308-617-7.

VA 88 $52.50

Cumberland Parish was formed at the same time Lunenburg County was created and was coextensive with the county. Lunenburg County was formed from Brunswick County in the year 1745. The Parish of St. Andrews which was located in Brunswick County was also divided and that which was located in the "new" Lunenburg County would be called Cumberland Parish. These records are considered official because the Vestry was responsible for them and not the county clerks. First of the records mentioned are the well-known Rev. John Cameron's Register of Marriages. This register follows him through his Rectorship in Bristol Parish, 1784-1793; Nottoway Parish, 1794-1795; and Cumberland Parish, 1796-1815. Also, a register of Baptisms and funerals for Cumberland Parish for the year 1815 is given. These records are followed by the Vestry Book of Cumberland parish, 1746-1816. In these Minutes of the Vestry, many of the same things are mentioned as in other vestry books, but of special note are the mentioning of land records. These land records range from conveyances, deeds, to mortgages. Also, there is much of this periodic.

Lunenburg County, Virginia Wills 1746-1765. By: Katherine Elliott, Pub. 1967, Reprinted 2016, 178 pages, soft cover, Index, ISBN #0-89308-377-1.

VA 53 $23.50

Lunenburg County was created in 1746 out of Brunswick County, VA. The earliest records in Lunenburg County cover this entire area. The records included in this volume have been abstracted from wills and administrations found in the back of Deed Book I and Will Book I & II. Because some of the early records of Lunenburg County do not seem to have been preserved, the compilers have included in this volume some 20 pages of records abstracted from ORDER BOOK 1-6. These notes from the order books give names of deceased persons not of record in the will books, and names of orphans and other notes pertaining to the period covered in Volumes 1 and 2 of these reprints. Also found is a listing of marriages taken from Deed Books and other vital records, as well as apprenticeships, guardianships and much other valuable data important to the person searching this area of Virginia. There are more than 2,200 names of persons found in the above records listed in the full-name index.

Lynchburg, VA. *and* Nelson County, Virginia Wills, Deeds, *and* Marriages, 1807-1831. By: Rev. Bailey Davis, Pub. 1985, Reprinted 2016, 256 pages, Index, ISBN #0-89308-289-9.

VA 37 $30.00

The city of Lynchburg sits within Campbell County and was created in 1786 but not incorporated until 1805. While Nelson was created in 1808 from Amherst County. Lynchburg Will Book "A" covers the period 1809-1830, the first Marriage Book of the city of Lynchburg begins in 1807 through 1828, and Deed Book A of the city of Lynchburg covers the period of 1805-1813. The Nelson County records include Will Book A, Deed Book 1 and the marriage records all from 1807-1831.

Lynchburg *and* Its Neighbors. By: Rosa F. Yancey, Pub. 1935, reprinted 2021, 522 pages, Index, soft cover, ISBN #978-1-63914-007-7.

VA 188 $48.50

The city of Lynchburg sits within Campbell County and was created in 1786 but not incorporated until 1805. This book is not too different from other county history books of this era. With such topics as trade and transportation, labor, churches, politics, slavery and Civil War - all important in the development of the county - are carefully discussed. This type of county history book can help one develop ideas or paths to those missing ancestors by showing the customs and traditions of the local residents. A particular useful feature of this book are the 200 plus pages of extensive biographical sketches for: Adams (2), Addison, Ambler, Anthony, Armistead, Aunspaugh, Barksdale, Bass, Beale-Hite, Beale-Gatewood, Bias, Bell, Bigbie, Bowman, Bragassa, Bransford, Breckenridge, Brown (2), Burks, Burton, Busey, Cabiness, Calhoun, Camm, Carroll, Carson, Caskie, Clark, Coleman, Collins, Craighill, Dabney. Davis, Dillard, Dirom, Evans, Edmunds, Faulkner, Fisher, Fleet, Fleming, Franklin (2), Featherstone, Floyd, Ford, Forsberg, Fouard, Gannaway, Garland, Gilliam (2), Gimer, Glass, Gooch, Gordon, Gregory (2), Guggenheimer, Hall, Halsey, Hamner, Hancock, Handy, Harrison, Holcombe, Horsley, Hutter, Isbell, Ivey, Jefferson, Jennings, Johnson, Jones, Jordan, Kean, Ket, Kinnier, Kirkpatrick, Kyle (2), Langhorne, Lee (2), Lucado, McDowell, McKinney, McLaughlin, McNamara, Macon (2), Manson, Massie, Miller (2), Mitchell, Montague, Montgomery, Moore, Moorman, Morgan (2), Morris, Morrison, Murrell, Nelson, Nowlin, Otey, Owen, Page (2), Paxton, Payne (2)Peak, Pendleton, Phelps, Percy, Perrow (2), Peters, Pettyjohn, Priddy, Radford, Rockenbach, Rodes, Ryland, Sale, Saunders (2), Schewel, Scott, Shaner, Shumate, Silverthorn, Slatter, Slaughter, Smith, Spencer, Stabler, Statham, Steptoe, Stokes, Stratton, Strode, Strother, Suhling, Taylor, Terrell, Thornhill, Thurman, Tilden, Tucker (2), Tunsstall, Tuner, Valentine, Victor, Voorheis, Waller, Walpole, Walsh (2), Watts, Williams, Wilson, Winfree, Wingfield, Wingfield-Leftwich, Wooling, Wray, Wyatt, Wysor, Yoder, and Yancey (2).

Mecklenburg County, Virginia, Early Settlers *of.* (Volume #1) By: Katherine B. Elliott, Pub. 1964, reprinted 2017, 216 pages, Index, soft cover, ISBN #0-89308-379-8.

VA 57 $25.00

This book contains such things as land grants in Mecklenburg County, early Brunswick and Lunenburg County Deeds, Tithable lists of 1748 and 1752, land procession 1759, St. James' parish Tithable lists in 1746 and other miscellaneous records plus a valuable section titled "Notes on Some Early Settlers". There is also a list of some Mecklenburg people who went to some other states together with the name of the state and sometimes counties taken for deeds, wills, and other legal records.

Mecklenburg County, Virginia, Early Settlers *of.* (Volume #2) By: Katherine B. Elliott, Pub. 1965, reprinted 1220, 266 pages, soft cover, Index, ISBN #0-89308-380-1.

VA 59 $25.00

This book contains early Lunenburg and Mecklenburg County Deeds and other Lunenburg and Mecklenburg County records: Commonwealth land Grants, miscellaneous Order Book records, Orphans and Wards listed in the Guardian Book 1765-1800, Personal Property Tax Lists for 1800 and an appendix which contains the 1782 Mecklenburg County Census.

Mecklenburg County, Virginia 1765-1810, Marriage Records ***of.*** By: Katherine B. Elliott, Pub. 1963, reprinted 1984, 190 pages, soft cover, Index, ISBN #0-89308376-3.

VA 49 $25.00

Mecklenburg County was created in 1765 from Lunenburg County, VA. It did suffer some loss of legal records but did not as the result of the Civil War.

Mecklenburg County, Virginia 1811-1853, Marriages ***of.*** By: K. B. Elliott, Pub. 1962, reprinted 1983, 236 pages, Index, ISBN #0-89308-375-5.

VA 51 $25.00

Mecklenburg County was created in 1765 from Lunenburg County, VA. It did suffer some loss of legal records but did not as the result of the Civil War.

Mecklenburg County, Virginia Revolutionary War Records ***of.*** By: K.B. Elliott, Pub.1964, reprinted 2020, 216 pages, soft Cover, Index, ISBN #0-89308-381-X.

VA 61 $25.00

With the exception of one Militia Muster Roll - that of Capt. Reuben Vaughn, 1779 - all the muster rolls and other records of the Militia of Mecklenburg County for this period have been lost. This volume contains abstracts of all military and patriotic services by Mecklenburg County residents which can now be satisfactorily or completely documented. These records include the Committee of Safety, names of gentlemen justices who served during the period, the names of all militia officers appearing on the order books, the muster roll and commission of Capt. Vaughan, notes from pension applications, notes from the order books of the county pertaining to the Revolutionary War and other notes and records. There are more than 1,500 people being mentioned in this book.

Mecklenburg County, Virginia 1765-1799, Early Wills ***of.*** By: Katherine B. Elliott, Pub. 1963, reprinted 2017, 221 pages, soft cover, Index, ISBN #0-89308-378-X.

VA 55 $27.50

This volume contains abstracts of all the wills and administrations recorded in Will Book 1, 2, 3, and a part of Will Book 4, totaling 1,290 original manuscript pages. There are over 4,000 people mentioned in this volume.

Middlesex County, Virginia, 1740-1852, Marriages ***of.*** By: The Virginia Genealogical Society, Pub. 1965, Reprinted 2023, 124 pages, Index, soft cover, ISBN #0-89308-265-1.

VA 29 $18.50

Middlesex County was formed in 1673 from Lancaster County, VA. Although it is not a burned county, it is situated in that part of the state that was settled early and borders on counties where records have been destroyed. The earliest marriage records are found in Christ Church Parish Register.

Middlesex County, Virginia, 1625-1812, The Parish Register ***of*** **Christ Church.** By: N.S. C.D. in the state of VA., Pub. 1897, Reprinted 2019, 360 pages, New Index, ISBN #0-89308-631-2.

VA 34 $35.00

Middlesex County was created in 1669 from Lancaster County and parish. Sometime before 1666 that parish was divided into two portions, separated by the Rappahannock River and the new parishes were names Lancaster and Pyanketank. In 1666, they were reunited under the name Lancaster, but a few years later were again separated and acquired the organization which they retained through the colonial period as Christ Church, Lancaster and Christ Church, Middlesex.

Middlesex County did suffer some loss of legal records but did not as the result of the Civil War. Information to be found within this book: Burials & deaths, births & christenings, marriages and births of slaves naming mother and owners' name. This new reprint has a NEW INDEX that not only mention approximately 33,000 persons but 4,000 slaves that are grouped alphabetically under their owner's names for ease of research in a new Errata section in the rear.

(Middlesex County) The Vestry Book ***of*** **Christ Church, Virginia 1663-1767.** By: C.G. Chamberlayne, Pub. 1927, reprinted 2006, 394 pages, Index, Hard Cover, ISBN #0-89308-229-5.

VA 97 $38.50

Middlesex County was created in 1669 from Lancaster County, VA. It did suffer some loss of legal records but did not as the result of the Civil War. In preparing this book the author expended great care in following the original book in every eccentricity of spelling and abbreviation and in all mistakes. The VESTRY BOOK itself contains the names of approximately 8,000 individuals either as Vestry members or as those who had been appointed to procession land of property owners; apprentice young people to other in the parish for training in crafts or livelihoods; binding out young slaves for training; clothing and feeding and general care and welfare of the poor in their midst.

Nansemond County, Virginia, 1743-1793, The Vestry Book ***of the*** **Upper Parish.** By: Wilmer L. Hall, Pub. 1949, Reprinted 2019, 400 pages, Index, ISBN #0-89308-824-2.

VA 143 $35.00

Nansemond County was created in 1646 from Upper Norfolk. And prior to that was part of Elizabeth City County. Even though the county is extinct now, it was originally a large source of early migration into the Colony of Virginia. When the parishes were formed by the General Assembly of Virginia, the Vestries were assigned some of the civil administrative functions and all such civil functions were official in nature and the records of actions taken were recorded in the vestry books. Such records contained in the Vestry book contained among other things such things as: upkeep of bastard children; payment for the upkeep of the ferry; prosecution of fornicators; appointment of road work crews; apprentice young people to others in the parish for training in crafts or other livelihoods; providing clothing, food and shelter for the poor and elderly; burial of the dead and many, many other similar duties.

New Kent County, Virginia, Records ***of.*** By: Martha Washington Chapt. of DAR, Pub. 1938, Reprinted 2017, 78 pages, Index, ISBN #0-89308-783-1.

VA 118 $12.50

This "BURNED" county was created from York County, VA. in 1634. This book includes the first extant census for the county - 1810 and also the 1850 census for the county. The 1850 census is the first one that gives the names of every inhabitant of the county. Also included in this volume are abstracts of the application papers of the Revolutionary War pensioners.

(New Kent & James City Co's) The Vestry Book ***of*** **Blisland, 1721-1786.** By: C.G. Chamberlayne, Pub. 1935, Reprinted 2017, 336 pages, soft cover, Index, ISBN #0-89308-869-2.

VA 144 $30.00

Considering the fact that New Kent County is a "BURNED" county prior to 1865, makes this book one of only a few sources of information about this county during this colonial period. This BURNED County was formed from York County in 1654 and is the parent county of: Hanover, King William, and King & Queen counties. James City County was created in 1634 and was one of the eight original shires. It is considered the mother county of the state, and within it lie the first church & parish. It is the parent county in whole or part to: Charles City, New Kent, Surry, & York, counties. This county has suffered great loss of records due to the Civil War.

(New Kent & James City Co's) The Vestry Book ***and*** **Register** ***of*** **St. Peter's Parish, 1706-1786.** By: C.G. Chamberlayne, Pub. 1937, Reprinted 2019, 866 pages, Index, ISBN #0-89308-870-6.

VA 145 $58.50

Considering the fact that New Kent County is a "BURNED" county prior to 1865, makes this book one of only a few sources of information about this county during this colonial period. This BURNED County was formed from York County in 1654 and is the parent county of: Hanover, King William, and King & Queen counties. James City County was created in 1634 and was one of the eight original shires. It is considered the mother county of the state, and within it lie the first church & parish. It is the parent county in whole or part to: Charles City, New Kent, Surry, & York, counties. This county has suffered great loss of records due to the Civil War.

When the parishes were formed by the General Assembly of Virginia, the Vestries were assigned some of the civil administrative functions and all such civil functions were official in nature and the records of actions taken were recorded in the vestry books. Such records contained in the Vestry book contained among other things such things as: upkeep of bastard children; payment for the upkeep of the ferry; prosecution of fornicators; appointment of road work crews; apprentice young people to others in the parish for training in crafts or other livelihoods; providing clothing, food and shelter for the poor and elderly; burial of the dead and many, many other similar duties.

New Kent County, Virginia 1680-1878, The Parish Register ***of*** **Saint's Peter's,** By: NSCD, Pub. 1904, reprinted 2004, 210 pages, soft cover, Index, ISBN #0-89308-770-X.

VA 83 $27.50

Considering the fact that New Kent County is a "BURNED" county prior to 1865, makes this book one of only a few sources of information about this county during this colonial period. This is a very valuable resource tool when researching in this county. This BURNED County was formed from York County in 1654. New Kent County is the parent county to Hanover, King William, and King & Queen counties. This book includes Births, Baptism, Marriage & Death records as recorded in their original order along with a complete index.

(New Kent County) The Vestry Book ***of*** **St. Peter's Parish, Virginia 1682-1758.** By: NSCD of Virginia, Pub. 1905, reprinted 2006, 242 pages, soft cover, Index, ISBN #0-89308-738-6.

VA 66 $28.50

Considering the fact that New Kent County is a "BURNED" county prior to 1865, makes this book one of only a few sources of information about this county during this colonial period. This BURNED

County was formed from York County in 1654 and is the parent county of: Hanover, King William, and King & Queen counties. When the parishes were formed by the General Assembly of Virginia, the Vestries were assigned some of the civil administrative functions and all such civil functions were official in nature and the records of actions taken were recorded in the vestry books. Such records contained in the Vestry book contained among other things such things as: upkeep of bastard children; payment for the upkeep of the ferry; prosecution of fornicators; appointment of road work crews; apprentice young people to others in the parish for training in crafts or other livelihoods; providing clothing, food and shelter for the poor and elderly; burial of the dead and many, many other similar duties.

Norfolk County, Virginia 1706 -1792, Marriages of. By: Elizabeth Wingo, Pub. 1961, reprinted 2011, 98 pages, soft cover, Index, ISBN #0-89308401-8.

VA 84 $18.00

In 1691 Lower Norfolk County was divided into two new counties: Norfolk and Princess Anne. It is believed that 60% of these early settlers of Lower Norfolk County (1637) were indentured servants coming from overseas. These marriage records start with the earliest known surviving marriages for the county. It is believed that the earlier dates were lost or destroyed during the Revolutionary War. This is the first time that this book has ever been reprinted since its 1961 original publication.

Norfolk County, Virginia Revolutionary War *and* War *of* 1812 Application *for* Pensions, Bounty Land Warrants *and* Heirs *of* Deceased Pensioners. By: Elizabeth Wingo, Pub. 1964, Reprinted 2019, 204 pages, Index, ISBN #0-89308-408-5.

VA 87 $25.00

Norfolk County, Virginia Tithables, 1730-1750. By: Elizabeth Wingo, Pub. 1979, Reprinted 2019, 258 pages, Index, ISBN #0-89308-496-9.

VA 81 $27.50

A Tithable refers to a person who paid, or for whom someone else paid, one of the taxes that the General Assembly of the state/colony imposed for the support of the civil government of that state or colony. These tithables permit the identification of county residents and provide information about various family relationships in crucial years prior to the American revolution. Another useful aspect to these records: the naming of slaves. This can be a very useful tool when trying research slave ancestry. The Original lists are so badly damaged that examination in now restricted. The care taken to ensure the accuracy of these transcriptions will, however, make this book an adequate substitute.

Norfolk County, Virginia Wills, 1637-1710, Brief Abstracts of Lower Norfolk and. By: Charles McIntosh, Pub. 1914, Reprinted 2018, 224 pages, Index, soft cover, ISBN #0-89308-322-4.

VA 11 $25.00

Lower Norfolk was created in 1637 when New Norfolk was divided and abolished. It became extinct in 1691 when it was split into Princess Anne and Norfolk counties. It is estimated that 60% of her early settlers of this coastal colony were indentured servants. Wills are a wonderful source for genealogical research due to the persons being mentioned within.

Norfolk County, Virginia Wills, 1710-1753. By: Charles McIntosh, Pub. 1922, Reprinted 2018, 344 pages, Index, ISBN #0-89308-324-0.

VA 12 $30.00

This is the second volume of books on the Wills of this county by Charles McIntosh. Lower Norfolk was created in 1637 when New Norfolk was divided and abolished. It became extinct in 1691 when it was split into Princess Anne and Norfolk counties. It is estimated that 60% of her early settlers of this coastal colony were indentured servants. Wills are a wonderful source for genealogical research due to the persons being mentioned within.

Norfolk County, Virginia 1711-1800, Collection *of* Unrecorded Wills. By: Elizabeth B. Wingo, Pub. 1961, Reprinted 2016, 148 pages, soft cover, Index, ISBN #0-89308-403-4.

VA 82 $22.50

Until now, this book has been out-of-print shortly after its original printing in 1961. Research has revealed that there are almost one hundred unrecorded wills and deposition among the Norfolk County, Norfolk Town or Norfolk Borough records from 1711-1800. These records are a must for those researchers who have been unable to locate those ancestors in this area of coastal Virginia.

Northumberland County, Virginia 1850 Census. By: Bayne P. O'Brien, Pub. 1972, reprinted 1982, 118 pages, soft cover, Index, ISBN #0-89308-307-0.

VA 40 $27.50

Northumberland County, Viginia Records. (Vol. #3). By: Beverly Fleet, Pub. 1938, reprinted 2006, 138 pages, soft cover, Index, ISBN #0-89308-389-5.

VA 119 $20.00

Northumberland County was created in 1645. Many of her early residents were from Maryland and in turn many of her residence later moved on to Essex & Stafford Counties and to other counties South of the James River. This book contains the Register of St. Stephen's Parish, Northumberland County, VA. This book contains the BIRTHS from 1661-1810 (with a few deaths being mentioned).

Northumberland County, Virginia Records 1678-1713, (Vol. #1). By: Lindsay O. Duvall, Pub. 1952, reprinted 1920, 156 pages, soft cover, Index, ISBN #0-89308-062-4.

VA 2 $20.00

This book contains the Court Minutes of the county from 1678-1713.

Northumberland County, Virginia Records. (Vol. #2). By: Beverly Fleet, Pub. 1938, Reprinted 2018, 144 pages, Index, soft cover, ISBN #0-89308-942-7.

VA 136 $20.00

Northumberland County was created in 1645. Many of her early residents were from Maryland and in turn many of her residence later moved on to Essex & Stafford Counties and to other counties South of the James River. This book contains Court order Book #2, 1652-1656 and Court Record Book #14, 1652-1655.

(Northumberland County, VA) Northumbria Collectanea, 1645-1720. (Vol. 19 & 20) By: Beverly Fleet, Pub. 1938, Reprinted 2018, 246 pages, soft cover, ISBN #0-89308-390-9.

VA 179 $27.50

Northumberland County was created in 1645. Many of her early residents were from Maryland and in turn many of her residence later moved on to Essex & Stafford Counties and to other counties South of the James River. This book contains Court order Book #1-13, 1650-1756 and Court Record Book #14-23, 1652-1749. This book is listed in alphabetical order.

(Old) Rappahannock County, Virginia 1656-1692, Wills *of*. By: William M. Sweeny, Pub. 1947, reprinted 1998, 194 pages, Hard Cover, Index, ISBN #0-89308-625-8.

VA 86 $30.00

Even though Rappahannock County was created from the Northern portion of Culpeper County in 1833, this book deals with the wills of "OLD" Rappahannock County (Richmond & Essex Counties). These wills were not conveniently copied and recorded by the clerk in a set of books known as "Will Books" but were scattered through the Deed Books and Order Books. In selecting the wills, it was necessary for the author to read over all the record books of Old Rappahannock, and all the early records of Essex and Richmond.

Orange County, Virginia Families, Vol. #2. By: William E. Brockman, Pub. 1957, reprinted 2010, 283 pages, New Index, soft cover, ISBN #0-89308-794-7

VA 128 $27.50

Orange county was created from Spotsylvania County, VA. in 1734. In turn it is the parent county of: Augusta, Culpeper, Greene & Frederick. The records contained within this volume are: 2000 marriage bonds from 1747-1824; a list of Importations from 1735-1756 giving persons names and origin of country; Military Commissions from 1735-1793 giving names, dates and rank; a list of Revolutionary soldiers giving dates of enlistments along with any known additional information of service; a list of Bonds & Administrations from 1752-1796, Chancery Suits from 1739-1760; a list of Bonds 1735-1799; Court Orders-Military Services 1738-1785; a list of persons from Orange county who served in the War of 1812 & Mexican War; Military Claims 1785-1795; Tithable 1736-1758; and genealogies of Brockmans, Collins, Gaydens, Merrys, Sims, Rhodes, and Woolfolks.

Orange County, Virginia Families, Vol. #3. By: W.E. Brockman, reprinted 2010, 229 pages, New Index, soft cover, ISBN #0-89308-795-5.

VA 129 $27.50

The records contained within this volume are: Clerk Browning's abstracts of various information from loose papers and supplemented by items not recorded and are believed to be the only source for this valuable information; Military Commissions in the State Militia 1735-1793 listing dates & ranks; and family genealogies/detailed information on: Ballard, Catterton, Chapman, Collins, Dowell-Salmon-Brockman, Salmon-Mundy Bible record, Edwards Bible record, Ellis, Graves Bible record, Hume of Culpeper, Macon, Masons of Gunston Hall, Montagues, Quisenberry, Rhodes, Shotwell Bible record, Simms, Terrett, Towles-Clark-Smoot, Willis family of Orange, Step-Stap-Stapp, Brockman, Tribble-Gordon-Burris, Marshall-Durrett, Robert E. Johnson Bible record, John Vaughan Miller Bible record, Wood Bible record.

Orange County, Virginia Marriages, 1747-1810. By: Catherine Knorr, Pub. 1959, Reprinted 2017, 120 pages, soft cover, Index, ISBN #0-89308-252-X.

VA 15 $17.50

Orange county was formed in 1734 from Spotsylvania County and comprised as area on both sides of the

Blue Ridge Mountains out of which has subsequently been formed more than 36 counties. In 1743, Fredericksburg County was formed from Orange and in 1745, Augusta County was formed. In 1749, Culpeper County was formed from it and in 1838 Greene County was formed from Orange. It is surrounded by Albemarle, Louisa, Spotsylvania, Culpeper, Madison and Greene.

Patrick County, Virginia 1791-1850, Marriages of. By: Lela C Adams, Pub.1972, reprinted 1984, 165 pages, soft cover, Index, ISBN #0-89308-357-7

VA 46 $20.00

Patrick County was created in 1791 from Henry County, VA. Over time Patrick County has donated some of her lands back to Henry County along with the counties of: Carroll, Franklin & Grayson.

Patrick County, Virginia 1791- Aug. 1800, Abstracts *of* Order Book "O". By: Lela C. Adams, Pub. 1984, 130 pages, soft cover, Index, ISBN #0-89308-427-1.

VA 100 $20.00

This order book contains brief description of court cases, and in some instances, the names of people involved in court cases that are carried over to another session of the court for disposition. It contains cases of the Commonwealth; grantor and grantee of deeds are listed; surveyors of the roads are names as well as people in the area who happened to work on the roads; lists of people appointed to the militia (officers) and appointments of commissioners, justices of the peace and sheriffs are also found in these records, as well as licenses for people to operate taverns and grist mills; lists of administrators of estates and those who were to inventory the particular estates in question are also found among other valuable information.

Patrick County, Virginia, 1791-1823, Abstracts *of* Wills, Inventories *and* Accounts *of.* By: Lela C. Adams, Pub. 1972, Reprinted 2019, 110 pgs, Index, soft cover, ISBN #0-89308-356-9.

VA 42 $15.00

Patrick county was created in 1791 from Henry County. It is the parent county to: Carroll, Grayson, and Franklin. Wills are wonderful source for the researcher due to many and variety of family members being mentioned. Many times, marriages of various family members can be discovered within a will.

Pittsylvania County, Virginia, History *of.* By: Maud Carter Clement, Pub. 1929, Reprinted 2018, 380 pages, soft cover, Index, ISBN #0-89308-848-X.

VA 173 $35.00

Pittsylvania County was created in 1767 from Lunenburg and Halifax Counties. This well-documented book not only covers the county from its creation but also includes material from its parent counties as well the continuous counties of Bedford, Campbell, Franklin, Henry, and Patrick. Besides the traditional information found in similar books of the era, such as discussions of: Indians, First settlements, creation of the county, its involvement in the French and Indian War along with the Cherokee War, Churches/Religion, Pre- and Post-Revolutionary War, the War of 1812, the Civil War and WWI. All of this helps in developing pathways and ideas of how the citizens of the county dealt with the development of the county. The reader will also discover a 1767 list of tithables of the county with the names of approximately 1,000 land and property owners. This book has loads of extremely useful and detailed tidbits of genealogical information along with mini biographies of these early settlers interspersed throughout the book included within the tremendous numbers of footnotes. The reader may discover those lost relatives thru the mentioning of marriages, Wills, Deeds, Military and Court records. The index within this book mentions approximately 5,000 individuals.

Pittsylvania County, Virginia Deeds 1765-1774. By: Lucille C. & Neil G. Payne, Pub. 1991, reprinted 2017, 218 pages, soft cover, Index, ISBN #0-89308-466-2.

VA 69 $25.00

Pittsylvania County was created in 1767 from Halifax County, VA. It was a important migration path for early settlers moving into Tennessee, Georgia and North & South Carolina. Deeds are GREAT source for genealogical research due to the many and varied family members that are mentioned. Not only will the reader find the deed transaction itself, but often times such things as: marriages, relinquishment of dower, divisions of family farms among heirs, remarriages of widows are just a few of the matters you can anticipate finding within records of deeds.

Pittsylvania County, Virginia Deeds 1783-1790. By: Gayle Austin, Pub. 2007, 282 pages plus index, soft cover, ISBN #0-89308-711-4.

VA 123 $35.00

Deeds are GREAT source for genealogical research due to the many and varied family members that are mentioned. Not only will the reader find the deed transaction itself, but often times such things as: marriages, relinquishment of dower, divisions of family farms among heirs, remarriages of widows are just a few of the matters you can anticipate finding within records of deeds.

Pittsylvania County, Virginia 1767-1805, Marriage Bonds *and* Ministers' Returns. By: Catherine L. Knorr, Pub. 1956, Reprinted 2006, 120 pages, Index, soft cover, ISBN #0-89308-260-0.

VA 23 $15.00

Pittsylvania County was created in 1767 from Halifax County, VA. Many of her early settlers were from Pennsylvania, including Germans, Quakers, Welch and Scotch-Irish. Also, many families throughout Virginia relocated here from such counties as: Brunswick, Charlotte, Amelia, Prince Edward, and other Tidewater counties.

Pittsylvania County, Virginia Land Tax Lists: 1782-1802. By: Gayle Austin, Pub 2007, 322 pages, Index, 8 1/2"x11" soft cover, ISBN #0-89308-712-2.

VA 124 $38.50

Some of the least know records for the state of Virginia are the Land Tax Lists. Within these land tax lists, you will discover not only the owner's name and acreage but with a little effort you will be able to follow a family through its land holdings. You can see when a person dies, when he sells out and leaves the county, when he passes his land down to his children. The reader will also discover the inclusion of Land Patents. Of special interest, after the owners name sometimes a set of initials will appear. These can mean one of several things: they can be the initials of the person he purchased the land from, or they can mean the location of the land such as a creeks name or geographical feature. These tax lists can be extremely important because sometimes when there was not a will or a deed, the transaction appears in these lists and nowhere else. It can also be used to help cover the gap of the missing 1800 & 1810 census records.

Pittsylvania County, Virginia 1767-1820, Wills *of.* By: Lela C. Adams, Pub. 1986, reprinted 2014, 274 pages, soft cover, Index, ISBN #0-89308-581-2.

VA 75 $30.00

Pittsylvania County was created in 1767 from Halifax County, VA. It was a important migration path for early settlers moving into Tennessee, Georgia and North & South Carolina. Many of her early settlers were from Pennsylvania, including Germans, Quakers, Welch and Scot Irish. Also, many families throughout Virginia relocated here from such counties as: Brunswick, Charlotte, Amelia, Prince Edward, and other Tidewater counties. This book contains not only wills of individuals, but also guardians and administrator's bonds, bastardy, apprentice, trustees, sheriffs and treasurer's bonds, and inventories of estates. The names of approximately 14,500 persons are found in these legal records of this important county.

Powhatan County, Virginia 1777-1830, Marriage Bonds *and* Minister's Returns of. By: Catherine Lindsay Knorr, Pub. 1957, reprinted 1983, 96 pages, map, soft cover, Index, ISBN #0-89308-258-9.

VA 21 $15.00

Powhatan county was created in 1777 from Cumberland County, VA. and later additional lands from Chesterfield County in 1850. These lands saw large numbers of Huguenots settlers in the 1700's.

(Powhatan County) Vestry Book *of* King William Parish, Virginia 1707-1750. By: R.H. Fife, Pub. 1905-1906, Reprinted 2006, 155 pages, Hard Cover, Index, ISBN #0-89308-354-2.

VA 142 $28.50

Powhatan county was created in 1777 from Cumberland County, VA. And even though this book begins before Powhatan County was created, it does reflect the portion of Powhatan County that was carved out of Henrico County, VA in 1777. This parish is very unique in that it is one of a few areas that the Huguenots settled in Virginia. This Huguenot District is filled with wonderful history. Prof. Fife has transcribed the vestry book from French to English so that it might provide some useful help to those tracing their Huguenot ancestors. When the Parishes were created by the general Assembly of Virginia, the Vestries were assigned some of the civil administrative functions and all of such civil functions were official in nature and the records of actions taken were recorded in the vestry book. This book serves as a unique as well as double purpose in that it contains two different sets of records: the minutes of the vestry (civil functions) and also the order for Processing. The later was the surveying of land to attempt to eliminate lawsuits over boundary lines. This book is filled with hundreds of early inhabitants.

Prince Edward County, Virginia 1754-1810, Marriage Bonds *and* Ministers' Returns *of.* By: Catherine Lindsay Knorr, Pub. 1950, reprinted 2018, 108 pages, map, soft cover, Index, ISBN #0-89308-263-5.

VA 26 $15.00

Prince Edward county was created in 1754 from Amelia County, VA. and later gave portions of her lands to Appomattox County, VA.

Prince George, County, Virginia 1666-1719, Vol. #6. By: Lindsay O. Duvall, Pub. 1962, reprinted 2011, 80 pages, Index, soft cover, ISBN #0-89308-067-5.

VA 7 $15.00

Prince George was created in 1703 from Charles City County and in turn it gave birth to Brunswick and Dinwiddie Counties. Many of the county's records were destroyed by fire during the Revolutionary & Civil Wars. Even though the county was not created until 1703, these records (Land Patents) begin in 1666 when it was part of Charles City and continue on through 1719.

(Princess Anne County) The Colonial Vestry Book *of* Lynnhaven Parish, Virginia 1723-1786. By: George C. Mason, reprinted 2004, 162 pages, 8 1/2" x 11" soft cover, Index, ISBN #0-89308-737-8.

VA 111 $28.50

The parish of Lynnhaven encompasses the whole county of Princess Anne. Princess Anne County was created from the Eastern third of Lower Norfolk County in 1691. These boundaries ran from the lower reaches of the Chesapeake Bay going South to the North Carolina State line along the Atlantic Ocean. These coastal counties were a great source of migration of early pioneers headed West. These minutes of the vestry contain 5,000 individuals either as Vestry members or as those who had been appointed to possession land of property owners, apprentice young people to others in the parish for training in crafts or livelihoods, binding out young slaves for training, clothing and feeding and general care and welfare of the poor in their midst.

(Princess Anne Co.) Gateway *to the* New World: A History *of* Princess Anne County, Virginia, 1607-1824. By: Florence K. Turner, Pub. 1984, reprinted 2020, 322 pages, Index, maps, ISBN #0-89308-523-5.

VA 139 $35.00

Gateway to the New World is the history of one of the oldest counties of Colonial Virginia. It tells about both the adventurous and ordinary lives of people in 17th, 18th and 19th century Princess Anne County, Virginia. Here is a tale of seven or eight generations.... How they lived, loved, and endured through thick and thin, told with candor, humor, sympathy and respect.

Princess Anne County, Virginia 1749-1821, Marriages *of*. By: Elizabeth Wingo, Pub. 1961, reprinted 2011, 154 pages, soft cover, Index, ISBN #0-89308-404-2.

VA 80 $20.00

Princess Anne County was created in 1691 out of Lower Norfolk County, VA. Even though these marriages do not start with the creation of the county, they are the first of the known marriage bonds that exist for this county. This is the first time that this book has ever been reprinted since its 1961 original publication.

Richmond County, Virginia Marriages, 1668-1853. By: George H. King, Pub. 1964, reprinted 2015, 312 pages, soft cover, Index, ISBN #0-89308-579-0.

VA 73 $35.00

Richmond County was created in 1692 from OLD Rappahannock County. Since Richmond was the state capital and a center of commerce for a wide area, the marriages abstracted here frequently refer to persons in other states, and other areas of Virginia. Many of the notices are from the "burned counties" of Virginia.

(Richmond Co.) The Registers *of* North Farnham Parish, 1663-1814 *and* Lunenburg Parish, 1783-1800, Richmond County, Virginia, By: George Harrison Stafford King, Pub. 1966, reprinted 2021, 236 pages, Index, soft cover, ISBN #0-89308-580-4.

VA 58 $28.50

Richmond County was created in 1692 from Old Rappahannock County. This is a very important research tool when working in Richmond County as it contains: Births, Baptisms, Marriages and Death records as recorded in their original order with a complete index.

Richmond Virginia Newspapers 1780-1820, Marriages *and* Deaths *from*. By: The Virginia Genealogical Society, Pub. 1983, reprinted 1987, 286 pages, Hard Cover, Index, ISBN #0-89308-619-3.

Since Richmond was the state capital and a center of commerce for a wide area, the marriage and death notices abstracted here frequently refer to persons in other states, and other areas of Virginia. Many of the notices are from the "burned counties" of Virginia. Some of the notices included were news items rather than obituaries or social notes. Many were obviously copied from out-of-town papers of unknown dates and a number of these were apparently included for their humor content or strangeness. The notices of deaths are in alphabetical order, followed by the marriage notices in alphabetical order by groom. There is a separate index of brides. The newspaper name has been indicated by initials, the key to which is in the introduction.

Richmond County, Virginia 1692-1724, Records *of*. By: Beverley Fleet, Pub. 1942 & 1943, reprinted 2006, 231 pages, soft cover, Index, ISBN #0-89308-823-4.

VA 31 $28.50

Richmond County was created in 1692 from OLD Rappahannock County. This book is a consolidation of two books by Mr. Fleet into one user friendly volume. This book consists of Deeds from 1692-1696 and Court Orders from 1699-1724.

Rockingham County, Virginia Marriages 1778-1816. By: Harry M. Strickler, Orig. Pub. 1928, reprinted 2010, 128 pages, soft cover, ISBN # 0-89308-740-8.

VA 78 $17.50

Rockingham County was created in 1778 from Augusta County, VA. It was later divided to created Page County, VA and Pendleton County, WV. Many of its early settlers came from Maryland and Pennsylvania. Because of its geographical position, thousands of persons migrated through and into the county heading west to Kentucky and Tennessee. This book contains an alphabetical listing of marriage records for the years 1778-1816.

Some RUSSELL County, Virginia 1853-1866. By: Thomas Colley, Pub. 1996, 192 pages, Hard Cover, Index, ISBN #0-89308-494-8.

VA 96 $30.00

Records within this volume: Births & Deaths for the years 1853-1866.

Shenandoah County, Virginia, A History *of*. By: John W. Wayland, Pub. 1927, Reprinted 2021, 874 pages, Index, ISBN #978-1-63914-006-0.

VA 163 $65.00

Shenandoah County was created in 1778 from Dunmore which was created in 1782 from Frederick County, Virginia. This book is not too different from other county history books of this era. With such topics as formation of county, Indians, trade and transportation, labor, churches, schools and Civil War - all important in the development of the county - are carefully discussed. This type of county history book can help one develop ideas or paths to those missing ancestors by showing the customs and traditions of the local residents. The reader will also discover the author has included additional information such as heads of families in 1785, lists of militiamen and soldiers, public representatives and church members, Births and Baptisms 1773-1782, Marriages 1782-1800, and Civil War muster rolls. But the reader will find the 150 plus pages devoted to biographical sketches of immense help when researching family members of this region.

Southampton County, Virginia 1750-1810, Marriage Bonds *and* Ministers' Returns *of*. By: Catherine Lindsay Knorr, Pub. 1955, reprinted 1982, 152 pages, maps, soft cover, Index, ISBN #0-89308-255-4.

VA 18 $18.50

Southhampton County, VA. Wills, *and* Administrations, 1775-1800. By: Blanche Adams Chapman, Pub. 1958, Reprinted 2016, 238 pages, Index, ISBN #0-89308-883-8.

VA 149 $25.00

Southampton County was created in 1774 from Isle of Wight and Nansemond Counties, VA. Wills are wonderful source for the researcher due to many and variety of family members being mentioned. Many times, marriages of various family members can be discovered within a will.

Spotsylvania County, Virginia Records. By: William A. Crozier, Pub. 1905, reprinted 2016, 576 pages, soft cover, Index, ISBN #089308-884-6

VA 147 $48.50

Spotsylvania County was created in 1721 from Essex, King & Queen and King William counties. Spotsylvania saw its full share of early settlers heading from Maryland & Coastal Virginia heading west to Culpeper, Madison and Orange counties. The records within this book are: Wills 1722-1800, Marriages 1722-1750 & 1795-1800, Guardians' bonds 1725-1798, Deeds 1722-1800, a list of Colonial Militia from the Order Books 1724-1782, Revolutionary Records from Order Books 1774-1786, and Revolutionary Pensions from Order Books 1829-1838.

(Stafford County) The Register *of* Overwharton Parish, Virginia 1723-1758. By: George HS King, Pub. 1961, Reprinted 2010, 292 pages, soft cover, Index, ISBN #0-89308-576-6.

VA 70 $30.00

Stafford County was created in 1664 from Westmoreland County, VA. It in turn was the parent county to Prince William, Fauquier, Fairfax, and Loudoun Counties. This book includes Births, Baptism, Marriage & Death records as recorded in their original order along with a complete index.

(Surry & Sussex Co's) The Register *of* Albemarle Parish, Virginia 1739-1778. By: NSCD, Pub.1958, Reprinted 2010, 308 pages, soft cover, New Index, ISBN #0-89308-042-X.

VA 102 $35.00

Albemarle Parish, a lineal descendant of the earliest parish in Virginia, has claim to distinction. James City Parish, when first laid out, included land on both sides of the James River; soon new parishes were organized on the south side, one of them in Surry County, which then stretched southward to the North Carolina line. Even though the influx of settlers made it impossible to govern such a large tract with one council and Sussex County was created from the southern half of Surry. Practically all of Albemarle Parish lay within the confines of the new county and a judicious alternation of boundary lines shaped the parish to fit into Sussex; small fringes of land on the north that had belonged to the parish were clipped off and abundant compensation provided by the addition of more fertile acres to the southward. There are approximately 5,000 baptisms between 1739 and 1778 of individuals. Besides the baptisms, this register also lists the names of parents and God parents, which approximate 24,000 in number. Also contained in this book is a register of births of Negroes, mulattos, and slaves, with the date of their birth; and this list contains the names of some 800 of the aforementioned, plus the name of their owner, as well as the name of the person who was supplying this information regarding the slaves. The Register of Deaths of White Persons contains the names of some 1,900 deceased individuals, plus the names of those individuals who furnished the information for the Parish register.

Colonial SURRY. By: John Bennett Boddie, Pub. 1948, Reprinted 2019, 260 pages, Index, ISBN #0-89308-059-4.

VA 167 $25.00

Surry County was formed in 1652 from James City County, which was one of Virginia's 8 original counties. John B. Boddie is a well-respected author who has completed numerous books on southside area of Virginia. Contents of this book: early history of the county, various genealogical data on pre-revolutionary time frame, Surry County Land Grants, 1624-1740, Surry County Censuses 1668, 1678, 1688, 1698 and 1782, Surry County Tithables 1668, 1674, 1678, 1683, 1688, 1694, 1698 and 1702, Surry County Militia 1687, Quint Rent Rolls for Surry County 1704, some Surry County Marriages 1679-1791, some Sussex County Marriages 1755-1781 and Sussex County Census 1782.

Surry County, Virginia, 1768-1825, Marriage Bonds *and* Ministers' Returns *of.* By: Catherine Lindsay Knorr, Pub. 1960, reprinted 2020, 110 pages, maps, Index, ISBN #0-89308-256-2.

VA 19 $18.50

Surry County was created in 1652 from James City County. Due to the loss of court records of many surrounding counties, such as Charles City, Dinwiddie, James City, and Prince George, the records of Surry County take on a more profound importance because of the early movement across county lines and the James River.

Surry County, Virginia Wills, Estates *and* Inventories, 1730-1800. By: Lyndon H. Hart, Pub. 1983, Reprinted 2016, 182 pages, soft cover, Index, ISBN #0-89308-325-9.

VA 10 $23.50

Surry County was created in 1652 from James City County. Due to the loss of court records of many surrounding counties, such as Charles City, Dinwiddie, James City, and Prince George, the records of Surry County take on a more profound importance because of the early movement across county lines and the James River. This book contains not only wills of individuals, but also guardians and administrators' bonds, bastardy, apprentice, trustees, sheriffs and treasurer's bonds, and inventories of estates. The names of approximately 7,000 persons are found in these legal records of this important county.

Sussex County, Virginia 1754-1810, Marriages *of.* By: Catherine Lindsay Knorr, Pub. 1952, reprinted 1982, 118 pages, map, soft cover, Index, ISBN #0-89308-257-0.

VA 20 $16.00

The Annals of Tazewell County, Virginia, 1800-1852. (2 Volumes) By: John Newton Harman, Pub. 1922, Reprinted 2020, 469 pages, NEW INDEX, Soft Cover.

Vol. #1, 1800-1852: 469 pages, ISBN #0-89308-955-9.

VA 181 $45.00

Until now, this book has been extremely difficult to use for research due to its lack of a through and complete INDEX. We have created a brand-new FULL NAME Index that contains the names of approximately 11,000 persons. Tazwell County was formed in 1799 from Wythe and Russell Counties. This volume contains abstracts of court orders, wills, and deeds; the names of all civil and military officers of the county; all lawyers admitted to the bar; all preachers licensed to celebrate the rites of matrimony and an exact copy of the Tazewell marriage registers from 1800 to 1852; every deed made to churches of all denominations from 1800 to 1922; the names of all Tazewell representatives in the General Assembly of Virginia from 1800 to 1852; and a list of Revolutionary Pensioners.

Vol. #2, 1853-1922: 655 pages, ISBN #0-89308-956-7.

VA 182 $58.50

We have created a brand-new FULL NAME Index that contains the names of approximately 20,000 persons. Tazewell County was formed in 1799 from Wythe and Russell Counties. Volume II continues the principal features of Volume I from 1853, with marriage records to 1868; the names of all devisers and devisees of wills to 1924; lists of Tazewell soldiers in the Revolutionary War, the Civil War, and World War I; various court orders; and a fairly complete list of Tazewell churches and church officers in 1924. The concluding 250 pages of the book, moreover, consist of lengthy genealogies of pioneer families of Tazewell County.

Washington County, Virginia Records, Vol. 34. By: Beverly Fleet, Orig. Pub. 1949, reprinted 1985, 96 pages, soft cover, Index, ISBN #0-89308-392-5.

VA 76 $15.00

This book is the marriage register for the years 1782-1810.

Westmoreland Co., Virginia Records, Vol. 23. By: Beverly Fleet, Orig. Pub. 1945, reprinted 1985, 104 pages, soft cover, Index, ISBN #0-89308-393-3.

VA 77 $15.00

Westmoreland county was created in 1653 from Northumberland County, VA. These are abstracts of Deeds, Wills, and Patents for the years 1653-1657.

Westmoreland County, Virginia Wills 1654-1800. By: Augusta Fothergill, Pub. 1925, Reprinted 2016, 238 pages, Index, ISBN #0-89308-323-2.

VA 9 $25.00

Westmoreland County was created from Northumberland County in 1653. It is the parent county of Stafford, Prince William, King George, & Fauquier. Many of Westmoreland's early records are missing especially the marriages which do not start until 1772. Wills are wonderful source for the researcher due to many and variety of family members being mentioned. Many times, marriages of various family members can be discovered within a will. The Index mentions approximately 5,500 persons.

(York County) Charles Parish, York County, Virginia 1648-1789. History *and* Register *of.* By: Landon C. Bell, Orig. Pub. 1932, reprinted 2014,293 pages, soft cover, Index, ISBN #0-89308-865-X.

VA 135 $30.00

York County was formed in 1634 as Charles River County and renamed York County in 1643. It is the parent county for Gloucester and New Kent counties. This book includes Births 1648-1789 & Death records 1665-1787 as recorded in their original order along with a complete index.

York County, Virginia 1633-1657, Records *of.* (3 Volumes) By: Beverly Fleet, Pub. 1945, reprinted 2013, soft cover, Index.

Vol. #1, 1633-1646: 108 pages, ISBN #0-89308-515-4.

VA 131 $15.00

Vol. #2, 1646-1648: 112 pages, ISBN #0-89308-516-2.

VA 132 $15.00

Vol. #3, 1657-1659: 108 pages, ISBN #0-89308-517-0

VA 133 $15.00

York County was formed in 1634 as Charles River County and renamed York County in 1643. It is the parent county for Gloucester and New Kent counties. The material within these three volumes are Deeds, Court Orders and Wills for the years 1633-1657

York County, Virginia Wills, Deeds *and* Orders, 1657-1659. By: Lindsay O. Duvall, Pub. 1961, reprinted 1978, 94 pages, soft cover, Index, ISBN #0-89308-066-7.

VA 6 $17.50

York County was created in 1642 from Charles River County. It is the parent county to Gloucester and New Kent Counties

Miscellaneous Records

Cavaliers *and* Pioneers: Abstracts of Virginia Land Patents *and* Grants, 1623-1666. By: Nell Marion Nugent, Pub. 1934, Reprinted 2018, 799 pages, Index, soft cover, ISBN #0-89308-945-1.

VA 183 $68.50

This book is a record of the Virginia Land Grants under the name of patentee or grantee from 1623 -1666. Within these records one will discover the number of acres, locations and dates of settlement, and many times the names of various family members. The family historian will also discover references to marriages, wills, and other legal instruments. It also has the names of thousands who were transported or brought over by the early settlers as "headrights." The index contains the names of approximately 20,000 persons.

The Colonial Clergy *of* Virginia, North Carolina *and* South Carolina, 1607-1776. By: Frederick Lewis Weis, Pub. 1955, Reprinted 2021, 108 pages, soft cover, ISBN #978-1-63914-031-2.

VA 193 $17.50

This book is alphabetical list of approximately 950 colonial clergymen from 1607-1776 who settled in Virginia, North Carolina and South Carolina. These annotations furnish such useful genealogical data as date & place of birth, date & place of death, names of parents, college of matriculation, date of ordination, denomination, names of parishes, dates in which tenure was held, and a variety of other similar data.

Early Virginia Immigrants, 1623-1666. By: George Cabell Greer, Orig. Pub. 1912, Reprinted 2018, 376 pages, Index, ISBN #0-89308-814-5.

VA 122 $35.00

A useful companion to Nugent's Cavaliers and Pioneers, this work provides an exhaustive list of immigrants to Virginia, 1623-1666, who were not original patentees of land. As the records stand it is very difficult to discover names of persons who came to Virginia unless they were patentees of land, and the great majority of immigrants to the colony were not Patentees but "Headrights". Nearly 25,000 names have been collected from the original records in the Virginia State Land Office and arranged in alphabetical order. Every immigrant from 1623 down to 1666 is noted long with the name of the patentee or party sponsoring him and the date and place or residence.

Emigrations *to other* States *from* Southside Virginia. (2 Volumes) By: K. B. Elliott, Pub. 1966, reprinted 2017, soft cover, Index.

Vol. #1: 120 pages, ISBN #0-89308356-8.
VA 63 $17.50

Vol. #2: 138 pages, ISBN #0-89308-366-3.
VA 65 $17.50

The term "South side Virginia" is used in these two volumes to include the counties of Amelia, Appomattox, Bedford, Brunswick, Campbell, Charlotte, Dinwiddie, Franklin, Greenville, Halifax, Henry, Lunenburg, Mecklenburg, Nottoway, Patrick, Pittsylvania, Prince Edward, Prince George, and Sussex. These south side counties contributed heavily to the settlement of N.C., S.C., GA., TN., and KY. The records in these volumes are documented from the county court records and include some notes on more than one generation of some of the listed. Though research has necessarily had to be limited, the compiler has included notes and other records deemed of value in tracing these families. Besides the states already mentioned into which people from south side VA. moved, reference is also made to these other states, viz: AR., FL., IL., IN., MS., MO., OH., PA., VA., LA., and N.Y.

English Duplicates *of* LOST Virginia Records. By: Louis des Cognets, Pub. 1958, Reprinted 2018, 386 pages, Index, soft cover, ISBN #0-89308-880-3.

VA 189 $27.50

This book was compiled from material found in the Public Record Office in London. The records within this book contain a great deal of out-of-the-way information. These records cover the counties of: Accomack, Brunswick, Caroline, Charles City, Elizabeth City, Essex, Hanover, Henrico, Gloucester, Goochland, Isle of Wight, James City, King & Queen, King William, Lancaster, Middlesex, Nansemond, New Kent, Norfolk, Northampton, Northumberland, Prince George, Princess Anne, Richmond, Spotsylvania, Stafford, Surry, Warwick, Westmoreland and York.

Free Negro Labor *and* Property Holding *in* Virginia, 1830-1860. By: Luther Porter Jackson, Pub. 1942, Reprinted 2020, 288 pgs, ISBN #0-89308-859-5.

VA 165 $27.50

Despite being a person of color and facing countless abuses, many of these free persons stayed in Virginia and made it their home. One must turn past the political reasons and look at the economic side as to why a free person of color would stay. This book is 3-decade study into the lives of these persons and the advancements they made in spite of the laws of the land. The author has included two appendix's that list these free persons who owned property valued over $1000 in Petersburg and Free persons of color who owned more than 100 acres of land throughout the state. The reader will also discover numerous amounts of detailed data concerning these free persons within the footnotes throughout this book. This book will deliver great insight into the lives of these person. Even if you don't have Afro-American genealogy in your family, this book should be a MUST read for anyone interested in Virginia History and Genealogy as a whole.

Petitions *of the* Early Inhabitants *of* Kentucky *to the* General Assembly *of* Virginia, 1769-1792. By: James R. Robertson & John F. Dorman, Pub. 1914, Reprinted 2019, 326 pages, Index, ISBN #0-89308-206-6.

KY 20 $30.00

Robertson's petitions are verbatim transcripts of the text of 110 petitions between 1769 and 1831 relating to the earliest settlers, together with a list of the persons who signed the petitions keyed to the petition number. An index covers names and subjects mentioned in the petitions. A 44-page addendum section containing additional petitions of Kentuckians to the Virginia Legislature has been included. This additional section was taken from "The Kentucky Genealogists" and prepared by Mr. John Frederick Dorman, F.A.S.G.. The NEW FULL NAME INDEX that was produced for this addendum section mentions approximately 2,250 individuals.

The Planters *of* Colonial Virginia. By: Thomas J. Wertenbaker, Pub. 1922, reprinted 2022, 260 pages, Index, ISBN #0-89308-054-1.

VA 194 $25.00

This book tries to explain to the reader how the headright system, tobacco cultivation and the importation of slave labor transformed the colony of Virginia from a society of small farmers to the aristocracy of large plantation life. At the turn of the eighteenth century most Virginia landowners were still self-sufficient small farmers holding a few hundred acres of land. The appendix in this book is the closest thing to a census for the years 1704-1705. The appendix is made up of over 7,000 Rent Rolls of individual landholders, listing them by county with the numbers of acres they had.

The History *of* Virginia's Navy *of the* Revolution. BY: Robert Armistead Stewart, Orig. Pub. 1934, Reprinted 2021, 279 pages, Index, soft cover, ISBN #978-1-63914-039-8.

VA 189 $27.50

This book is broken up into two main sections. The first is a general history of the organization along with its exploits. The second section is an alphabetical roster of its officers and enlisted men. These entries of the roster include, wherever possible, rank or status of officers and others, names of vessels served upon, length of service, native county, and, in main cases, information about their heirs and descendants.

Virginia Revolutionary War State Pensions. By: Virginia Genealogical Society, Pub. 1980, reprinted 2015, 192 pages, soft cover, Index, ISBN #0-89308-268-9.

VA 33 $25.00

Abstracts of some 465 pension records of the soldiers in Virginia. In the majority of these files, the date of death of the soldier or his widow is shown, and the name of the executor or administrator is often given. If the soldier was killed in service, the place or the name of the battle, as well as statement of his wounds, appear. This book contains the names of more than 10,000 individuals.

Revolutionary War Records Virginia: Virginia Army and Navy Forces with Bounty Land Warrants for Virginia Military District of Ohio and Virginia Military Scrip from Federal and State Records. By: Giaus Marcus Brumbaugh, Pub. 1936, Reprinted 2019, 748 pages, ISBN #0-89308-928-1.

VA 166 $55.00

This book is a MUST on anyone doing research of Virginia. It is a massive collection of Virginia's Revolutionary War source materials. It is a treasure trove of information about Virginians in the Revolutionary War. It contains list after list of soldiers and sailors extracted from bounty land warrants, pension applications, land scrip records, records of the State Line and the Continental Line, militia records, Half Pay applications, and along with a few that have never before been published.

Virginia MILITIA *in the* Revolutionary War. By: J.T. McAllister, Pub. 1913, Reprinted 2017, 338 pages, soft cover, Index, ISBN #0-89308-920-6.

VA 162 $35.00

The Virginia Militia played a large role in the American Revolution. At one point, it numbered around 45,000 persons. This book does not profess to be a history of the Virginia Militia in the Revolution but more of a summary the services of the militia arranged by county but also containing 1) Declarations of 250 Virginia Militia pensioners, these declarations give such information as dates of birth, dates of death, spouse's name, marriage dates, service records in great detail, and other miscellaneous information. 2) A list of militia officers appointed, nominated or qualifying during the Revolution in the counties of: Albemarle, Amelia, Augusta, Bedford, Berkley, Botetourt, Caroline, Charlotte, Chesterfield, Cumberland, Fauquier, Fluvanna, Frederick, Goochland, Greenbrier WV, Montgomery, Orange, Powhatan, Prince Edward, Rockbridge, Rockingham, Shenandoah, Spotsylvania, and Washington. 3) Pensioners residing in Virginia in 1835 who received pensions as Militia Militiamen. 4) Pensioners residing outside Virginia in 1835 who received pensions as Virginia Militiamen from such states as Alabama, Georgia, Kentucky, Illinois, Indiana, Maryland, Missouri, North Carolina, Ohio, South Carolina, and Tennessee. 5) the mentioning of the vast numbers of soldiers he had served with.

Southside Virginia Families. (2 Volumes) By: John Bennett Boddie, Pub. 1956, Reprinted 2019, soft cover, Index

Vol. #1, 1800-1852: 398 pages, ISBN #0-89308-876-5..

VA 185 $38.50

The Tidewater area of Virginia was one of the early regions within the colonies that received large amounts of colonial settlers. This set of books on the early families of this are among some of the most frequently consulted works on that area due to Mr. Boddie's impressive and detailed research. The first volume in this valuable two-volume set contains genealogies of families from the early counties of Isle of Wight, Prince George, and Surry. The families covered are as follows: Allen, Bailey, Ballard, Barker-Bradford-Taylor, Batte, Bell, Bennett-Pierce, Bishop-Stokes, Blunt, Boyce-Scott-Tatum, Braswell, Biggs, Browne, Burges, Cato, Champion, Clark, Cocke, Cooke, Corker, Dixon, Eaton, Faulcon, Flake, Fort, Goodrich, Gordon, Graves-Hancock, Hamblin-Hamlin, Hancock, Hill, Hines, Howle, Irwin, Jennings-Hill, Johnston, Jones, Jordan, Lanier, Lewis, Long, Massengill, Norfleet, Overton-Harris-Day, Pitt, Plummer, Rudulph, Sitgreaves, Sledge, Smith, Sweeney, Tyrus, Weldon, West, and Whitmel. The index to this volume has approximately 10,000 names.

Vol. #2, 1853-1922: 428 pages, ISBN #0-89308-877-3

VA 182 $58.50

This second volume of the set covers families from the early counties of Isle of Wight, Surry, and Sussex. Genealogies are for the families of Arrington, Bailey, Barham, Barker, Branch, Chappell, Cloud, Cocker, Cofer, Coffer, Coker, Collier, Copher, Darden-Durden, Edmunds, Foliot, Green, Gurgany, Hargrave, Hart, Harvin, Herbert, Hill, Holt, Judkins, Lane, Lucas, McKain, Macon, Mann, Norwood, Perry, Philips, Rogers, Sorrell-Earle-Warren, Stover, Taylor, Tyas-Tyus, Westbrook, and Worsham-Marshall. The index to this volume has approximately 10,000 names.

Virginia Settlers *in* Missouri. By: Dorothy Ford Wulfeck & A. Maxim Coppeage, Pub. 1960, Reprinted 2018, 158 pages, ISBN #0-89308-651-7.

VA 175 $25.00

This interesting book takes a look at early settlers leaving the East Coast and headed west in search of new lands and new lives. The authors have used various sources such as: Atlases, maps, census records, newspapers, Cemetery Inscriptions and etc., to show the relationship between these early settlers who moved from Virginia to Missouri by showing where they came from and where they have ended up. They have also included 64 mini/biographies various person that have crossed their paths while preforming this research.

Virginia Wills *and* Administrations, 1632-1800. By: Clayton Torrence, Orig. Pub. 1931, Reprinted 2017, 483 pages, soft cover, ISBN #0-89308-923-0.

VA 138 $38.50

This invaluable index, by a distinguished genealogist, list more than 50,000 names of individuals for whom wills and administrations were recorded in the counties of Virginia (colony and state), some of which are now in West Virginia.

Virginia Wills *before* 1799. By: William M. Clemens, Orig. Pub. 1924, reprinted 2017, 106 pages, soft cover, ISBN #0-89308-922-2.

VA 138 $38.50

This is a complete abstract register of all names mentioned in over 600 wills recorded before 1799. These wills were obtained from the courthouse records of: Amherst, Bedford, Campbell, Loudoun, Prince William, and Rockbridge Counties. They are arranged alphabetically by the name of the Testator. There are approximately 3000 names, mainly relatives, who were listed in the Will, plus the place and date of the will was filed.

The Virginia Company *of* London 1607-1624, Vol. 3. By: Lindsay O. Duvall and Beverly Fleet, Pub. 1950, reprinted 1983, 118 pages, soft cover, Index, ISBN #0-89308-064-0.

VA 4 $17.50

WEST VIRGINIA

Sims Index *to* LAND GRANTS *in* West Virginia. By: Edgar Sims, Pub. 1952 & 1956, reprinted 2020, 886 pages, Index, ISBN #0-89308-911-7.

WV 11 $68.50

This book is a MUST have and should be in everyone's collection who is researching family members within the states of West Virginia and Virginia. These Land Grants were made by Lord Fairfax prior to the creation of the Virginia Land Office in 1779, as well as those issued by the Commonwealth of Virginia for land now located in West Virginia, and by the State of West Virginia under its First Constitution. This book is a comprehensive collection of 1772-1867 land records in West Virginia of which was created out of Virginia in 1863. There are more than 50,000 entries with each containing the name of the grantee, amount of acreage, location and date of grant, and the grant book and page numbers. Sims meticulously examined each record to ensure that the spellings of the names of grantees, location, and descriptions of tracts were accurate, and that any variations of spellings of grantees' names were also indexed or noted. Records are listed for Barbour, Berkeley, Boone, Braxton, Brooke, Cabell, Calhoun, Clay, Doddridge, Fayette, Gilmer, Grant, Greenbrier, Hampshire, Hancock, Hardy, Harrison, Jackson, Jefferson, Kanawha, Lewis, Logan, Marion, Marshall, Mason, McDowell, Mercer, Monongalia, Monroe, Morgan, Nicholas, Ohio, Pendleton, Pleasants, Pocahontas, Preston, Putnam, Raleigh, Randolph, Ritchie, Roane, Taylor, Tucker, Tyler, Uphur, Wayne, Webster, Wetzel, Wirt, Wood, and Wyoming counties, West Virginia, as well as for the portions of Augusta, Bath, Botetourt, Frederick, Montgomery, Russell, Tazewell, and Wythe counties, Virginia, that were used in the formation of West Virginia. Special Note: This reprint includes the 16-page Supplement of 1956 covering grants of Fincastle, Giles, and Rockingham counties.

Cabell County, West Virginia Annals *and* Families. By: George Selden Wallace, Pub. 1935, Reprinted 2018, 608 pages, Index, soft cover, ISBN #0-89308-950-8

WV 1 $50.00

Cabell county was formed in 1809 from Kanawha County. It sits on the western side of the state bordering Ohio and Kentucky. It sits only a few miles south of the one of the main migration routes of the 19th century of persons headed West in search of land. This book is not too different from other county history books of this era. With such topics as trade and transportation, labor, farming, politics, and race relations - all important in the development of the county - are carefully discussed. This type of county history book can help one develop ideas or paths to those missing ancestors by showing the customs and traditions of the local residents. A particular useful feature of this book is the extensive biographical sketches that the author included on: Abbott, Altmeyer, Archer, Beuhring, Billups, Bostick, Bradshaw, Broh, Brown, Buffington, Burdette, Campbell, Cox, Darlington, Douthat, Everett, Foster, Frampton, Francis, Freemna, Gallaher, Gibson, Gideon, Hall, Hampton, Hannan, Harrison, Harshbarger, Hatfield, Haworth-Carmack-Matthews, Hite, Holderby, Hollenbeck, Hull, Jenkins, Johnston, Kail, Kilgore, Kyle, Laidley, Lane, Layne, LeSage, Long, Love, Lyon, Marcum, Martin, Maupin, McComas, McCormick, McGinnis, McLaughlin, Meek, Miller, Moore, Morris, Naglee, Nash, Neal, Oley, Page, Paine, Pancake, Pine, Poage, Quirk, Richmond, Ricketts, Russell, Rutherford, Samuels, Samworth, Scales, Scherr, Scott, Seamonds, Shepherd, Shoffstall, Sikes, Simmons, Spurlock, Staley, Switzer, Taylor, Thornburg, Tynes, Binson, Wallace, Walton, Wellman, Werninger, Wiatt, and Wilson. These biographical sketches represent approximately 1/3 of the entire book.

(Harrison County) History *of* Prospect Valley, West Virginia. By: Nettie B. Cooper, Pub. 1940, Reprinted 2018, 186 pages, soft cover, ISBN #0-89308-951-6.

WV 2 $22.50

Prospect Valley is located in Harrison County which was formed in 1784 from Monongalia County, WV. It sits in the northern portion of the county close to the town of Shinnston. This book covers the gypsies who lived in this area, the natural environment of the region, the economic and social side of this region of Harrison County, educational development, churches, newspapers, assorted family genealogies, and railroads.

Jefferson County, West Virginia, A History *of*. By: Millard K. Bushong, Pub. 1941, Reprinted 2019, 458 pages, Index, ISBN #0-89308-026-8.

WV 17 $40.00

Jefferson County was formed in 1801 from Berkeley County. It sits in the Shenandoah Valley and is the eastern most county in West Virginia, bordering Washington County, Maryland and Loudoun, Clarke, & Berkeley Counties, Virginia. This book is not too different from other county history books of this era. With such topics as county creation, trade and transportation, labor, farming, Revolutionary War, Civil War, Harper's Ferry, politics, and race relations - all important in the development of the county - are carefully discussed. This type of county history book can help one develop ideas or paths to those missing ancestors by showing the customs and traditions of the local residents. A particular useful feature of this book is the extensive biographical information included. This volume contains biographical sketches on: Baylor, Beall, Bedinger, Boteler, Brooke, Chew, Craighill, Cutshaw, Dandridge, Darke, Douglas, Gates, Gibson, Gwynn, Hagan, Hamtramck, Hawks, Hoff, Hopkins, Humphries, Hunter, Lee (2), Lucas (3), McDonald, Morrgan, Porterfield, Quick, Reynolds, Rutherford, Stephen, Stephenson (2), Washington (4), & Wilson (2). The author has included several appendix's that have rolls of soldiers who served in the Revolutionary War, War of 1812, Mexican War, Civil War, Spanish-American War, and WWI.

Upper Monongahela Valley, West Virginia, Genealogical *and* Personal History of. (3 Volumes). By: James Morton Callahan, Pub. 1912, Reprinted 2019, Soft cover, Index.

Monongah Valley lies in the northern portion of the state of West Virginia boarding Pennsylvania. The counties of: Marion and Monongalia lie within its boundaries. Monongalia County was created in 1776 from Augusta County, VA. From it the following counties were created: Barbour, Harrison, Lewis, Marion, Preston, Randolph, Taylor, Tucker and Upshur and they too are represented in these three volumes with Genealogical Sketches of its early settlers.

Vol. #1: 454 pages, ISBN #0-89308-952-4.

WV 6 $40.00

Vol. #2: 618 pages, ISBN #0-89308-953-2.

WV 7 $52.50

Genealogical Sketches to be found within this volume: Alexander, Allen (3), Allender, Amos, Anderson, Armstrong, Arnett (3), Atchison, Avis, Bailey (3), Bardett, Barncord, Bartlett, Beaty, Bentley, Black (2), Blackshere, Bland, Boso, Bovers (2), Bowman, Brand (3), Brandon, Brown, Brownfield, Bumgardner, Callahan, Carder, Carpenter, Carr, Carter (2), Casselberry, Church, Clark (2), Clifford, Coffman (3), Cole, Conaway, Conley, Conrad, Corley, Cox, Cunningham, Cure, Davis (11), DeBolt, Demain (2), Despard, Doheny, Douthat, Dudley, Duff, Duncan, Dunnington, Durrett, Dye, Edmondson, Elder, Ernst,

Evans, Ferry, Flanagan, Fleming (2), Finly, Finnell, Fisher (2), Fitch, Gaston, Glancy, Gordon (2), Grant (2), Green, Gregg (2), Hale, Hall, Halterman, Harmer, Harr, Hatfield, Hartley, Hawkins, Hayden, Hayes, Haymond, (3), Haynes, Hefner, Heinze, Hennen (2), Henry, Highland, Higinbotham (2), Hite, Hodges, Holden, Holland, Hough, Howard (2), Huffman, Hughes, Hursley, Irvin, Jackson, Jacobs, Jenkins, Johnson, Johnston, Jones (3), Kelley, Keller, Kessler, Kincaid, King, Koblegard, Langfitt, Latham, Lazear, Lazier, Leps, Lewis, Lightburn, Lilley, Lane, Leonard, Lockwood, Lough, Loving, Lowe, Lucas, Lyon, Madeira, Maloy, Manown, Martin, Mathers, Maxwell, McClelland, McDaniel, McDonald, McGregor, McGrew, McGuire, McIntire, McNeely, McVicker, Meredith (2), Miller, Mitchell, Moore (3), Moreland, Morgan (2), Morrison, Mumford, Musgrave, Newcomb, Newlon, Nichols, Nutter, Offner, Ogden (2), Orr, Parkes, Payne, Peck, Perine, Phillips, Pickenpaugh, Post, Potter (2), Powell, Price (2), Race, Rainey, Reed (2), Robinson, Rogers (2), Rohrbough, Rosier, Ruhl, Rumbaugh, Schwaner, Schwenck, Shaw, Shinn, Short, Sivey, Skidmore, Smith (5), Smoot, Snider, Snyder, Southern, Steel, Steele, Stewart, Stockert, Stockton, Strosnider, Stuart, Supler, Swiger (3), Swisher, Tate, Thorn, Thomas, Vandervort, Vance, Walker, Ward, Warman, Washington, Watson, Wendel, Wiedebusch, White (3), Whitehill, Whiteman, Whitescarver, Williams (3), Wood, Yeager, and Young.

Vol. #3: 500 pages, ISBN #0-89308-954-0.

WV 8 $48.50

Genealogical Sketches to be found within this volume: Abbaticchio, Alexander, Alford, Allen, Anthony, Arnet, Arnold, Ashcraft, Baker, Barnes, Barrickman, Batten, Bennett, Bevington, Bico, Bland, Bond, Bowcock, Boydston, Britten, Brock, Buchanan, Burnside, Burton, Butcher, Campbell, Casey, Clayton, Cole, Conway, Cordray, Costello, Cox, Crile, Currey, Danser, Davidson, Dean, Defrost, Dent, Devison, Dille, Douthitt, Downs, Durrin, Eddy, Elliott, Evans, Faris, Ferguson, Fife, Findley (2), Fisher, Fisk, Fletcher, Ford, Francis, Francois, Furbee, Gandy, Garlow, Garrett, Gaskin, Glasscock, Goff (2), Goodwin (2), Gore, Grant, Greene, Griffin, Hall (4), Hanes, Hardesty, Hardy, Harrison (2), Hart, Hartley, Haught, Haymond (2), Heavner, Hennen, Hess, Hiner, Hogg, Holt, Hood, Hornor, Huey, Huston, Hutton, Ice, Jarrett, Jarvis (2), Keener, King, Krebs, Law, Layton, Lazzelle, Leahy, Lewis (2), Lodge, Long, Lorentz, Lowe, Loyd, Lucas, Malloy, Martin (4), Mason, Maxwell (3), McCray, McGraw, McIntire, McKinley, McKone, McLane, McNeil, McReynolds, Miller, Mills, Morfit, Morgan (4), Morris, Morrison, Moore, Neely, Ogden (2), Orr, Parsons, Parrish, Patterson, Pepper, Phillips, Pigott, Pratt, Price, Proudfit, Purinton, Randall, Randolph, Reay, Reed (2), Reeder, Rice, Riedy, Rightmire, Roane, Robinson, Rogers, Ross (2), Rudeheaver, Satterfield, Scott (2), Shaver, Shields, Shinn, Showalter, Shriver, Shuman, Simmons, Simpson, Slater, Sloan, Smalley, Smith (2), Snider, Snyder (2), Sommers, Sperry, Spindler, Stewart (2), Syout, Strother, Sturgiss, Sutherland, Sutton (2), Swager, Swartz, Taylor (3), Tetrick, Trach, Vance, Van Voorhis, Wade, Warder (2), Weaver, Whetsell, White (3), Wiedebusch, Willis, Wilt, Wilson, Withers, Wood, Woodley, Worley, and Yost.

Monroe County, West Virginia, History of.

By: Oren Morton, Pub. 1916, Reprinted 2019, 556 pages, Index, soft cover, ISBN #0-89308-024-1.

WV 10 $48.50

Monroe county was created in 1799 from Greenbrier County, WV. Which in turn was created out of Botetourt, VA and in turn from Augusta County, VA. It lies in the southeastern corner of the state boarding Virginia. This book begins with a detailed history of the county covering such topics as: creation of the county, geography, Indians, religion, towns & villages, agriculture, slavery, its involvement in various wars, the Militia system & its officers' and miscellaneous other data. The reader will also discover that the author has included abstracts of Greenbrier record books and petitions for 1780- 1800 and Monroe County for 1799-1860. Also surveys and patents under Augusta, VA. Botetourt, VA., and Greenbrier County, WV Along with early land conveyances mostly under Greenbrier County, WV. 1786-1815. Approximately 25% of this book is devoted to biographical sketches of 292 early settlers of the county.

Randolph County, W.V., History *of.*

By: Dr. A.S. Bosworth, Pub. 1916, Reprinted 2019, 450 pages, Index, ISBN #0-89308-902-8.

WV 5 $40.00

Randolph County was formed in 1787 from Harrison County. This book is a detailed history of the county starting out with the pioneer era then moving to the creation of the county starting with its inclusion in Harrison County. It moves into data concerning land records from Patents, Land Entries, and Conveyances. The author has included chapters covering the roads of the county, Education, Civil War Period, Various Laws concerning the county and commerce. Then the reader will discover that almost half of this book is devoted to biographical sketches / genealogies of the following families and individuals: Addison, Arnold, Arbogast, Armentrout, Armstrong, Baker, Ball, Barlow, Barnard, Barron, Bennett, Bent, Bosworth, Booth, Bond, Bogard, Buffington, Blarir, Buckey, Butcher, Brown (2), Caplinger, Carr, Crouch, Collett, Chaffey, Channell, Crickard, Cobb, Coff, Conner, Corder, Curtis, Cassity, Connolly, Chenoweth, Clingerman, Crawford, Coberly, Corley, Cowger, Conrad, Cunningham (2), Curry, Currence, Daniels, Dann, Darden, Davis, Dean, Dilworth, Doerr, Downs, Dulaney, Earle, Eberly, Eberman, Elkins, Ellis, Elza, Elder, Evans, Fisher, Fitzwater, Friend, Ferguson, Fowler, Gainer, Gandy, Gear, Gibson, Goddin, Godwin, Goff, Greynolds, Hansford, Harding, Harmon, Harper, Hart, Haigler, Haymond, Haddan, Harris, Hedrick (3), Hicks, Hinchman, Hornbeck, Howell, Hutton, Isner, Jackson, Keenan, Keer, Keim, Kildow, Kimmell, Kittle, Knaggs, Kump, Kyle, Lantz, Levitt, Lloyd, Logan, Long, Lough, Lucas, Manning, Marshall, Marteny, Martin, Marstiller, Maxwell, McCollum, McLaughlin, McLean, McQuain, Miller (2), Moore, Morgan, Morrison (2), Mullenix (2), Neal, Nestor, Parrish, Pedro, Pennington, Phares, Pickens, Poling, Potts, Pritt, Probst, Quick, Rains, Riffle, Ringer, Rooney, Rosencranse, Rowan, Roy, Russell, Ryan, Schoonover, Scott, See, Seitz, Shaffer, Skidmore, Simmons, Smith (2), Snyder, Sutherland, Strader, Stalnaker, Strum, Sturms, Swecker, Talbott (2), Tallman, Taylor, Teter (4), Thomas, Trembly, Triplett, Tuning, Tyre, Tyree, Updike, Wamsley, Ward, Warthen, Warwick, Weese, Weimer, Weir, Westfall, Weymouth, Whetzel, White, Wilson (2), Wilt, Whitman, Wilmoth, Woolwine, Wymer (2), and Yokum.

West Virginia *in the* American Revolution.

By: Ross B. Johnston, Pub. 1939-47, Reprinted 2018, 322 pages, soft cover, ISBN #0-89308-990-7.

WV 3 $35.00

Considering West Virginia did not become a state until 1863, the author has identified soldiers who at one time or another lived in what is now the State of West Virginia. Their military duties having been discharged in the service of other states, notably Pennsylvania, Virginia and Maryland. The information found within: the name, age, date of birth, service record, date pension applied for and granted, place of residence, and names of wife & children.

West Virginia Revolutionary Ancestors.

By: Anne Walker Reddy, Pub. 1936, Reprinted 2019, 94 pages, Index, ISBN #0-89308-414-X.

WV 5 $40.00

This is a list of names of approximately 2,000 West Virginians whose Public Claims are on record in manuscripts at the Virginia State Library. Claims were registered for people who nursed the sick and wounded, fed the troops, furnished supplies, buried the dead, rode express, and manufactured firearms. This list was compiled for the benefit of those who desire to trace ancestors who gave service in the Revolutionary War but whose names do not appear in the published indexes and rolls of Revolutionary soldiers and sailors. This index to the Public Claims is particularly valuable, therefore, because it contains names of patriots whose services are recorded in no other place unless they rendered military as well as non-military service. Each patriot is identified by name and county of residence. At the back of the volume the researcher will find a selection of excerpts from Revolutionary Warrants taken from the records of Berkeley, Botetourt, Greenbrier, Hampshire, and Monongalia counties, Virginia.

AFRO-AMERICAN and SLAVE Genealogy

Free Negro Owners *of* Slaves *in the* United States *in* 1830.

By: Carter G. Woodson, Pub. 1924, reprinted 2021, 86 pages, soft cover, ISBN #978-1-63914-008-4.

USA 5 $15.00

This book will make a great addition to anyone's collection of research books especially when it concerns Afro-American Genealogy. This book contains the names of the Head of Household along with their approximate age, gender, and number of persons within his or her family. Information is broken down by state and then into counties.

Free Negro Heads *of* Families *in the* United States *in* 1830.

By: Carter G. Woodson, Phd., Pub. 1925, Reprinted 2021, 354 pages, Index, soft cover, ISBN #0-89308-668-1.

USA 4 $35.00

This book will make a great addition to anyone's collection of research books especially when it concerns Afro-American Genealogy. This book contains the names of the Head of Household along with their approximate age, gender, and number of persons within his or her family. Information is broken down by state and then into counties. The 53-page introduction includes sections devoted to preventing the increase of the Free Negroes, the Free Negro before the Law, economic achievement along with other information concerning the Free Negro. The index for this book identifies over 40,000 individuals.

Free Negro Labor *and* Property Holding *in* Virginia, 1830-1860.

By: Luther Porter Jackson, Pub. 1942, Reprinted 2020, 288 pgs, ISBN #0-89308-859-5.

VA 165 $27.50

Despite being a person of color and facing countless abuses, many of these free persons stayed in Virginia and made it their home. One must turn past the political reasons and look at the economic side as to why a free person of color would stay. This book is 3-decade study into the lives of these persons and the advancements they made in spite of the laws of the land. The author has included two appendix's that list these free persons who owned property valued over $1000 in Petersburg and Free persons of color who owned more than 100 acres of land throughout the state. The reader will also discover numerous amounts of detailed data concerning these free persons within the footnotes throughout this book. This book will deliver great insight into the lives of these person. Even if you don't have Afro-American genealogy in your family, this book should be a MUST read for anyone interested in Virginia History and Genealogy as a whole.

Slavery *and* Servitude *in the* Colony *of* North Carolina. By: John Spencer Bassett, Phd., Pub. 1896, reprinted 2023, 86 pages, soft cover, ISBN #978-1-63914-129-6.

NC 123 $17.50

FAMILY HISTORIES

The Alstons *and* Allstons *of* North *and* South Carolina. By: Joseph A. Groves and Rev. S.E. Lucas, Jr., Pub. 1901 & 1976, Reprinted 2015, 668 pages, Hard Cover, Index, ISBN #0-89308-013-6.

FH 4 $60.00

There were two major Alston-Allston lines: one in North Carolina from which the author descends and which is a very comprehensive genealogy of this family; the other was the Allston family of South Carolina, in which the author concentrated on the male line. This reprint updates the South Carolina line of Allston family, emphasizing the female lines. Contains excellent genealogies of the LaBruce, Ward, Pawley families of the Waccamaw area. The publisher has added a very comprehensive photo section of various descendants of the Allstons, LaBruce, Pawleys and Wards from photographs and oil paintings, as well as family jewelry and other items dating from the 1730's. This is a MUST book for anyone with roots in the Low Country of South Carolina due to the many intermarriages between these four families and other illustrious families of Colonial South Carolina.

The Berryhill Family History. By: Viginia T. Brittain, Pub. 1962, reprinted 1982, 338 pages, Soft Cover, Index, ISBN #0-89308-293-7.

FH 16 $35.00

This book is primarily concerned with the descendants of William Berryhill, born about 1780, possibly in Georgia, and died between 1861 and 1864 in Marion Co., Alabama, and his wife Margaret Weeks, born in GA. about 1780/90 and died about 1845/46 in Marion Co., AL. and their 18 children.

The Dodson (Dotson) Family *of* North Farnham Parish, Richmond Co., VA.: A History *and* Genealogy *of their* Descendants. (Volume #1) By: Mrs. Sherman Williams and Rev. S. Emmett Lucas, Jr., Pub. 1998, 1212 pages, Hard Cover, Index, ISBN #0-89308-349-6.

FH 10 $55.00

Chapter 1: "The First Five Generation Descended from Charles Dodson, Sr. of Richmond Co., VA." Each of these individuals is assigned a number and there are charts giving a graphic illustration of these five generations. Chapter 2: "Dodson Descendants from the Fifth Generation to the Present", contains descendants from each person in the fifth generation to the extent that information is available. Some of these lineage's have been worked out from census and courthouse records, although much of this material has been donated by Dodson relatives and researchers. Many of these lineage's come down to current generations. Chapter 3: "Photographs" This is a 145-page section containing some 288 photographs, tintypes, old Bible records, etc.. of descendants of the various branches of the family.

The Dodson (Dotson) Family *of* North Farnham Parish, Richmond Co., VA.: A History *and* Genealogy *of their* Descendants. (Volume #2) By: Mrs. Sherman Williams and Rev. S. Emmett Lucas, Jr., Pub. 1989, reprinted 2015, 740 pages, Hard Cover, Index, ISBN #0-89308-599-5.

FH 11 $65.00

Chapter 4: "Dangling Dodsons" This is information and genealogies on various Dodson-Dotson lines that have as yet not been connected to Charles Dodson of North Farnham Parish because of lack of records, which, however, are more than likely descendants of Charles, or of other Dodson-Dotson lines from PA. and New England. Chapter 5: "Legal Documentation for Dodson Descendants, Chapters 1, 2, and 3. Chapter 6: "Dodson of Chapter 1 and 2 received too late to be included in their proper places (in Chapter 2)." Chapter 7: "Rochester, Pyles, and Allied Lines of the Publisher." INDEX: A full name index of 96,000 descendant.

The Polks *of* North Carolina *and* Tennessee. By: Mrs. Frank M. Angellotti, New England Historical Society, Orig. Pub. 1923-1924, Reprinted 2017, 166 pages, soft cover, Index, ISBN #0-89308-543-X.

FH 22 $20.00

This is a detailed reprinting of the descendants of William Polk of Maryland, who settled in NC about 1750 and through his sons, four of whom were officers in the Revolutionary War, and was the ancestor of the distinguished Polk Family of North Carolina and Tennessee to which James Knox Polk, 11th President of the United States, and Leonidas Polk, bishop and Confederate General, belonged. A brief account is also given of the first 2 generations of Polk's in America, in order to show the family connections of William Polk of Maryland and North Carolina and his descent from Robert Polk, the immigrant ancestor of the family.

The Powell Families *of* Virginia *and the* South. By: Rev. S.E. Lucas, Jr., Pub. 1969, Reprinted 2015, 724 pages, Hard Cover, Index, ISBN #0-89308-027-6.

FH 9 $65.00

This book is a detailed study of the 8 major Powell families of VA. and their descendants in VA, NC, SC, GA, AL, MS, TN and KY. Contains genealogies of the Norfolk and Elizabeth City counties, VA lines complete revised, the Isle of Wight county, VA family lines; the York county, VA family; the Nicholas Powell family of Northampton county, VA; the Walter Powell family of Accomack, Northampton and Prince William counties, VA and Somerset county, MD; the old Rappahannock county, VA lines consisting of: the Essex county, VA line, the Caroline, Culpeper-Orange counties, VA lines. Also, vast sections of legal records for miscellaneous Powells in Virginia, South Carolina, North Carolina, Georgia, Alabama, Kentucky, Tennessee, Mississippi, etc. and genealogies of unconnected lines. The MOST comprehensive work ever undertaken on Powells in the South. This reprint does not include the approximately 125 additional pages of Powell descendants that originally appeared in the editor's book: The Powell Family of Norfolk and Elizabeth City counties, VA which deals primarily with the descendants of Catherine Powell and Benjamine Wills Powell.

IMMIGRATION

A Collection *of* Upwards *of* 30,000 Names *of* German, Swiss, Dutch, French *and other* Immigrants *in* Pennsylvania *from* 1727 *to* 1776. By: I. D. Rupp and M.V. Kroger, Pub. 1876 and 1935, 826 pages with Index, soft cover, ISBN #978-1-63914-100-5.

PA 4 $62.50

This book is considered one of the most useful tools for identifying persons who came to North America between 1727 and 1776. It contains 319 ships passenger list with more than 30,000 names. Its main emphasis is on the early Palatine immigration. The lists are arranged in chronological order according to date of arrival, listing the names of the ships on which the passengers arrived and the places from which they emigrated. In addition, the appendices list over a thousand early settlers who landed at some port other than Philadelphia, but who afterwards came to Pennsylvania from New York, North Carolina, and Georgia. Included are "Names of the First Palatines in North Carolina, 1709 and 1710," and "Names of Salzburgers Settled in Georgia, 1734-1741." To make this book even more useful, we have included Kroger's 232-page full name index of which the original is lacking. Without the index, this book can be difficult to use.

Early Virginia Immigrants, 1623-1666. By: George Cabell Greer, Orig. Pub. 1912, Reprinted 2018, 376 pages, Index, ISBN #0-89308-814-5.

VA 122 $35.00

A useful companion to Nugent's Cavaliers and Pioneers, this work provides an exhaustive list of immigrants to Virginia, 1623-1666, who were not original patentees of land. As the records stand it is very difficult to discover names of persons who came to Virginia unless they were patentees of land, and the great majority of immigrants to the colony were not Patentees but "Headrights". Nearly 25,000 names have been collected from the original records in the Virginia State Land Office and arranged in alphabetical order. Every immigrant from 1623 down to 1666 is noted long with the name of the patentee or party sponsoring him and the date and place or residence.

Emigrants *from* England, 1773-1776. By: Gerald Fothergill, Pub. 1913, Reprinted 2020, 206 pages, Index, ISBN #0-89308-455-7.

USA 3 $22.50

This book on English passenger arrivals to ports along the eastern seaboard during the years immediately preceding Independence presents a list of about 6,000 names copied from Treasury Records in the Public Record Office in London. For each passenger the following information is given; age, occupation, place of origin, name of ship, destination, and reason for emigration. These new immigrants were Georgia; North & South Carolina, Virginia; Maryland; Pennsylvania; New York, Massachusetts, Barbados, St. Kitts, St. Vincent's, Jamacia, Antigua, Montreal, Quebec, Dominica, Fort Chamberland, St. Christophers, Tobago, Nevis, Grenada, and Bermuda.

Emigrants *from* Scotland *to* America, 1774-1775.

By: Viola Root Cameron, Pub. 1930, reprinted 2023, 120 pages, Soft Cover, Index, ISBN #978-1-63914-103-6.

USA 13 $17.50

These records have copied from old Treasury Papers in the Public Record Office in London. This book lists approximately 2,000 persons by age, station, occupation, residence in Scotland, destination in America, and reasons for emigrating. Ports of entry in the US were: New York, NY; Philadelphia, PA; Wilmington, NC; Savannah, GA; Charleston, SC; and ST. Johns Island. This work is of great value in bridging the Atlantic during the years of 1774-1775.

The English Ancestry *and* Homes *of the* Pilgrim Fathers.

By: Charles Edward Banks, Pub. 1929, reprinted 2022, 198, Index, soft cover, ISBN #978-1-63914-065-7.

USA 9 $22.50

This book is a compilation of 112 biographical sketches of passengers who sailed on the first four ships to New England: Mayflower (1620), Fortune (1621), Anne (1623), and Little James (1623). The author begins with historical evidence including Pilgrim sources in England, Children of the Mayflower, Unlisted Mayflower passengers, London as a Pilgrim Centre, and Story of the Mayflower. It is then followed up with the individual biographical sketches of these passengers' giving data on origins within England and family connections including such things as: names of spouse, children, parents, occupations, dates of baptisms and etc....

Naturalizations *of* Foreign Protestants *in the* American *and* West Indian Colonies, 1740-1772.

By: Montague S. Giuseppi, Pub. 1921, reprinted 2023, 210 pages, Index, ISBN #978-1-63914-120-3.

USA 14 $27.50

This book contains copies of all the Returns of Naturalizations of foreign Protestants sent from the Colonies to the Lords Commissioners for Trade and Plantations during the period 1740 to 1772. It covers approximately 6,500 persons who were naturalized. These Returns are from the colonies of South Carolina, North Carolina, Virginia, Maryland, New York, and Pennsylvania, along with some from Jamaica in the West Indies. The Returns from Pennsylvania making up the bulk of these persons within. The entries generally include name, religion, town and county of residence, and date of naturalization.

Original Lists *of* Persons of Quality, 1600-1700: Emigrants, Religious Exiles, Political Rebels, serving men sold for a term of years, Apprentices, children stolen, Maidens Pressed, and others who went from Great Britain to the American Plantations.

By: John Camden Hotten, Pub. 1874, Reprinted 2020, 604 pages, Index, ISBN #0-89308-178-7.

USA 2 $48.50

This book should be a part of everyone personal library who is researching their family history. This book is probably the most famous of all ships' passenger lists of English-speaking immigrants of the colonial period ever published. It was transcribed from the records of the British State Paper Office, it contains the names of over 11,000 immigrants. Data to be found within: names & ages, former places of residence, and the names of ships in which they embarked. The use of the book is greatly enhanced by a 66-page index, giving the Christian as well as the family name of all immigrants cited in various lists throughout the work.

REVOLUTIONARY WAR

The German Allied Troops *in the* North American War *of* Independence, 1776-1783.

By: Max Von Eelking, Pub. 1893, reprinted 2023, 360 pages, Index, soft cover, ISBN #978-1-63914-119-7.

PA 42 $40.00

This book is a history of the German troops (i.e., Hessians, Brunswickers, Waldeckers, etc.) who fought for the British during the American Revolution. The author has devoted approximately 70 pages to a List of the Officers of the Hessian Corps who served during 1776-1783. This list names about 1,500 men, arranged by regiment and thereunder by rank, with dates of service and other records. Since many of these German "auxiliaries" were captured and ultimately remained in America, this work should interest many researchers with ancestors from the Revolutionary era.

Known Military Dead *during* The American Revolutionary War, 1775-1783.

By: Clarence Stewart Peterson, Pub. 1959, reprinted 2021, 198 pgs, Index, soft cover, ISBN #978-1-63914-028-2.

USA 6 $22.50

This book is an alphabetically list of approximately 10,000 "Known" military dead during the American Revolution. Information to be found within: names with rank, date of death, and state of birth or service or place where buried.

ROYALITY

The Blood Royal *of* Britain. Being a Roll of the Living Descendants of Edward IV and Henry VII Kings of England and James III, King of Scotland.

By: The Marquis of Ruvigny and Raineval, Pub. 1903, reprinted 2023, 672 pages, Index, ISBN #978-1-63914-091-6.

USA 11 $60.00

Unlike previous works on Royal Descents which have been principally, if not wholly, confined to setting out the specific descents of those persons who have paid for that purpose, every attempt has been made in this book to trace out ALL the descendants of the above-named Kings, of which no fee or charge was made for their insertion. The author traces all the living descendants of King Edward III as of the date of original publication (1903), with some 48,000 individuals and with over 300,000 lines of descent between them. Included in the Roll are the names of all the crowned heads of Europe; of the majority of hereditary peers; of all the royal and princely houses of Europe; of many of the higher nobility of France, Germany, Austria, Hungary, Poland, Bohemia, Italy, Spain, Portugal, Russia, and Belgium; and of the old aristocracy of the Southern States of America, together with baronets and county gentry.

An Index *of* Hereditary English, Scottish, *and* Irish Titles *of* Honour.

By: Edward Solly, Pub. 1879, reprinted 2023, 214 pages, soft cover, ISBN #978-1-63914-102-9.

USA 12 $20.00

This book is an index of approximately 5,750 titles of honour, arranged in alphabetically order. It gives the family name for all the English, Scottish and Irish Peerages and Baronetages both existing and extinct at the time the work was originally published. It also lists the date when each separate title was conferred, the family seat, and the changes which the titles underwent. Since hereditary titles of honour often are used by direct male descendants and, in some creations, by heirs in general, the family names themselves are little known. Identification of family hereditary honours is thus facilitated through the use of this index.

The Magna Charta Barons *and their* American Descendants.

By: Charles H. Browning, Pub. 1898, reprinted 2022, 463 pages, index soft cover, ISBN #978-1-63914-066-4.

USA 10 $40.00

For Americans claiming lineal descent from the Magna Charta Barons, this is the book. This book follows the pedigrees of the founders and members of the Order of Runnemede up to 1898. The bulk of this work follows the pedigrees of these founders. It is followed up by a history of the Magna Charta of 1215; by lists of the Magna Charta Barons; and by biographies of the Sureties who were the twenty-five barons designated to enforce the Magna Charta. Founders, for whom pedigrees are given, are as follows: Ballord, Betts, Bigelow, Bispham, Bleecker, Browning, Bulkeley, Cadwalader, Darling, Earle, Fleete, Greene, Griffith, Hancock, Lawrence, Lawton, Lee, Lyman, Marsh, Parsons, Pomeroy, Richardson, Riker, Saltonstall, Schieffelin, Spotswood, Terry, Throckmorton, Waddell, Ward, Whitney, and Winston.

Families Directly Descended *from* All the Royal Families *in* Europe, 495-19323 *and* Mayflower Descendants

By: Elizabeth M. Leach Rixford, Pub. 1932, reprinted 2023, 254 pages, Index, soft cover, ISBN #9787-1-63914-126-5.

USA 15 $30.00

This work shows connections to the royal and noble families of Europe. The notable ancestors traced by the author include Cerdic, first of the West Saxon Kings; Alfred the Great; Robert Bruce; Kings Henry I, II, and III; Kings Edward I, II, and III; and many lines through Charlemagne, Louis I, the Earls of Warren, the Dukes of Normandy, the Royal House of Portugal, the House of Capet, the Counts of Anjoy, the Kings of Jerusalem, and more. Part two of this volume, the author has included how several Mayflower lines are connected to all the members of the Vermont Society of Mayflower Descendants. Surnames of the following royal, noble or Mayflower households: Aquitaine, Angouleme, Anjoy, Baskerville, Beauchamp, Bray, Bulkeley, Capet, Castille, Cheney, James Chilton, Francis Cooke, Courtenay, Rixford, De Vere, Farleigh-Hungerford, Devereux, Douglas, Drake, Eaton, Ferrers, Fitz-Alan, Flanders, Graves, Greene, Gregory, Hainault, Heydon, Johnson, William Latham, Lawrence (John and Isaac), Lisle, Marshall, Milbourne, Moore, Mowbray, Phelps, Port, Province, Rogers, Russell, Seymour, De Spineto, Smith and Georges, Sir Henry Smith, Stanley, Throckmorton, Tailefer, Vermandois, Warren, Washburn, Washington, Winnington (Wynnington), Gov. Thomas Welles, Whitney, William the Conqueror, Winslow, and Wyne.

Date: ____________________

E-MAIL: southernhistoricalpress@gmail.com

To: Southern Historical Press, Inc.
[redacted]
Greenville, SC 29602-1267

Please me the following books below. My check / money order or cash in the amountof $________ in payment of this order is enclosed. (Libraries may be Invoiced.) Please add a postage and handling charge in the remittance. ***$6.00 for the first book and $2.00 for each additional book on the order.***

BOOK CODE	# of Copies	Title of Book *(Indicate Vols if a set)* *Please Print*	AMOUNT

Visa / Master Card #: ______________________________ **TOTAL $**____________

Expiration Date: ____________________ **Shipping / Handling $**____________

CVV: __________ **S.C. Residents add 6% Sales Tax $**____________

AMOUNT DUE $____________

Ship To:

NAME : ______________________________

ADDRESS: ______________________________

CITY: ______________________________

STATE: __________ **ZIP:** ______________

E-Mail: ______________________________

Telephone #: ______________________________

(Please Send a Catalog To:)

NAME : ______________________________

ADDRESS: ______________________________

CITY: ______________________________

STATE: __________ **ZIP:** ______________

E-Mail: ______________________________

Date: ____________________

E-MAIL: southernhistoricalpress@gmail.com

To: Southern Historical Press, Inc.
[redacted]
Greenville, SC 29602-1267

Please me the following books below. My check / money order or cash in the amountof $________ in payment of this order is enclosed. (Libraries may be Invoiced.) Please add a postage and handling charge in the remittance. ***<u>$6.00 for the first book and $2.00 for each additional book on the order.</u>***

BOOK CODE	**# of Copies**	**Title of Book** *(Indicate Vols if a set)* *Please Print*	**AMOUNT**

Visa / Master Card #: ________________________________ **TOTAL $**______________

Expiration Date: ________________ **Shipping / Handling $**______________

CVV: __________ **S.C. Residents add 6% Sales Tax $**______________

AMOUNT DUE $______________

Ship To:

NAME : ______________________________

ADDRESS: ______________________________

CITY: ______________________________

STATE: __________ **ZIP:** ______________

E-Mail: ______________________________

Telephone #: ______________________________

(Please Send a Catalog To:)

NAME : ______________________________

ADDRESS: ______________________________

CITY: ______________________________

STATE: __________ **ZIP:** ______________

E-Mail: ______________________________

www.southernhistoricalpress.com
Southern Historical Press, Inc.
[redacted]
1071 Park West Road
Greenville, S.C. 29602-1267